KT-369-071

The Body Machine

Christiaan N. Barnard

is Professor of Surgical Science at the University of Cape Town, South Africa. In 1967 he performed the first human-to-human heart transplant and in 1974 the first double heart ('piggyback') transplant. Less well known, but of immense importance to many hundreds of people, are the surgical techniques he has pioneered for treating various congenital heart conditions, and the prostheses he has developed for replacing diseased heart valves. His outstanding contribution to medicine has been acknowledged all over the world, by states, cities, universities and professional bodies. Professor Barnard is also a recipient of the Dag Hammarskjöld Peace Prize—he has consistently championed the underprivileged in South Africa, regardless of creed or colour. Among the eight books to his credit are an autobiography and two novels. These reveal him to be controversial, certainly, but also courageous and compassionate and fully alert to the important social and ethical issues of today.

John Illman

Co-ordinating Editor, is one of Britain's finest medical journalists and the recipient in 1978 of the Medical Journalists' Association's special award. He has written extensively for the *Sunday Times* and for other leading newspapers, and is a past editor of *General Practitioner* and founder editor of *New Psychiatry*. His wide experience and dynamic style are evident throughout the book.

Consulting Panel

Lester Breslow
Professor and Dean, School of Public Health, University of California, USA

Sir John Butterfield
Regius Professor of Physic, University of Cambridge, United Kingdom

Chen Zhong-wei
Head of Orthopaedic Department and Research Laboratory for Replantation of the Severed Limb, Sixth People's Hospital, Shanghai, Chinese Peoples' Republic

Robert Corringham
Research Fellow, Cancer Research Campaign, United Kingdom

Maurice Katz
Head of Fertility and Endocrine Research Unit, University College Hospital, London, United Kingdom

Malcolm Lader
Professor of Clinical Psychopharmacology, Institute of Psychiatry (University of London), United Kingdom

Michael J. G. Harrison
Director of Department of Neurological Sciences, Middlesex Hospital, London, United Kingdom

Richard S. Lazarus
Professor of Psychology, University of California, Berkeley, USA

Yoshio Mishima
Professor of Surgery, University of Tokyo, Japan

A. John Rush
Director of Clinical Services and Associate Professor, Department of Psychiatry, University of Texas, Dallas, USA

J. M. Tanner
Professor of Child Health and Growth, Institute of Child Health, University of London, United Kingdom

Richard W. D. Turner
Senior Research Fellow in Preventive Cardiology, University of Edinburgh, United Kingdom

The Body Machine

Your Health in Perspective

Christiaan Barnard
Consultant Editor

John Illman
Co-ordinating Editor

HAMLYN
London · New York · Sydney · Toronto

This book was devised and produced by
Multimedia Publications Inc.

Publishing Controllers: Leonard Kristal, Arnon Orbach
Editor: Anne Cope
Assistant Editor: Catherine Ingoldby
Production Director: Arnon Orbach
Designer and Art Director: Martin Bronkhorst
Assistant Designer: Tassos Xeni
Picture Editor: Leonard Kristal
Picture Researchers: Anne Horton, Tessa Paul
Artists: Olivia Beazley, Jane Cope, John Davies, Chris Forsey,
David Gifford, Richard Lewis, Josephine Martin,
Terry Oakes, Charlotte Emma Styles,
Kathy Wyatt, Tassos Xeni

Copyright © 1981
Multimedia Publications Inc., Willemstad (Curacao)

This edition published 1981 by
The Hamlyn Publishing Group Limited
London · New York · Sydney · Toronto
Astronaut House, Feltham, Middlesex, England

All rights reserved. No part of this publication may be
reproduced, stored in a retrieval system or transmitted in any
form or by any means, electronic, mechanical, photocopying,
recording or otherwise, without the permission of
The Hamlyn Publishing Group and the Copyright holder.

British Library Cataloguing in Publication Data
Barnard, Christiaan
The Body Machine
Includes index

ISBN 0 600 33212 8

B/W and colour origination: D. S. Colour International Inc., London, UK
Typesetting: Western Printing Services Ltd, Bristol, UK
Printed in Spain by Graficromo S.A., Cordoba

Contents

Introduction

The concept of the human body as a machine is a controversial one, seen by some as a threat or insult to human individuality and uniqueness. It is neither of these things. We are unique, yet we have thousands of characteristics in common with machines. Like the automobile we derive energy from a high octane fuel, and like automobiles we are developed on assembly lines, though each of us is a product of a unique assembly line programmed by the genes, the units of heredity.

In fact, the analogy should be turned round. It is the machine which is like the body. After all, the body came first and it incorporates all the best patents. Machines are man's attempt to make inanimate objects perform like living things—so it is not surprising that machines built for man by man are built in his own image.

How does the human machine compare with the automobile? The average small family saloon is 170 in (4.3 m) long, about 18 cwt (0.91 tonnes) in weight and 50 in (127 cm) high. The adult body tends to be rather higher but it weighs much less—the normal range is between 100–120 lb, or 45–54 kg— and it contains much more. It is the most compact feat of mechanical engineering known. It is far more versatile, far more flexible and has an operational span ten times longer than the automobile.

The automobile is of course faster. The fastest speed achieved by the body machine is some 23 miles per hour (37 km/h) and that required a super-tuned model who was only able to maintain the speed for a few seconds. The automobile is also more powerful. A well-trained athlete can produce 1.6–2.0 horsepower in bursts lasting 5–10 seconds, or as much as 6 horsepower in bursts of less than one second. In contrast the six-wheeled Jameson Concorde generates 1,760 horsepower.

Let's take a more elaborate example. The endocrine system, which secretes the body's hormones or chemical messengers, is not fully understood. But we do know that it employs what is known as a negative feedback system. Central heating works in the same way. If the temperature in the house drops below a certain preset limit the thermostat 'instructs' the boiler to pump out more heat to push the temperature back up to the desired level. Likewise, the boiler reduces its output if the house is too hot.

When body temperature drops, blood temperature drops, resulting in a flow of cold blood through the brain. This activates the thermostat, causing it to release hormones to create energy and reduce further heat loss by cutting off the blood supply to the skin, particularly to the feet and hands. But because nature is an economical designer this same thermostat is incorporated within a mechanism which also regulates basic drives, and feelings like stress, violence, anger, fear and grief. No man-made thermostat is so versatile. Perhaps the most sophisticated human application of negative feedback is that found in guided missiles; these are equipped to track and even predict evasive action by the target, and to twist and turn accordingly. But their design is elephantine compared to that of the endocrine system, and they are required to operate once only. The thermostat in the human brain lasts a lifetime.

The machine-like nature of the body was recognised some centuries ago. In fact this book is in some ways a second edition of *The Body Machine*—the first was written by the French philosopher René Descartes (1596–1650) under the title *Treatise of Man* but it was not published until after his death because it did not conform to mid-17th-century ideas about the body. Descartes compared the body to the mechanical contrivances of his age.

A contemporary of Descartes, the Englishman William Harvey, whose work laid the foundations of modern medical science, is also remembered for his mechanical interpretation of the body. He was the first to recognise the pump-like mechanism of the heart. A graduate of the University of Cambridge, Harvey studied medicine in Padua under the famous anatomist Fabricius of Aquapendente. Fabricius deduced that the veins contained valves which stopped the flow of blood from the centre of the body to its extremities. Harvey demonstrated that what the valves really did was ensure that the blood flowed in one direction only, away from the heart via the arteries and back into the heart via the veins. And so the circulation was discovered.

Concepts are not developed in a vacuum. They evolve, often slowly. So it is with the Body Machine concept. Descartes and Harvey forged two links in a long chain which stretches back to ancient civilisations and forward to the distant future.

One of the best known man-machine analogies of this century was that offered by R. Buckminster Fuller in 1938: "A self-balancing, 28-jointed adapter-based biped; an electrochemical reduction plant, with segregated stowages of special energy extract in storage batteries for . . . thousands of hydraulic and pneumatic pumps with motors attached; 62,000 miles of capillaries . . . the whole extraordinary complex mechanism guided with exquisite precision from a turret in which are located telescopic and microscopic self-registering and recording range finders, a spectroscope, etc., the turret control being closely allied with an air conditioning intake-and-exhaust, a main fuel intake . . ." and so on.

But the body machine is not a hard machine like the automobile or tank. It is a soft machine. However, like the automobile it needs proper care and maintenance. The principles of good body maintenance are now well established; the problem is to persuade people to adopt them and the lifestyles that go with them. We hope this book will help towards this end.

Many people alive today owe their existence to cardiac pacemakers, artificial heart valves, and synthetic joints. This is why we examine the major advances which have saved life and improved the quality of life. Thirty years ago Bionic Man and Bionic Woman had not even been conceived. Now they are beginning to assume a sharp definition. Perhaps one day our mechanical creations will be as good as the biological originals. Opinions vary, but of one thing there is no doubt: nature holds all the best patents. These are the products of evolution and, according to one theory, part of a great experiment conducted by our genes in the laboratory we know as the world.

It is impossible in a book of this size to draw a fully comprehensive picture of the body machine—each section could make a book in its own right, and so what we have done is to present a general picture.

We start by describing what are known as body systems, treating each as a separate entity. But it is important to remember that the body machine functions as an integrated whole—any attempt to break it down into its constituent parts invariably involves overlap. We have tried to avoid duplication and to limit the number of cross references from one section to another. However, in the interests of continuity, there are some sections where information is duplicated. For example, the aorta is described in two sections: the heart and the blood. We hope this will accommodate the needs of the reader who does not read the book from beginning to end, but who dips into the different sections at random. Having said that the logical place to start is at the beginning—with the cell, the basis of life.

Body systems

The basic unit of life

Charles Darwin (1809–1892)
The splendid isolation of the animal species on the Galapagos Islands, and the differences between them and related mainland species, first gave Darwin the idea of evolution. He believed—and his ideas provoked much controversy—that selection occurs within species, so that only the fittest individuals survive to pass on their genes.

Each human adult has an estimated 60 million million cells. Together these units of life give the body substance, shape and form. Remarkably, each human cell, except for mature red blood cells which have no nucleus, is potentially capable of forming a complete human being.

The cells are controlled by genes, the units of heredity, and every cell in an individual has the same set of genes. There are many thousands of genes within each cell; exactly how many is a subject of scientific dispute.

The genes are biological blueprints which shape and form the body on a production line making long lines of identical cellular models, millions of them every day. Invention and innovation are the lifeblood of industry in the outside world but in the internal world of the body there are no new cellular models; each new cell is a replica of an old one—except for the occasional mistake.

Division and differentiation

All the cells in our body arise from the solitary cell created by the fusion of a sperm from the father and an ovum (egg) from the mother. This cell divides to create more cells and then they divide and sub-divide. The first cells formed by the fertilised ovum are identical. Then a complicated process called differentiation occurs, creating cells of different shape, size and texture, each of which has a specific task. Muscle cells are concerned only with movement, nerve cells only with co-ordination and so on.

The role of the cell determines its structure and shape because cells are built only for efficiency. This characteristic is not usually synonymous with beauty but there are few things to match the rich visual diversity of animal cells. They encompass grace, elegance, form and symmetry, and include every conceivable shape from boxes to balls and from cylinders to trees. As an example, the small, simple oxygen-carrying red blood cells are saucer-shaped because this is the most efficient shape for carrying oxygen to the other cells and carbon dioxide away from them. Nerve cells have particularly long extensions because these are efficient for transmitting messages. In contrast, liver cells are square-shaped and very tightly packed together. The cells which line some of the ducts in the body have hair-like extensions called cilia which facilitate the passage of various materials through them. And these cilia have exactly the same structure as those found in one-celled animals alive today and alive when life on earth had just begun.

The pictures on page 12 show the wonders of cellular structure. But they should be visualised as action pictures; cells are living things which move and change shape to balance the biological accounts within the body machine.

The walking aquarium The body is a community of cells divided into industrial centres or groups of specialised cells. Each such group of cells is known as a tissue and because tissues cannot work independently they are grouped together into organs. Each tissue is packed in a watery substance called tissue fluid which creates a waterway or canal system between the cells and the blood.

We are, in fact, walking aquaria, the descendents of elementary forms of life that lived in the prehistoric seas some 2,000 million years ago. Water accounts for about 60 per cent of a man's body weight and about 50 per cent of a woman's; the average woman has a larger proportion of fat which contains no water. Therefore, the average man's body weight includes about 9 gallons (40 l) of water, more than half of which is found inside the cells. In turn water makes up more than three-quarters of the weight of individual cells.

Cell composition

All living cells are composed of protoplasm which consists of organic and inorganic salts, glucose, lipids (fatty substances) and nitrogenous substances. The protoplasm is encased by a very fine membrane which regulates entry of raw materials into, and expulsion of waste materials from, the cells. These materials include organic substances such as proteins, carbohydrates and fats, and inorganic elements such as sodium, potassium and chloride. Substances taken into individual cells vary according to their function. For example, bone cells need calcium salts for building purposes and bone marrow cells need iron to incorporate into the haemoglobin of the red blood cells made there.

The membrane gateways, made from lipids and protein threads, are punctuated by minute perforations through which substances such as oxygen can pass into the protoplasm and waste products such as carbon dioxide can pass out. Larger molecules which are too big to pass through are dissolved in the lipid membranes and then carried inside. Other nutrients such as glucose, fatty acids and amino acids, from which proteins are formed, are taken into the cell by chemical substances simply known as carriers. Cells discriminate keenly between the molecules they admit and discharge.

Beneath the membrane is the cytoplasm which takes its name from the word elements 'cyt' meaning cell and 'plasm' meaning matrix or 'something moulded'. It is a watery substance which gives the cell bulk and provides the medium in which chemical changes occur. Composed of many dissolved substances and chemical particles riddled by a system of linked tunnels, the cytoplasm supports the cellular production plant, the endoplasmic reticulum.

Cross references
Composition of blood 100
Heredity 14
Fertilisation 20
From embryo to foetus 136

The cradle of life

Out of the sea came life on earth. All animals are descended from primitive sea creatures. The body fluids of marine and land animals are similar, resembling the salt content of the sea itself. To this day all simpler marine organisms can automatically vary the concentration of their body fluids with changes in the surrounding sea. In slow succession the earth has seen the development of invertebrates (animals without backbones), fishes, amphibians (living partly on land and partly in water), reptiles, birds, mammals, primates and Man.

Cell: the complete survival kit

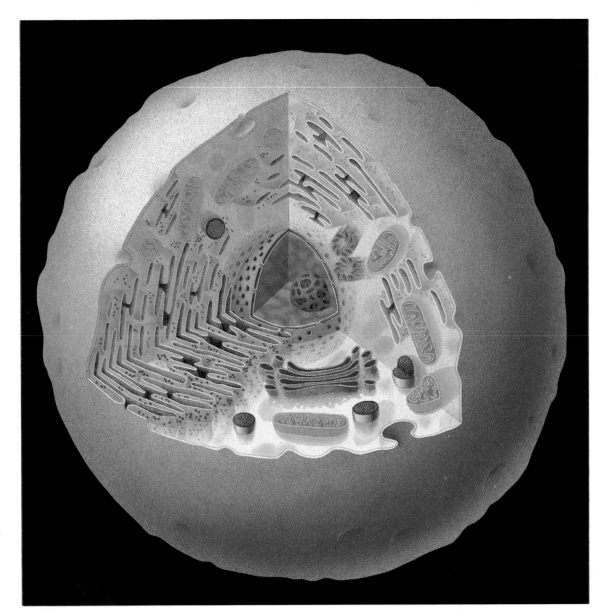

Inside the human cell
At the centre of the cell sits the nucleus. It contains 23 pairs of chromosomes made up of thousands of genes, each coding for an individual protein. The maze-like structure connecting the nucleus with the cell surface is the endoplasmic reticulum—the vital pathway for hormones and enzymes moving within the cell. The small bean shapes are the mitochondria, the cell's main energy sources containing highly specialised enzymes capable of breaking down fat and glucose to produce ATP.

Traffic inside the cell
Hormone molecules outside the cell activate messenger molecules on the cell's surface. These then pass into the endoplasmic reticulum to relay their chemical messages.

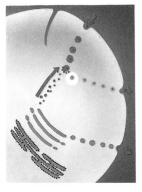

The basis of life Proteins, named from the Greek word meaning 'first importance', are the chemical basis of life on earth and they are synthesised or manufactured in the endoplasmic reticulum. They account for about 12 per cent of body weight and shape the characteristics of individual cells providing most of their structural material; they also control the multitude of chemical changes taking place simultaneously within cells.

Key products such as hormones and enzymes are formed from proteins. Hormones are chemical messengers carried in the blood which, among other things, regulate growth, the biological clock and basic drives and emotions. Enzymes are catalysts that stimulate biochemical reactions without taking any direct part in them. Within any one cell there may be dozens of simultaneous chemical reactions occurring, each and every one of which depends upon the interlocking activity of the enzyme system. Usually each enzyme sparks off only one chemical reaction. Every cell contains several thousand different kinds of enzyme molecules, all of which are essential for building up the cell, maintaining it and helping to carry out its specific duties. The combustion of glucose would rarely, if ever, occur without a complex series of enzyme reactions.

Proteins are formed by the linking together of hundreds of amino acid molecules. Twenty-three different sorts of amino acids or building blocks are found inside the body and all but ten of these can be synthesised or manufactured by cells. The remainder are consumed in the diet in the form of proteins which are broken down into amino acids during digestion and then built up again into the proteins required by the body.

The composition of specific proteins is determined by the way different amino acids are

Cross references
Endocrine system 66
Diet 186
Energy conversion 39

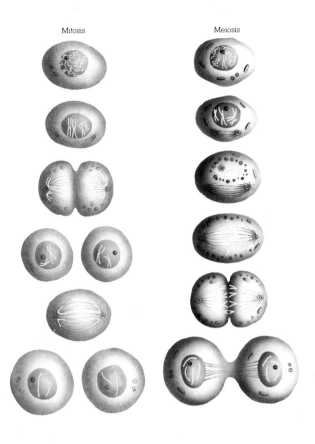

Mitosis

Meiosis

Divide and survive
Most cells in the body divide by mitosis, the sequence of events shown on the left. Cells in the ovaries and testes divide by meiosis, the sequence on the right. Mitosis begins when the chromosomes in the nucleus arrange themselves into long thin intertwining threads. Then each chromosome splits into two strands, the chromatids. These gradually pull apart from a centre point, the centromere, and the distinction between the nucleus and the cytoplasm is lost. Then the centromeres split and the chromatids migrate to opposite poles of the cell. As the outer membrane of the cell constricts two daughter cells are formed, each equipped with the same number of chromosomes as the parent cell. Meiosis on the other hand involves two successive divisions. The parent cell first splits into two, and then both of the offspring divide, giving four daughter cells. These have only *half* the chromosomes of the parent cell.

where the blueprints for life are stored in a 'library' composed of 46 chromosomes arranged in 23 pairs of different shapes and sizes. A chromosome, a large collection of genes, can be thought of as one volume within this library and the genes as the pages which set out the building instructions.

The gene machine

No man or woman, however unique, is ever made only of himself or herself. We are all mosaics of other people and other influences assembled by the workmanship of circumstance into a more or less integrated whole. This is the work of our genes, the machine tools of evolution. In theory at least genes are immortal. As people we die but our genes pass from generation to generation in a process of biological hitch-hiking, with every new conception representing a new hitch. According to the British biologist Richard Dawkins, author of *The Selfish Gene*, the body is merely the genes' survival machine, something to be discarded once it has served its purpose, namely the production of one or more new survival machines.

An individual who cannot cope with the environment does not reproduce and as a result his or her genes die out. The fossil record of the earth has shown that this has happened many times as environments have changed in the past, so that entire species have been wiped out.

Those who cope with the changing environment do so because of some evolutionary change in their genes, some slight quirk which enables their offspring to survive. These changes are known as mutations. Hence, in an environment of fast-moving predators the slightly faster rabbit will live to pass on his athletic genes to his offspring whereas his slothful neighbour will never know what hit him.

If an individual were to live forever, eventually he would become an evolutionary contradiction, an organism carrying unchanging genes unable to adapt to the changing environment. Apart from overpopulation, which could in itself cause major changes in the environment, the species could quickly become obsolete.

The late Sir George Pickering, Professor of Medicine at Oxford University, expressed this very aptly when he said: "Insofar as man is an improvement of monkeys, this is due to death. A new species, for better or for worse, can only start with a new life."

A half-century ago the author A. S. Warden wrote: "We live but to create a new machine of a little later model than our own, a new life machine that in some ineffable way can help along the great process of evolution of the species somehow more efficiently than we could do if we were immortal."

It is as if the world is a laboratory and we are the experiments.

Division in progress
Here a cell in the anther of a bluebell divides by meiosis. The two daughter cells are clearly seen half way through the second division. The resulting four cells will be the pollen grains which eventually penetrate and fertilise the ovary of another bluebell.

linked together into a chain or polypeptide. This sequence is in turn determined by the genes, which make known the building requirements through special chemical messengers composed of ribonucleic acid (RNA). RNA molecules form proteins by linking together the amino acids on small 'assembly benches' known as ribosomes which are attached to the endoplasmic reticulum.

The cell as a factory The cell can be compared to a factory. The ways in which the security guards, the outer membrane, regulate entry to and exit from the cell, how raw materials and waste are carried in and out, and how the production plant operates have already been described. The export packing department, known as the Golgi complex after Camillo Golgi, the Italian physician who discovered it in the brain cells of barn owls, receives the produce and moves it to the wall of the cell in membraneous bags for export.

The power plant is made up of machines called mitochondria, of which there may be many hundreds in a single cell. The mitochondria extract energy from the chemical bonds of nutrients for use in chemical, mechanical and electrical work. As we breathe in and out every minute of the day, glucose and fatty acid molecules undergo a series of chemical changes resulting in the formation of a high-octane fuel, adenosine triphosphate (ATP).

The control centre of the cell is the nucleus,

The mechanisms of inheritance

Spiral geometry of DNA
Just before a cell divides each chromosome can be seen to consist of a pair of chromatids, the tightly coiled structure of which is shown below. The angles at which the base molecules join to form the steps of the staircase dictate the double spiral pattern and the very tight coiling of DNA.

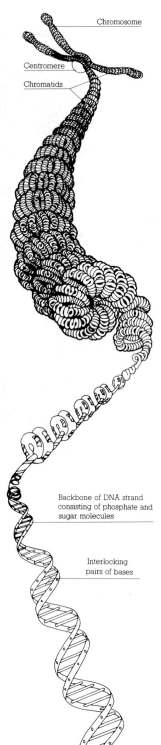

Chromosome

Centromere

Chromatids

Backbone of DNA strand consisting of phosphate and sugar molecules

Interlocking pairs of bases

The spiral staircase The way in which the genetic blueprints of life are stored in the 23 pairs of chromosomes lying within the nucleus of the cell has already been described. The chromosomes have a skeleton of protein, but the genes they carry are made of deoxyribonucleic acid (DNA). In fact the discovery in 1953 by James Watson, an American biologist, and Francis Crick, a British physicist, of the chemical structure of DNA is among the greatest of all biological discoveries.

Crick and Watson showed that the DNA molecule is shaped like a helix or spiral staircase built up of many thousands of steps. The sides of the staircase consist of sugar and phosphate, and the steps consist of one of four nitrogen-containing compounds: adenine, thymine, cytosine and guanine (A, T, C and G). Chemically these are bases (capable of combining with an acid to form a salt). Each step has two bases joining in the middle like the two sections of a drawbridge. Only certain pairs have room to unite; base A can join only with base T and vice versa, and base G only with base C and vice versa.

As a result there are four combinations which can be repeated on any one section of the DNA stairway. For example, AT may be followed by CG, then by TA, and then by AT, CG, GC, TA, AT and so on. Although there are only four combinations, there is no limit to the number of sequences which create diversity on the stairways, and thereby uniqueness in every individual.

The sequences create a chemical code which is copied by the other nucleic acid, ribonucleic acid on RNA, the cell messenger, which is then taken to the production plant and translated into proteins. This is the way that the genes determine the proteins to be manufactured within each cell and so control cellular characteristics. Every cell carries exactly the same information, meaning that within a muscle cell, for example, there are instructions for the construction of a nerve cell or a blood cell—in fact, for every cell. But the muscle cell ignores every instruction but its own.

Heredity

Genetics would be easier to understand if there were one gene which fashioned eye colour and another the size of feet and so on. However, most characteristics are shaped by many genes working together. There may, in fact, be as many as a hundred genes involved in one development process and it is often difficult to distinguish the role of one gene from that of another. And to make the issue even more complicated, the same gene can have different effects in different parts of the body.

Good genes, bad genes Just as people can be described in comparative terms, so too genes can be described as 'good', 'bad', 'recessive', 'weak' or

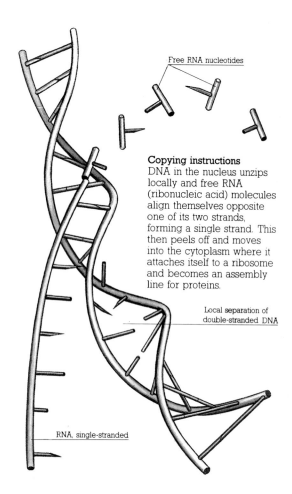

Free RNA nucleotides

Copying instructions
DNA in the nucleus unzips locally and free RNA (ribonucleic acid) molecules align themselves opposite one of its two strands, forming a single strand. This then peels off and moves into the cytoplasm where it attaches itself to a ribosome and becomes an assembly line for proteins.

Local separation of double-stranded DNA

RNA, single-stranded

even 'dominant'. As an example, brown eye genes are dominant over blue eye genes: two blue-eyed parents can expect to have only blue-eyed children but if one parent has two genes for blue eyes and the other two genes for brown eyes, their offspring will all have brown eyes. However, if two brown-eyed parents both possess the recessive blue gene, they are likely to have one blue-eyed child for every three brown-eyed—a genetic compromise.

Inheritance of characteristics determined by a large number of genes is more complicated. Children tend to be more 'average' than their parents. For example, most of the children of very tall parents tend to be tall but less so than their parents. Most of the children of very bright, or very dull, parents are in turn bright or dull but less so than their parents. A good home with many books, newspapers, intelligent conversation and other intellectual pursuits will not prevent this overall process of 'regression to the mean'. This is not to say, however, that intelligence and other inherited attributes are established by heredity in an unbreakable mould. Environment is immensely important. In the USA the children of Japanese immigrants tend to be taller than their parents, perhaps because of dietary factors. However, it seems that there is a limit to the average height any population can reach, regardless of nutrition.

The inheritance of intelligence is less

straightforward because it is much more difficult to measure than height. It has been suggested that genetic disposition was responsible for the fact that black Americans gained lower scores in IQ tests than white Americans. However, it has also been said that these same tests were biased towards the white culture—this was supported by IQ tests specifically designed for blacks and on which they did significantly better.

Genes and behaviour Scientists have tried to sort out the environmental and cultural components from the genetic components of particular traits by studying 'biological accidents' such as twins and 'social accidents' such as orphans or adopted children. Many studies have shown that the personalities and intelligence of adopted children are more in line with those of their true parents than of their adoptive ones. The same is true of mental abnormality and, to a small extent, of criminal behaviour.

There are two sorts of twins: identical or monozygotic (MZ) and fraternal or dizygotic (DZ). MZ twins are formed from a single fertilised egg which divides into two; they are always of the same sex and share 100 per cent heredity. DZ twins are the result of two eggs being fertilised by different sperm, so on average they share only 50 per cent heredity, no more and no less than ordinary siblings of the same parents. Even if identical twins are separated early in life and grow up in different places, they tend to develop remarkable similarities, as in the case of the Jim Twins.

In January 1979 James Lewis, a security guard in Lima, Ohio, traced his twin brother whom he had not seen since they were both adopted into different families at the age of five. The court which had arranged the adoption helped Lewis to trace his brother who was found to be one James Springer, then a record clerk in Dayton, Ohio, less than three hours' drive from Lima. A meeting was arranged between the brothers—39 years after the twins had last seen each other. It emerged that both brothers had married women called Linda. Subsequently both brothers had divorced and re-married, again both marrying women called Betty. Lewis had named his first son James Alan; Springer called his son James Allan. Both had owned dogs as boys, and called them Toy. Both men had worked part-time as deputy sheriffs; both had been employed by McDonalds, the hamburger chain, and both had been attendants in filling stations. Both brothers had the same favourite subject at school—maths—and both were poor spellers. The brothers have the same sleeping problems and share the same smoking and drinking habits. They also share 'tension headaches' that begin in the afternoon and develop into migraines. Both have had two confirmed or suspected heart

The DNA code breakers Francis Crick (third from left) and James Watson (second from right) received the Nobel Prize in 1962. Between them is John Steinbeck, winner of the Nobel literature prize that same year.

Mixing genes always means that some are suppressed and others expressed. No question as to which skin colour won out here!

Identical twins Arise from a single fertilised egg which divides into two embryos. About 1 in 90 pregnancies results in twins.

attacks and both have haemorrhoids.

The Jim Twins are one of 300 sets of twins to have been studied at the University of Minnesota. Sixteen pairs of identical twins underwent intense scrutiny. These included two British women, Margaret Richardson and Terry Connally, who underwent 46 hours of medical and psychological investigation and answered some 15,000 questions about themselves. Interestingly, it was discovered that they had both been married on the same day in 1965 within half an hour of each other.

The Minnesota researchers also found twin pairs where one twin smoked and the other did not. However, it was found that the state of the lungs of the smoking twin was almost exactly the same as that of the non-smoking twin. This lends circumstantial support to the idea that some people may be genetically resistant to the effects that smoking appears to cause in others.

Number 23: the sex chromosomes

Sexual deviance The Minnesota findings also challenged the widespread belief that people are genetically predisposed towards homosexuality. There are identical twins where both are homosexual; and there are other pairs where one is homosexual and one apparently fully heterosexual.

The genetic 'explanation' for sexual deviance has been popular for two reasons: for the homosexual it provides a simple means of explaining his sexual preference, while for the heterosexual it provides a means of compartmentalising a baffling deviation. The genetic argument is one of several about the origins of sexual deviance and currently it has little scientific support. It may be that the science of genetics is not yet advanced enough to detect the link, if one exists.

Which sex? Of the 23 pairs of chromosomes within a body cell, 22 are matching pairs. In women the 23rd pair is also identical and these are known as the X chromosomes. Men have two chromosomes that do not match: one is an X chromosome, as in women, the other is a Y chromosome. Paternal and maternal chromosomes fuse at conception to create an XX combination (female) or an XY combination (male).

But there are other combinations which arise either from an absence of one chromosome or the appearance of a third, or even a fourth. One example is XO, where O signifies no chromosome. XO individuals have external female genitalia but lack internal sex organs, a condition known as Turner's syndrome.

The combination XXY, Klinefelter's syndrome, produces a sterile man with a small penis, small testicles, and often a slight degree of mental handicap. Other chromosomal mistakes can lead to anomalies such as XXX, XXXY and XYY.

Examination of chromosomal abnormalities among criminals suggests that there is a case for cytological evidence to be produced in court before a defendant is put in the dock. In one British prison, for example, it was found that 20 per cent of men who were more than 6 ft (1.8 metres) tall were XYYs. Since the Y chromosome shapes masculine characteristics it was thought that XYYs might be aggressive and prone to wildness. In fact, they are associated more with trivial crime such as shop-lifting and pilfering. In 1969 a Los Angeles judge ruled that the XYY abnormality cannot be used to excuse crime. According to one recent estimate there are 700 'normal' XYs for every one XYY, and many quite 'normal' men are XYY.

Hermaphroditism is a sex anomaly hundreds of times rarer than XYY. Hermaphrodites are people with both male and female gonadal tissue, both testes and ovaries. Most hermaphrodites, however, have external genitalia which contradict their chromosomal sex, and for this reason are called pseudohermaphrodites. A female pseudo-hermaphrodite has female chromosomes, gonads, hormones and internal sex organs, but because of a genetic anomaly which produces excess male hormone during the foetal stage, she is born with a small penis and a scrotum. At puberty breasts develop and her true sex is revealed.

The moral is, your chromosomes may say you are one thing, but your genes may say you are something slightly different.

Genetic disease Natural selection, the survival of the fittest, is no longer the major determinant of human survival. With scientific and other advances the physically weak and the mentally retarded can now live long enough to marry and have children. In other words, survival no longer depends solely upon individual capacity for keeping warm, hunting and killing and beating competition from rival species. Social and cultural forces as well as natural ones determine the patterns of human reproduction to an unprecedented extent.

A case in point is the way in which genetically determined disorders can now be partly controlled. Haemophilia is one such disorder and it arises from a DNA 'copying' error. Because they lack a substance called Factor VIII, which promotes blood clotting, haemophiliacs are prone to internal bleeding and to prolonged bleeding from even slight external injuries. Women carry the disorder—the gene concerned is on the X chromosome—but only males suffer from it, because their X chromosome has no pair. Children of carriers have a one in two chance of carrying a haemophiliac gene.

One of the most famous carriers was the British Queen Victoria. Her eighth child, Prince Leopold, died after a minor fall resulted in major bleeding, while two of her daughters, Alice and Beatrice, carried the disease into the Prussian, Russian and Spanish royal families. Most haemophiliacs die prematurely, some in childhood. Treatment is by transfusion of plasma containing Factor VIII.

Some defective or mutant genes can pass undetected through many generations of a family. The offspring are not at risk unless the family is sexually united with another carrying family. This is what happens in the case of cystic fibrosis, a severe gland disorder. The children of two carriers have a one in four chance of contracting the disease, two chances in four of becoming a carrier and one chance in four of inheriting normal genes.

Mutant genes can also have positive effects. In West Africa, for example, particular mutant genes inherited from both parents can produce sickle-cell anaemia, a killer blood disorder. However, if a child inherits the recessive gene from only one parent, he or she has stronger than average resistance to malaria.

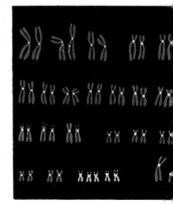

Under a microscope each group of human chromosomes (here the different colours correspond to the different groups) has a distinctive appearance. The 23rd pair (grey) are the sex chromosomes, in this case X and Y. The presence of the extra chromosome in pair 21 is abnormal and associated with Down's syndrome. Normal individuals have only 46 chromosomes

Cloning Some scientists now believe that it will become possible to produce long lines of identical human beings, in much the same way as factories produce long lines of identical automobiles.

The process in humans is called cloning and it involves production of a new individual with an identical gene make-up to one of the parents; in other words maternal and paternal genes are not mixed together in the usual way. Thus a mother could produce a baby that would be her own 'identical twin'. Similarly, a father could also produce an identical, though of course younger, 'identical twin'. The process involves taking a cell from a single 'parent' and removing the nucleus containing the genetic memory bank. This is injected into a fresh human egg from which the nucleus has been removed and allowed to mature normally in the womb.

Frogs and mice have already been cloned, although most biologists argue that human cells are too small to clone with available techniques. However, the rapidly expanding science of molecular biology will probably overcome such problems, but several basic ethical questions will have to be answered first. Does man have the right to play at creator? What will happen if he does? Will he be able to replicate genius in the test tube? He may replicate the genes of a genius without actually producing a carbon copy genius; after all, environment too is immensely important.

Life and death of cells

Although each one of us is born only once and can die only once, there is a constant cycle of life and death within all our bodies; every second some 50 million cells die but they are immediately replaced. Some cells in the intestinal lining live for only one and a half days; white blood cells survive for only a few days; and the oxygen-carrying red blood cells survive for about four months. New cells are created by the division of old ones in a process known as mitosis. In this process each of the 46 chromosomes splits in half along its length to form pairs (like splitting a log rather than sawing it across the middle). The two halves, each containing a portion of all parts of the original, move to opposite sides of the cell and each half then forms a new nucleus. The middle of the original cell then constricts and divides. The result is two new cells arising from what are known as the daughter nuclei (see diagram on page 13).

Sexual reproduction involves a different kind of division, meiosis. The sex cells—sperm in the man and ova in the woman—divide as before but the chromosomes do not split into two sets of pairs. As a result each sex cell has only 23 chromosomes and not 23 pairs of chromosomes (see diagram on page 13). As described earlier, the 23 single chromosomes become 23 pairs at fertilisation.

Down's syndrome
commonly referred to as mongolism, is a chromosomal disorder which affects roughly 1 in 700 babies, with increased frequency in babies born to older mothers. Down's children have a typically slant-eyed, immature appearance. Abnormality in chromosome 21 is the usual cause.

Screening procedures
for genetic diseases have increased dramatically in recent years. Spina bifida and anencephaly (in which the neural tube in the spine or skull fails to close) can be diagnosed very early.

The royal disease,
as haemophilia was once referred to, is a sex-linked disorder. Eighty per cent of cases are caused by a gene on the X chromosome which is expressed in males but only carried by females. Queen Victoria was a carrier: one of her sons, three of her grandsons and seven of her greatgrandsons were haemophiliacs. For a woman to be a haemophiliac, haemophilia genes must be present on both X chromosomes; in other words her mother would have to be a carrier and her father haemophiliac.

Woman: the inside story

Labia majora
Entrance to vagina
Labia minora
Hood of clitoris
Urethral meatus
Perineum
Anus

The female vulva
or external sexualia. The clitoris is ideally located to receive the maximum possible stimulation during lovemaking, but many men, and too many women, are only half aware of its importance.

The words 'it's a boy' or 'it's a girl' are almost invariably the first words that mark the arrival of a newborn baby. In the delivery room, during those first few seconds, there is only one visible distinction between the sexes—the genitals. Everything else is indistinguishable. In fact, the similarities between the sexes are so marked that it would be strange if their genitals were not in some way similar as well, as indeed they are.

The clitoris, for example, is the female equivalent of the male penis. Like the penis, the clitoris is even hooded by a foreskin and it too swells with blood during sexual excitement. From puberty both the male and female genitals are shrouded in pubic hair. Internally too the female ovaries and the male testes produce hormones that regulate the reproductive system and influence the size and shape of the body.

These similarities are examined in detail later in this section. But it is worth mentioning now that the text is accompanied by diagrams and pictures, some of which are based on *composite* findings. Illustrations such as these can create as much worry as enlightenment among people who believe they are in some way 'different' and therefore possibly abnormal.

But just as height, weight and appearance vary from individual to individual so too do the genitals. They are as much an expression of physical individuality as our faces. This is an important point to stress because people often conceal nagging doubts about the inadequacy of their genitals. Most people are brought up to hide their genitals or 'private parts', even to the point of feeling ashamed about looking at them closely. Later this feeling of guilt may subside, only to be replaced by a fear of admitting to ignorance about them. Yet understanding about the sexual systems can affect behaviour, confidence, personal esteem and our relationships with one another.

The female

A woman's sexual organs are more complex than those of a man because she plays a somewhat larger part than he does in the reproductive process. The man merely deposits the sperm in the woman's body; she produces eggs for the sperm to fertilise and nourishes the embryo for nine months until it emerges as a fully formed baby.

The vulva, the external part of the female genitalia, is a mouth with not one but two sets of lips, the labia majora and the labia minora. These part during sexual arousal, exposing the opening of the vagina. Enclosing and protecting the entrances to both the reproductive and urinary systems, the labia majora extend downwards from the mound of fatty tissue over the pubic bone (mons pubis) and join between the legs at the perineum, just in front of the anus.

One outer lip may be bigger than the other, but this does not affect function and is nothing to worry about. Similarly, one of the inner lips may be bigger than the other. Again, there is nothing unusual about this.

The outer lips surround the clitoris and the inner lips. The thinner, inner lips can be seen by pulling back the outer ones. Curving upwards to meet in the region of the clitoris, the labia minora change in colour from pink to red during sexual intercourse.

Clitoris Consisting of a small bud of tissue, the clitoris varies in size from 1/5–1 in (0.5–2.5 cm) in length and from 1/3–3/4 in (1–2 cm) in diameter. The clitoris contains two corpora cavernosa, twin columns of spongy tissue equivalent to those found in the penis, and enlarges during sexual arousal, but it only becomes truly erect and protuberant in a few women. The clitoris is believed to be the most sensitive structure in the female body, yet many people still do not recognise it as an erotic focus, believing instead that deep vaginal penetration is the key to sexual satisfaction. Just as a man does not have to possess a large penis to be a good lover, a woman does not have to have a large clitoris. Yet some women worry unnecessarily either because they fail to detect the clitoris or because it seems so small.

The clitoris is sensitive to pressure and to stretching as well as to touch, meaning that it is not necessary to touch it directly to achieve stimulation, although some women find this immensely pleasurable. In contrast, others experience extreme pain through direct clitoral contact, preferring stimulation of the surrounding areas, such as the labia minora, the vaginal vestibule or entrance, and the mons pubis. The latter cushions the impact between the male and female pubic bones during intercourse and therefore acts as a sort of shock absorber.

Vestibule and hymen The basin-shaped vaginal vestibule or entrance also contains the entrance to the urethral meatus or urinary tract. Many people worry about urine seeping into the vagina but in healthy people urine is usually sterile, so worry is rarely justified.

In a virgin the vaginal entrance is often partly blocked by a membrane called the hymen. Contrary to what many people believe the hymen does not completely seal the vagina; exit from the vagina is necessary for menstrual blood flow. The retention of the hymen ('maidenhead' or 'virgin's veil') is unique to our species. In lower mammals the hymen occurs only as an embryonic stage in the development of the urogenital system. In his best-selling book *The Naked Ape* Desmond Morris comments: "When evolution has gone to such lengths to render [the human female] as sexually

Cross references
Cystitis **218**
Adolescence **153**
Prenatal development **136**

responsive as possible, it is at first sight strange that she should also be equipped with what amounts to an anti-copulatory device. But the situation is not as contradictory as it might seem. By making the first copulation attempt difficult and even painful, the hymen ensures that it will not be indulged in lightly." The point is interesting, but disputable.

The hymen may be thin and easily ruptured without pain. On the other hand it may be thick enough to prevent penetration and may require surgical excision. In fact, it is not uncommon for a woman to reach the hospital delivery room with her hymen still intact, so an intact hymen does not necessarily indicate virginity. Yet in countries such as Italy and Japan, which place a high value on premarital chastity, women have even undergone surgery to give their hymens an intact appearance.

Vagina The purpose of the vagina is to accommodate the male penis and to provide a birth canal. It leads inwards and upwards to the womb or uterus. A hollow muscular tube, the vagina is between 3 and 5 in (7.5–12.5 cm) long, but it distends and elongates with stimulation, or it could not possibly contain a baby, let alone a penis. During sexual arousal the soft vaginal walls secrete a lubricating fluid so that the penis can slip smoothly in and out. It used to be believed that this 'love juice' emanated from glands around the vulva and the neck of the womb. William Masters and Virginia Johnson, the American husband and wife team who have made a major contribution to our understanding of the physiology of sexuality, detected the actual source of these secretions by inserting a camera into the vagina. They found that secretion from the vaginal walls marked the beginning of sexual excitement.

Uterus The uterus or womb is a pear-shaped organ slightly smaller than a woman's fist, situated in the pelvis immediately behind the bladder and supported by the muscular floor of the pelvis.

At the lower end of the uterus is the cervix or neck of the womb which protrudes into the vault of the vagina. At its upper end the uterus opens on each side into a Fallopian tube. Extending out like outstretched arms, these tubes have finger-like projections which envelope the ovaries.

The uterine walls have two main layers. The outer layer is thick and muscular. During pregnancy, in preparation for delivery, it increases in weight from about 1 oz (28 g) to 2 lb (900 g). During labour it exerts a tremendous force. A fit woman can double the total force by voluntarily contracting her abdominal muscles. Within a few weeks of birth the uterus reverts to more or less its original size.

The inner uterine layer is the womb lining or endometrium. If pregnancy does not occur this lining is shed each month in the process of menstruation; if pregnancy does occur the lining forms part of the placenta (afterbirth).

Ovaries The two almond-shaped ovaries are about 1½ in (3.5 cm) long. The primary reproductive organs and equivalent of the male testes, the ovaries lie on each side of the pelvis. They have two functions: to secrete female hormones into the bloodstream and to produce ova or eggs.

The ovaries of a newborn girl contain all the egg cells she will ever produce—as many as one million contained within follicles. These egg cells are rapidly depleted so that there are only about 300,000 remaining at puberty.

Ovum maturation or ripening follows a set pattern. In the first phase the oogonia (immature cells) develop into cells known as oocytes. Containing 23 pairs of chromosomes these cells divide or reproduce through a process known as meiosis. Meiosis differs from mitosis, the other sort of cell division, in that cells do not split into two sets of chromosome pairs to create two new cells with 23 *pairs* of chromosomes. Instead meiosis is a process which creates a sex cell with only 23 *single* chromosomes; that is, it halves the normal chromosomal complement. Likewise the male sperm contains only 23 single chromosomes, so that in this way the combination of male and female chromosomes (from sperm and egg) make up 23 pairs, the normal complement, in the fertilised egg.

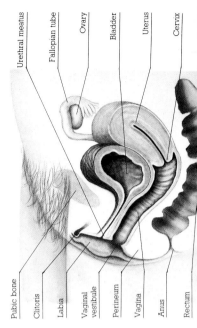

Urethral meatus
Fallopian tube
Ovary
Bladder
Uterus
Cervix
Pubic bone
Clitoris
Labia
Vaginal vestibule
Perineum
Vagina
Anus
Rectum

A woman's genitals are inside her body or hidden by pubic hair, hence much of the mystery and myth surrounding female sexuality. During sexual excitement the uterus draws up and away from the vagina. With orgasm the uterus, the vagina and the sphincter around the anus contract rhythmically.

Fertility rites as practiced by the Mechinacu Indians of Brazil. Even with today's advanced contraceptive practices, fatherhood and childbearing are everywhere regarded as fulfilling and socially respectable. Though less formal, fertility rites still exist in most societies however 'unprimitive'.

The beginning of a new life

Fertilisation The menstrual cycle lasts for about 28 days during which time the egg is available for fertilisation for only about 12–24 hours immediately after ovulation. Since ovulation tends to occur midway through the cycle—on the 14th day—it is theoretically possible to calculate when it will occur. In practice, however, it may not be that easy since the menstrual cycle is often erratic. To complicate the issue further, ovulation does not always take place half way through the cycle. Among women with regular menstrual periods, for example, ovulation may occur between 12 and 16 days before the next period, irrespective of the length of the cycle.

Finally, there are the sperm to consider. These can survive inside a woman's body for 24–48 hours or even longer, which is good if pregnancy is desired but bad if it is not.

In a single ejaculate there may be as many as 350 million sperm deposited around the cervix. These sperm face a formidable journey, thousands of times greater than their own length. Starting in the vagina they pass through the cervical canal and via the uterus to the Fallopian tube, and then up the tube towards the female egg. In fact, very few sperm—perhaps between 1,000 and 100,000—enter the Fallopian tube containing the ovum and of these perhaps only 100 will reach the ovum. A further 100,000 may enter the wrong tube but many more do not even penetrate the uterus. Detailed information about precisely why and where sperm falter is elusive. Similarly, detailed knowledge about the ultimate fate of sperm is scanty; many are destroyed while still in the vagina, others by white cells in the uterus. As a rule abnormal sperm—and as many as 40 per cent of the total sperm ejaculated may be abnormal—are kept out of the uterus by the cervix. This filter system is still not understood.

A sperm may spend several hours in the female before it is able to penetrate and fertilise the egg. During this time it undergoes a process called capacitation to make possible its penetration into the ovum. This process culminates in the shedding of the acrosome, the thin cap encasing its DNA-packed head. The acrosomal cap is believed to contain an enzyme which dissolves the protective outer coat of the ovum, making sperm penetration easier. This cap shedding is not only restricted to the sperm that subsequently penetrates the egg but also affects all the doomed sperm around the egg. This act of self-sacrifice is not without purpose. The enzyme from just one cap would be insufficient to break down the ovum membrane, but the enzyme from many thousands produces a strong concentrated enzyme mass. Therefore, contrary to popular opinion, it takes more than one spermatozoon to produce a baby.

It could be said that this process of fertilisation

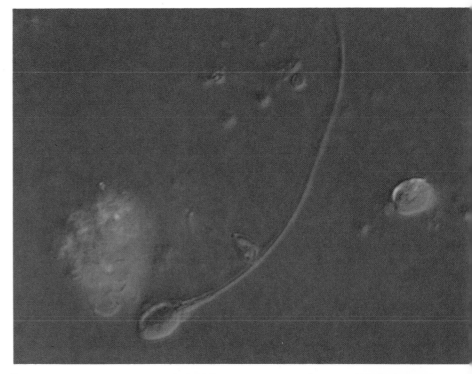

Egg meets sperm
One sperm cell, its rounded head packed with male chromosomes, meets an egg containing the female's. There is little evidence of chemical attraction between egg and sperm, but should they touch, the head and middle piece of the sperm penetrate the egg, leaving the long motile tail outside. Some 12 hours later the zygote so formed begins to divide.

leaves a great deal to chance. There is no mechanism to guarantee contact between spermatozoa and egg. New life hangs quite literally in the balance of random movement of sperm and egg in the Fallopian tube. In lower plants, by contrast, sperm are directly attracted to eggs. In bracken, for example, the eggs secrete malic acid to draw sperm to them (yes, bracken too has sperm). In humans, however, once the egg has been penetrated by a sperm it usually then resists overtures from any other sperm, except that is in occasional cases of twins, and in rare cases which result in the death of the embryo.

The sperm is engulfed by the egg. Only at this late stage does the egg complete its second meiotic division. The chromosomes of both sperm and egg then create two separate units. Known as the male and female pronuclei, these enlarge, move towards one another and meet in the centre of the egg. With the fusing of the two, the normal number of 46 chromosomes is restored.

Human embryo: fourth week
By the end of the first month the head and tail folds are complete. The brain and eyes are also developing, though the face is not yet recognisable. The heart is already present in primitive form and will soon begin to beat. At 28 days the embryo is still only ¼ in (5 mm) long.

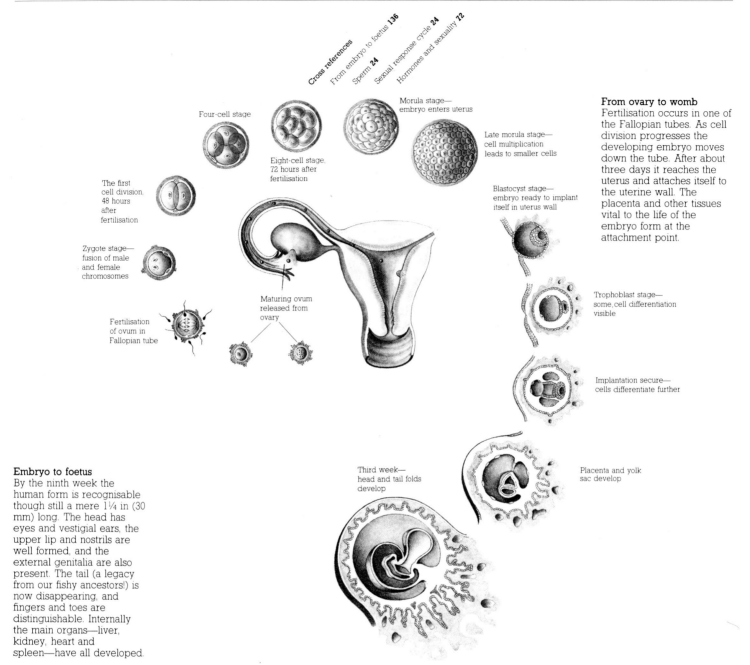

Cross references
From embryo to foetus **136**
Sperm **24**
Sexual response cycle **24**
Hormones and sexuality **72**

Four-cell stage

Eight-cell stage,
72 hours after
fertilisation

Morula stage—
embryo enters uterus

Late morula stage—
cell multiplication
leads to smaller cells

The first
cell division,
48 hours
after
fertilisation

Zygote stage—
fusion of male
and female
chromosomes

Fertilisation
of ovum in
Fallopian tube

Maturing ovum
released from
ovary

Blastocyst stage—
embryo ready to implant
itself in uterus wall

From ovary to womb
Fertilisation occurs in one of
the Fallopian tubes. As cell
division progresses the
developing embryo moves
down the tube. After about
three days it reaches the
uterus and attaches itself to
the uterine wall. The
placenta and other tissues
vital to the life of the
embryo form at the
attachment point.

Trophoblast stage—
some cell differentiation
visible

Implantation secure—
cells differentiate further

Third week—
head and tail folds
develop

Placenta and yolk
sac develop

Embryo to foetus
By the ninth week the
human form is recognisable
though still a mere 1¼ in (30
mm) long. The head has
eyes and vestigial ears, the
upper lip and nostrils are
well formed, and the
external genitalia are also
present. The tail (a legacy
from our fishy ancestors!) is
now disappearing, and
fingers and toes are
distinguishable. Internally
the main organs—liver,
kidney, heart and
spleen—have all developed.

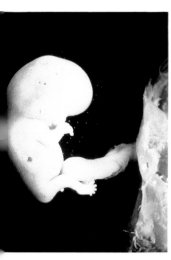

Menstrual cycle One egg ripens every month or so
between puberty, which marks the onset of a
woman's reproductive life, and the menopause,
which marks its end. Maturation and release of
eggs is controlled by hormones from the pituitary
gland. This is what happens in the average cycle.

Day 1 Even while a woman is menstruating a series
of egg-bearing follicles begin to ripen, stimulated
by FSH (follicle stimulating hormone). The
follicular cells produce oestrogen to reinforce the
womb lining in preparation for pregnancy.
Day 10–12 A surge of oestrogen signals the
pituitary gland to produce and release LH
(luteinising hormone).
Day 13 There is a surge in LH secretion which
causes the follicle to rupture.
Day 14 The egg or ovum is released, i.e. ovulation
occurs, and the ruptured follicle begins its
transformation into a yellow body, known as the
corpus luteum.

Day 15–25 The corpus luteum develops further
and releases, in addition to oestrogen, another
hormone, progesterone. These two sex hormones
build up the womb to maximum thickness in
preparation for pregnancy.
Day 26–28 If fertilisation and implantation occur,
progesterone and oestrogen from the corpus
luteum adapt the uterus to the needs of pregnancy.
If the egg is not fertilised, the corpus luteum
disintegrates in the last few days of the cycle and
the supply of progesterone to the uterus ceases.
Consequently the uterine lining breaks up causing
menstrual bleeding and a new cycle begins.

Eggs are transported from the ovaries to the uterus
through one or other of the Fallopian tubes, each of
which is about 4 in (10 cm) long. The egg is carried
downwards by contractions within the tube and by
a current formed by the beating of tiny, hair-like
structures called cilia.

Man: the inside story

Circumcision of Jesus, a painting by Andrea Mantegna. In many hospitals in the United States 80 per cent of male babies are circumcised in the first week of life. The operation is undoubtedly painful and stressful. Some psychologists argue that it not only adds to the trauma of birth but may also account for some assumed 'sex' differences which are in reality differences bred by cultural attitudes to maleness and femaleness. Clitoridectomy, cutting away of the clitoris, is an exceedingly rare and barbarous practice performed not for medical reasons but for the purpose of barring women from sexual pleasure.

The mass of coils and tubes making up the internal genitals of a mature male would extend for about 1,000 yards (metres) if they were to be unravelled. One of many examples of the body machine's compact structure, this remarkable design tends to be overshadowed by preoccupation with the size and shape of the visible parts. These consist of the testes or testicles and the penis. The testes manufacture and store sperm and also produce a hormone which promotes male characteristics. The penis deposits semen in the vagina of the female during sexual intercourse.

Penis The hydraulic power of the penis is derived from three cylinders of tissue attached to the pelvis and bound together by tough connective tissue. On the upper side of it are two cylinders, the corpora cavernosa, Latin for 'hollow bodies', which is exactly what they are when the penis is flaccid or unerect. In order to erect the penis these bodies have to fill with blood.

At the base of the penis the corpora cavernosa are covered by muscle strands to slow blood drainage and prolong erection. The third cylinder, the corpus spongiosum, is spongy and forms the underside of the penis and remains spongy even during erection. It provides a soft, protective coat for the urethra, the muscular tube about 8 in (20 cm) long which carries both semen and urine to the exterior. During sexual intercourse muscles at the neck of the bladder contract to prevent urine from entering the urethra and semen from entering the bladder. It is this mechanism which is defective in paraplegics.

The skin encasing the three cylinders is highly sensitive to touch and pressure. Sensitivity is greatest in the head and decreases markedly in the shaft which is more sensitive to pressure and less sensitive to touch.

Penile crown and acorn Much so-called medical language is more Latin and Greek than medical. It may seem intimidating but in fact it often describes the body machine in a colourful and imaginative way. Take, for example, the shape of the head of the penis. It could scarcely have a better name than the glans, the Latin word for 'acorn'. The rim separating the glans from the shaft is known as the corona, the Latin word for 'crown'. It is perhaps a shame that only the male reproductive system is biologically equipped with a 'crown'; a few new names would be chosen if somebody today was given the task of renaming the parts of the body.

Circumcision On an uncircumcised penis the skin forms a hood over the head; this is the foreskin or prepuce. The foreskin can usually be drawn back to expose the tip but adhesions between the head and the foreskin may prevent this, and the problem is simple for a doctor to deal with. In extreme cases the foreskin clings to the head. In this condition, called phimosis from the Greek word meaning 'muzzling', the foreskin fails to retract from the head of the penis, and the penis becomes trapped. Phimosis is treated by circumcision, the removal of the foreskin.

Circumcision is an emotive and controversial procedure. Although it is not usually necessary for medical reasons, most males in the USA are circumcised routinely after birth. Outside the USA the procedure is becoming increasingly rare, except when it is performed as a religious rite. Among Jews circumcision, performed when a boy is eight days old, affirms the Hebrews' covenant with God. Ritual circumcision is also performed among Muslims when a boy is aged between 7 and 13.

The argument for circumcision is that it promotes hygiene and makes the penis easier to clean. The argument against it is that the foreskin protects the penis' delicate head. Sex researchers Masters and Johnson have shown that there is no difference in sensitivity between a circumcised and an uncircumcised penis. Other people, however, maintain that circumcision does make the penis more or less sensitive. There is no conclusive evidence either way.

Dimensional neurosis The human male has the largest penis of any primate. When erect the human penis is not only extremely long but also very thick compared with that of other species.

Dimensions vary considerably and the popular idea of 'large' is frequently based on inaccurate hearsay. Even full frontal observations in the shower room can mislead because the penis is usually seen in its flaccid rather erect state. Erection tends to increase the size of a large flaccid penis by only 75 per cent; a smaller flaccid penis enlarges by as much as 100 per cent, sometimes more. Most adult penises are between 6 and 7 in (15–17.5 cm) long when erect, with the average length being about 6½ in (16.25 cm). In a survey made in the UK the smallest erect penis found was 4¾ in (11.9 cm) long and the largest 9 in (22.5 cm).

The old idea that tall strong men have larger penises than smaller weaker men is untrue. Measuring the flaccid length of more than 300 penises, Masters and Johnson found that the largest—which was 5½ in (13.75 cm)—belonged to a slim man of 5 ft 7 in (1.7 m) and the smallest —which was 2½ in (6.25 cm)—belonged to a man of 5 ft 11 in (1.8 m).

The belief that women prefer large penises is also untrue. More women report discomfort from large penises than dissatisfaction from small ones. And finally one more myth can be exploded: there is no correlation between race and penile size. This is a misconception with no factual basis.

Nervous pathways
of the male sexual response. Centres in the brain may be stimulated by the sight of a woman or by erotic imagery; equally they can be inhibited by taboos or fear of inadequacy. Erection and ejaculation are reflexes which can be helped or hindered by the brain. Provided the brain says 'go' and the nerve pathways from the penis and other erogenous zones are functioning normally, arousal is inevitable.

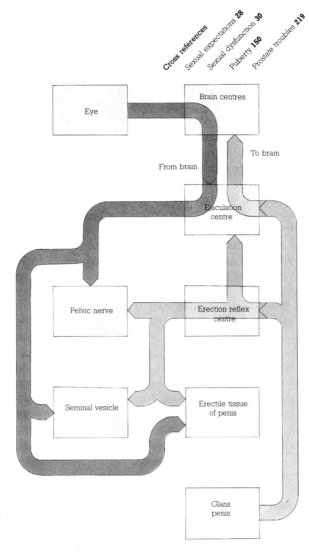

The male genitalia
lie outside the body. For many societies the erect penis has been a symbol of threat and aggression. Even apes and monkeys display their erect penis to ward off rivals and intruders. In some societies a man held his testes or penis when speaking under oath. Women, not equipped with either, could not 'testify' in court.

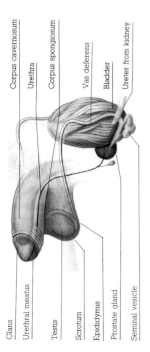

Glans
Urethral meatus
Testis
Scrotum
Epididymis
Prostate gland
Seminal vesicle

Corpus cavernosum
Urethra
Corpus spongiosum
Vas deferens
Bladder
Ureter from kidney

Testes The egg-shaped testicles, the male reproductive glands, hang together in a small pouch, the scrotum, below and behind the penis. Each measuring about 1 in (2.5 cm) thick, 1¾ in (4.35 cm) deep, and 1 in (2.5 cm) in length, the testes hang at different heights. In more than three-quarters of men the right one is above the left. This lopsided positioning is a mystery; perhaps the design is meant to prevent the testes from bumping into one another during ordinary movement. The testes are extremely sensitive and even slight pressure can cause considerable pain.

One testicle may be bigger than the other. Contrary to popular fears this does not decrease virility. Conversely a well-proportioned large pair does not increase virility. Many a bet has been won by men boasting of having three testicles. They win their bets by showing three swellings in the scrotum. However, surgical exploration would invariably show that one of these swellings is not a testicle, but a cyst.

The possession of three testicles is a biological impossibility. On the other hand, some men have only one. This rarely has an adverse effect on virility. One testicle is as effective as two.

In foetal life the human testes lie in the abdomen before descending to the scrotum shortly before birth. During their descent into the scrotum they pass through the inguinal canal in the crotch. Some only fall after birth but in two to five per cent of cases either one or both fail to fall of their own accord. In such cases either the testes remain in the abdomen or their descent is arrested in the crotch. If only one testicle is involved the defect is probably mechanical; if both are involved the cause may be hormonal, in which case injections of human chorionic gonadotrophin (derived from the placenta) encourage the testes to descend into the scrotum. Failing that they can be brought down surgically. This operation is best performed early, preferably before the age of seven or eight.

Normal body temperature is too hot for sperm production and so the testes must be kept at a lower temperature than that inside the body. There is a thermostatic muscle response within the scrotum, known as the cremasteric reflex, which relaxes and contracts it to adjust testicular temperature. If, for example, a man jumps into a cold pool of water, his testes will draw themselves up towards the crotch. Conversely, if he walks from the cold into a sauna, they will lower themselves.

Each testicle comprises many lobes containing about 1,000 seminiferous tubules. Each one of these spaghetti-like tubules is about 30 in (75 cm) long, giving a total of more than 550 yards (500 metres). They are lined with spermatogonia or parent cells which begin to divide (reproduce) from puberty onwards. Several complex divisions then produce immature cells called spermatocytes.

It takes about 74 days for a spermatogonium to become a mature sperm cell, and as many as 500 million mature daily. From the testes sperm pass into the epididymes, storage tanks consisting of some 20 ft (6 m) of coiled tubes. It is in these storage tanks that the maturation of sperm is completed. From the epididymis (singular) the mature cells move into one or other of the two 16-inch long (40 cm) tubes known as the vasa deferentia (singular, vas deferens). Surgical cutting of the vasa deferentia, known as vasectomy, is a method of birth control by which sperm are prevented from reaching the urethra. This does not significantly impede normal sperm production or the ability to have sexual intercourse.

From the vasa deferentia the sperm move into the seminal vesicles which also store sperm. In addition they produce fluids, sugars for nourishing the sperm and prostaglandin. The prostate gland, which surrounds part of the urethra, also contributes acids, trace elements and enzymes to the sperm to form a thick milky fluid—semen. Prostatic fluid gives semen its distinctive smell. In rape cases traces of acid phosphates in the vagina are used as evidence of coitus.

Sperm: the perilous voyage

Ejaculation At the climax of sexual intercourse the seminal vesicles pour semen into the urethra for ejaculation. The urethra is lubricated by a clear sticky solution, sometimes known as 'love drops', released from the mouth of the penis early in sexual arousal. This emanates from the bulbourethral glands that lie in the pelvic diaphragm. Love drops may contain sperm, making the widely-used coitus interruptus or withdrawal method a most risky means of contraception. When a man ejaculates the seminal fluid surges into the urethra which blows out to two or three times its normal width, producing an explosive feeling. Powerful muscular contractions propel the semen out of the penis in a series of about half a dozen surges.

The capacity for repeated ejaculation decreases rapidly after puberty. In his famous study *Sexual Behaviour in the Human Male* Dr Alfred Kinsey showed that about 20 per cent of 15-year-old boys can reach a repeated climax, compared with less than 10 per cent of 25-year-olds and less than 5 per cent of 40-year-olds. He also reports one man who for 30 years had four to five orgasms daily.

Sperm Semen is 90 per cent water, with sperm accounting for less than 2 per cent of volume. Some 60 per cent of seminal fluid is from the seminal vesicles and about 38 per cent from the prostate.

About $\frac{1}{500}$ in (0.005 mm) in length, the mature sperm cell is divided into five parts: head, neck, mid-piece, tail and end-piece. The head is packed with chromosomes which potentially make up half the genetic component of the next generation. Accounting for half the dry weight of the sperm head, the chromosomes are protected by a thin cap, the acrosome. This is shed immediately before the sperm penetrates the female egg, releasing an enzyme or catalyst to make penetration easier.

The rest of the structure is designed to propel the sperm cell or spermatozoon towards the egg. The cylindrical neck is believed to account for the long whip-like movements of the tail that keep the sperm motile. The mid-piece contains the powerhouse or mitochondria which release the energy necessary for movement. An axial filament, built up of two central fibres and nine peripheral ones, runs from the mid-piece to the tail.

Sperm reaches the uterus within about 30 seconds of orgasm, both because of ejaculatory force and vaginal muscle spasms and the swimming power of the sperms. Initially in fact the sperms are relatively inactive. Subsequently they swim forward at a speed of about $\frac{1}{10}$ in (3 mm) a minute by contracting in length, first along one side of the tail, then on the other. But only those that are capable of movement do so; many perish quickly. Speed and progress also depend upon where the sperm are. Sperm that fail to penetrate the cervix

Sexual freedom became most recently overt in the 'swinging' sixties. The hippies, with their long hair and free love, have mostly gone but more liberal attitudes towards pre-marital sex, abortion and cohabitation have persisted. Though marriage is no longer mandatory, most couples still seek stable, often contractual arrangements.

Artificial insemination by either husband or donor now enables many infertile marriages to produce children. Semen is stored and introduced into the woman at the optimum time for fertilisation. The machine shown here concentrates the seminal fluid to ensure that it contains a high sperm count. In the United States approximately 60,000 babies a year are conceived using AI.

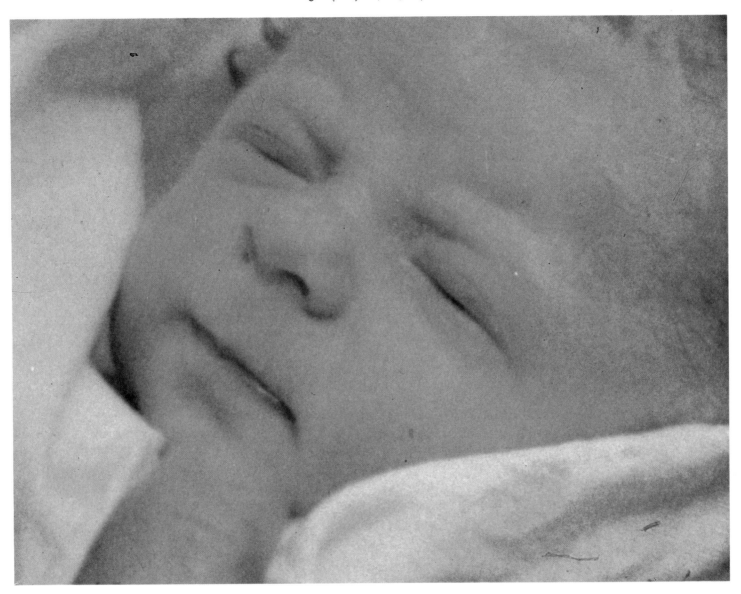

Conception outside the womb
The first baby to be conceived outside the womb was born in England in 1978. An egg was taken from the mother and transferred to a culture dish with sperm and nutrients. Once fertilised it was placed in another dish with more nutrients. Finally it was implanted in the mother's womb, after which gestation proceeded normally.

become motionless in the vagina after about one hour after ejaculation.

Sperm shapes vary. Those with normal oval-shaped heads account for about 80–90 per cent of the total in a typical ejaculation, though the normal healthy range extends from as high as 95 per cent to as low as 50 per cent. A high number of abnormal sperms can reduce fertility. Abnormal sperms have rounded heads or are double-headed or double-tailed; and some are giant-headed or pin-headed.

SPERM ANALYSIS A sperm count, expressed as the number of sperms in a millilitre of semen, is used to investigate suspected infertility. The range may vary from zero to several hundred million; a count showing more than 20 million per ml is accepted as normal. Most men produce about 3 ml (a small teaspoonful) of semen per ejaculation, and there are on average about 100 million sperm per ml. Fewer

than 20 million per ml may mean infertility.

It has become apparent in recent years that the quality of sperm movement is probably the most important factor in determining degree of fertility, even more important than sperm numbers. Where movement is very good, pregnancies have been recorded with sperm ejaculated by men with counts as low as 3 million per ml.

CRIME In much the same way as blood can be classified into groups, semen can also be classified into what are known as 'sperm prints'. These can help to identify the culprits of sex crimes if semen is found on the victims.

SPERM BANKS Human semen can be frozen and stored in sperm banks for use in artificial insemination (AI). Frozen rapidly in liquid nitrogen after chemical treatment, it can be stored for many years without losing its fertile condition.

Sexual response cycle

Theories on love
and attraction abound, but
recent attention has focused
on human pheromones,
odours we all emit but are
not necessarily aware of in
ourselves or others. Perfume
manufacturers have always
sought the essence of
ultimate attraction.
Researchers at Warwick
University, England, have
isolated a steroid from male
sweat which smells like
sandalwood and creates
'immediate empathy'!

In their remarkable research into the physiology of
sex, based on the observation of thousands of
sexual acts, Drs William Masters and Virginia
Johnson discovered that the body went through a
set or cycle of changes. They called this 'the sexual
response cycle'.

The female EXCITEMENT PHASE This begins with
the secretion of a fluid which lubricates the vaginal
walls. Some early investigators believed that this
fluid originated from the uterus and flowed through
the cervix. But Masters and Johnson saw full
vaginal lubrication among women who had had
hysterectomies and therefore possessed neither a
uterus nor cervix. Beads of moisture appeared on
the vaginal walls in much the same way as sweat
appears on the face.

The enlarging of the male penis and the
appearance of these beads in the vagina may seem
completely different responses but Masters and
Johnson believe they have a common cause.
During arousal there is an imbalance between the
amount of blood entering the tissues around the
vagina and the amount that can leave. More blood
entering than leaving produces vasocongestion.
Both the vaginal walls and the walls of smaller
blood vessels are semi-permeable membranes, that
is they retain fluids under some conditions but
release it in others. It seems that vaginal secretions
arise from leaks from congested blood vessels. So
both male erection and vaginal lubrication are
caused by engorgement of blood.

The clitoris also swells in size as a result of the
engorgement of blood vessels. In some women the
glans or head (equivalent to the glans of the penis)
may double in size. In other women the clitoral
swelling response may be slight. The clitoral shaft
also enlarges. Blood engorgement also increases
nipple size, although one nipple may become
erect before the other. Increases in breast size are
more apparent among women who have not
breast-fed babies.

As sexual arousal increases the inner two-thirds
of the vagina expand like an inflated balloon. At the
widest point the diameter of the vagina may be
three times bigger than normal. The uterus also
draws up and away from the vagina.

The skin becomes flushed as small blood vessels
enlarge; this response extends from the breasts and
shoulders to the lower abdomen. And heart rate
and blood pressure increase.

PLATEAU PHASE There is no sharply defined
moment when this phase begins. The most
dramatic change is in the formation of the
'orgasmic platform'. The tissues surrounding the
outer third of the vagina swell and engorge,
reducing the size of the diameter by as much as
half, so that the penis is gripped, increasing erotic
stimulation for the man.

The appearance of the orgasmic platform, which
does not mean that the woman is ready for orgasm,
is accompanied by a further ballooning of the inner
two-thirds of the vagina and further elevation of the
uterus. In women who have had babies the uterus
may double in size. The clitoris becomes elevated,
although it also seems to retract and is drawn
further away from the vagina. Following elevation
its shaft shortens by as much as half but it still
responds to stimulation.

Earlier responses become more pronounced.
Heart rate and blood pressure continue to increase
and the sexual flush may spread and intensify in
much the same way as a measles rash.

ORGASMIC PHASE The arousal period may last a few
minutes or several hours depending on the
preferences of the sexual partners. In contrast,
orgasm itself lasts only a few seconds. It is marked
by a series of rhythmic, muscular contractions of
the orgasmic platform, the outer third of the
vagina. The first few contractions occur every
four-fifths of a second. Subsequent ones are more
spaced out and less intense. An intense orgasm may
produce as many as 12 contractions; a mild one
three or four. In one extreme recorded case there
were 25 contractions within 43 seconds.

The uterus also contracts during orgasm, and
other muscles, such as the anal sphincter muscle,
may contract rhythmically as well. Heart rate,
blood pressure and breathing rate also reach a peak
and muscles throughout the body become taut.

Cross references
Birth control **210**
Blood pressure **106**
Sexual dysfunction and sex therapy **30**

RESOLUTION PHASE The uterus descends back to its original position, although the lower part of the cervical canal remains open for as long as 30 minutes, gently dipping into the semen so that sperm can swim towards the uterus. The vagina relaxes to its original size. Women differ considerably from men in that their resolution phase may go only as far as the plateau phase. With continued stimulation some women, unlike men, can experience a second orgasm or even a succession of orgasms.

The male EXCITEMENT PHASE The penis enlarges and becomes erect as arterial blood stretches the tissue taut. Erection may occur gradually or within just a few seconds. The spermatic cords from which the testes are suspended shorten, drawing the testes farther up the scrotum and closer to the body. Just as in women one nipple may become

Sexual arousal

sets in train a series of events which result in vasocongestion of the whole genital region. Ejaculation at orgasm is assisted by the tightening of the cremaster muscle which raises the testes. In the woman the inner part of the vagina distends and the outer part contracts. In both sexes the onset of orgasm is experienced as something beyond voluntary control.

Rest phase
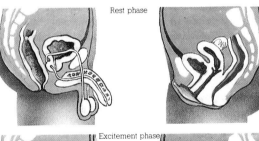

Excitement phase
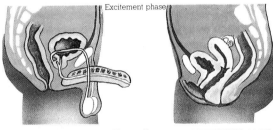

Plateau phase
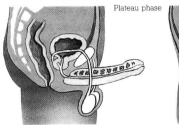
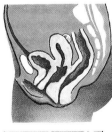

Orgasm
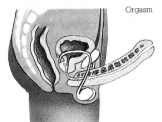
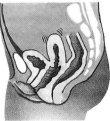

erect before the other, so too one testicle may rise before the other. Male breasts also respond to sexual excitement although not to such a marked degree as the female. Masters and Johnson observed partial nipple response among three-fifths of the males in their studies and this usually late in the excitement phase.

Heart and breathing rates increase as excitement mounts. In some men lubricating fluid appears at the tip of the penis even at this early stage. It is worth stressing again that this fluid may contain sperm, making it inadvisable to use coitus interruptus or withdrawal before ejaculation as a means of contraception. It is impossible to be certain that no sperm have been released.

PLATEAU PHASE Full erection of the penis is usually completed in the excitement phase, but during the plateau phase there may be a slight increase in diameter of the glans or head of the penis. The opening in the tip becomes more slit-like and in some men, on some occasions, the reddish-purple colour of the glans deepens.

The testes are drawn still closer to the body and may increase in diameter to about 50 per cent larger than their unstimulated size. The full elevation of the testes is a sign that the male is close to orgasm. If the nipples have not already become erect, they may do now. The imminence of ejaculation is marked by a sharp increase in heart and breathing rates and blood pressure. A sexual flush may appear over the shoulders, the chest, the neck and the forehead.

ORGASMIC PHASE Semen ejaculation is a complex process. Before orgasm, sperm collects in the seminal vesicles and in two flask-like containers, the ampullae of the vasa deferentia. The rhythmical contractions of these organs propels the semen into the urethra. The prostate glands contract at the same time to inject prostatic fluid into the urethra. These fluids are received by a bulb, which doubles or triples in size, near the base of the urethra. This bulb then contracts forcing the semen out of the penis under great pressure. Usually there are three or four major bursts of semen, one every four-fifths of a second. These are followed by more irregular, weaker muscular contractions.

As in women, the man's heart rate, breathing rate and blood pressure also reach a peak at the orgasmic phase.

RESOLUTION PHASE There may be a rapid decrease in penis size to about half its erect size, followed by a slower reduction to its normal state. During this phase there is a refractory period in which a second erection is impossible regardless of stimulus. The duration of this period varies with the individual and the occasion.

Sex: problem time or entente cordiale?

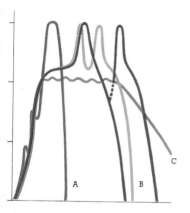

Sexual response patterns
Masters and Johnson found
that women are capable of
three patterns of sexual
response. **A** represents
rapid ascent to prolonged
orgasm, **B** gradual build-up
followed by several
orgasms, and **C** prolonged
hovering at the plateau
phase. The male response is
usually limited to one
orgasm.

Pink—female response

Blue—male response

Orgasm All the women in the Masters and
Johnson investigations achieved orgasm both
through masturbation and vaginal intercourse, so
it was concluded that orgasm is a natural part
of the human female sexual response. However, the
achievement of female orgasm is also strongly
influenced by cultural expectations. The
anthropologist Margaret Mead has suggested that
the human female's capacity for orgasm should be
viewed as a 'potentiality' that may or may not be
developed by a given culture. Virtually all
Polynesian women experience orgasm but the 1976
Hite Report, based on information provided by
3,000 women in the United States, suggests that
the majority of Western women do not regularly
experience orgasm during intercourse even though
they are quite capable of having orgasms when they
stimulate themselves. Shere Hite reported: "I
found that [70 per cent] of women do not
[regularly] reach orgasm as a result of intercourse.
An unrealistic expectation has placed a great
burden on women (and men). Women know very
well how to have orgasms when they stimulate
themselves—easily, quickly and with great physical
pleasure. Eighty-two per cent of women in the
study had masturbated and 95 per cent of those
achieved orgasms. Women are not dependent on
men to have orgasms, yet they are taught to act as if
they are. Why is there such a stigma on
masturbation? Why shouldn't women give
themselves orgasms while their partners are
cooperating by kissing them, etc? I am advocating
that women take power over their own bodies and
their own sexual lives."

A hundred years ago few people had even heard
of the female orgasm and even in the 1950s medical
students were told that about a quarter of women
were 'constitutionally frigid'. It is now known that
this is untrue and the number of Western women
unable to reach climax is steadily diminishing as
the 'potentiality' described by Margaret Mead is
realised and exploited.

In their recently published book *Sexual Decisions*
the North American authors Milton Diamond and
Arno Karlen postulate that the female orgasm may
be a relatively recent development. They say that
occasional reward can drive people harder than
regular reward. It would thus be biologically
adaptive, they suggest, for women to keep seeking
orgasm, ensuring a relatively regular supply of
sperm to help ensure conception.

Masters and Johnson found, as researchers had
before them, that middle class men believe they
have a responsibility for female orgasm. Such men
are more likely to try to delay their orgasms in an
attempt to help women reach theirs, while men
from lower social classes are more inclined to
believe that men should achieve orgasm when they
are ready for it.

Simultaneous orgasm can be very satisfying for a
couple, but those sex manuals that have stressed its
importance have also created anxiety among
couples who experience difficulty in reaching
climax together. In practice it does not matter at all
if the orgasms of the respective partners are one
minute, ten minutes or even further apart,
provided that the couple do not feel a sense of
failure or disappointment.

Sexual expectations

Today, now that respectable scientists have
brought sex from the shadows of the bedroom into
the searching light of the laboratory, far more is
known than ever before about the physiology of
sex. And there is no doubt that society as a whole is
benefiting from this new knowledge.

Many people are now far less inhibited about sex
and have been encouraged by the mass media to
enjoy what has been described as the 'new sexual
freedom'. However, many people do feel
imprisoned within the freedom of the sexual
expression they are supposed to enjoy. Freedom
means exercising choice—and choice, perhaps
paradoxically, can create anxiety. Many people
worry, for example, about sexual technique,
possibly because in so many marriage manuals
love-making sounds more like hard work than
pleasure. It is always worth remembering that there
is no sexual 'norm'; sexual capacity varies as much
from individual to individual as height and weight
do. Some people make love several times a week;
others only once a week or less frequently—the
whole question is a matter of personal preference.

While preferences do vary greatly, some factors
are almost universally considered important in
achieving a satisfactory sexual relationship. The
authors of *Sexual Decisions* believe that these
factors include relating to a partner as a person and
not just as a body. The authors claim that while not
everyone needs love in order to have satisfactory
sex, most people prefer something beyond body
contact. Certainly some people do fantasise or even
act out anonymity, prostitution, or rape during
sexual play but they usually already feel sexually
and emotionally secure with their partners.

The authors also advocate that a person should
be willing to please and accept being pleased: some
people gain greatest satisfaction from their own
pleasure, others enjoy giving their partners
pleasure, but perhaps for most people pleasure is a
combination of both. Unfortunately inhibition, low
self-esteem, difficulty in expressing passivity or
assertiveness, and other psychological factors can
stand in the way. It is important also to be flexible.
Something that is sexually exciting on one occasion
may not be so on another and vice versa. Likewise
something that pleases one partner may not please
another. If two people's sexual desires differ,

Cross references
Sexual dysfunction and
sex therapy 30

willingness to adapt and compromise is usually appreciated and in the long run may help both.

A couple should strike a balance between trust, seriousness and play. During sexual play most people are physically and emotionally vulnerable; if they are unable to trust each other they likewise cannot relax and fully respond. It can be particularly difficult to trust, admit need, and risk rejection and hurt when a relationship is new or when an established relationship seems insecure. Some people need verbal reassurance, others need physical contact. But either way, trust does open the door to emotional and physical responsiveness.

While for some people sex is a serious matter, for others sex is a game played for its own sake. Such differences in attitude can lead to misunderstanding or conflict. Some people, for example, resist factual or playful talk about sex because it seems to lack emotional sensitivity; they even suspect that being playful about sex indicates low capacity for intimacy. Conversely, people who are playful about sex may assume that those who are more serious are merely inhibited. Partners therefore need to be aware of each other's attitudes.

In general people communicate many subtle messages during sexual play. These can take the form of sighs, facial expressions, speech or silence. Unfortunately many messages are not given clearly or interpreted correctly. It is always admirable for a partner to explain his or her feelings, actions, or inaction directly or indirectly, and no harm is caused by partners telling each other what pleases or satisfies them. Asking a person to do something, however, may be more difficult and requires trust and confidence. It can be even harder for one partner to tell the other that a particular act is unappealing. However, this can usually be done with a tactful explanation that creates no shame, guilt, or feeling of rejection. Maintaining silence also expresses thoughts, feelings and attitudes. To keep communication open and clear, it helps to keep these points in mind:

☐ Indicate clearly your likes, dislikes, fantasies and desires.

☐ When turning down an invitation, say what you would rather do instead so that your partner does not feel rejected.

☐ Acknowledge what sexual activity you do enjoy and give your partner credit for it—compliment never hurts.

☐ Do not dwell on past grievances but suggest positive alternatives.

☐ When in doubt about a partner's wishes, ask instead of guessing.

Some experiences are memorable for their spontaneity and the best techniques can be frustrating failures if each partner's true feelings are ignored. If these are kept in mind, all but the most inept encounters can be satisfying.

For better or for worse, two people who have grown and worked together for more than 30 years. Without trust, honesty and affection their partnership could not have stood the strains of running a busy snack bar.

Untried affections Young love is often derailed by high expectations and unformed attitudes.

Sexual dysfunction and sex therapy

All problems formerly labelled frigidity or impotence are now termed 'sexual dysfunction'. Whatever the terminology used, well over 90 per cent of sexual difficulties are psychological rather than physical in origin.

Until the pioneering work of Masters and Johnson and others it was standard psychiatric practice to label a woman who was not orgasmic (unable to experience orgasm) as 'frigid'. But as William Masters (of Masters and Johnson) put it, frigidity "means a woman who doesn't have orgasm and it means a woman who has orgasm once a week and her husband thinks she ought to have it twice". In psychiatry, psychology and marital counselling the term has largely been abandoned as pejorative and vague, and been replaced by 'orgasmic difficulties' or 'orgasmic dysfunction'.

A whole range of male sexual problems comes under the heading of impotence, which like frigidity has become a highly derogatory term. It is more common now to talk of 'erectile difficulties' which may or may not include ejaculation problems or loss of interest in sex.

Dysfunction in women may be primary (anorgasmia or lack of orgasm under all circumstances) or situational (orgasm is experienced only in certain situations, e.g. during masturbation). Occasional orgasmic difficulty is often due to emotional dissatisfaction with the sexual partner, or to the man not maintaining erection for long enough. Also many women still suffer from society's double standard, which sanctions male sexuality but denies or ignores women's. Drugs, alcohol and fatigue decrease sexual responsiveness in women, though not to the point of making coitus impossible. Other forms of female dysfunction, such as vaginismus (spasm in the outer third of the vagina) and dyspareunia (pain during intercourse), usually have psychological causes, though the latter may be the result of vaginal infection.

Therapy for psychologically-caused dysfunction in women has traditionally tried to abolish performance-oriented sex, and emphasise non-demanding, mutual pleasuring and better verbal and non-verbal communication. 'Sensate focus' exercises encourage women to show their partners which kind of stimulation they find arousing. Most women who have primary orgasmic difficulty can become orgasmic through 'directed masturbation' therapy.

Male erection problems are categorised as primary (men who have never had intercourse successfully) and secondary (men who have). Both groups include men who have erections under some circumstances (on waking, during masturbation) and men who don't have erections at all. The secondary group includes men who can have intercourse on some occasions or with some

women–it is not uncommon for men to be impotent only with women they feel strongly about. Causes may be physical (severe diabetes, alcohol, certain drugs, fatigue) or psychological (guilt, fear, lack of knowledge, anxiety) or a combination of both. Although all men have erection difficulties on occasions, for some a single unsuccessful experience is enough to establish a pattern of 'performance anxiety', which of course creates and exacerbates the problem. Modern therapies (as practised by Masters and Johnson, J. and L. LoPiccolo and H. S. Kaplan) emphasise re-education, with gradual increases in intimacy under conditions designed to reduce anxiety about performance.

Sex therapy

Therapists regard and treat non-medical sexual problems as longstanding habits, which, like any habit, are difficult to break. The goal of therapy is to create an atmosphere where the natural processes of arousal and orgasm can occur unimpeded by anxiety. Contemporary sex therapists do not focus on creating sexual arousal or orgasm in situations where these responses are absent. Rather, and this comes as a surprise to most clients, they focus on breaking down the blocks to sexual responsiveness. Once the blocks of anxiety, inhibition or fear are removed, it is assumed that natural sexual responsiveness will emerge.

The goal of treatment is for the individual or couple to have one successful experience as a result of improved technique, understanding, trust and communication. Once the goal (firm erection, presence of pleasure, orgasm, etc.) is attained, the individual or couple is encouraged to identify the factors that contributed to their success, and make them part of their lovemaking. Therapy ends when the individual or couple is confident that the new patterns are well established. Follow-up research suggests that the level of performance which marks the end of therapy is not usually maintained; nevertheless the ultimate level of performance and satisfaction is usually significantly better than the pre-treatment level.

Correcting misinformation Many problems stem from misunderstanding the processes of sexual response and the range of individual differences. Education is an important, some would say the most important, way to ease sexual problems.

For example, girls are usually given inadequate information about their genitals and their different functions. Information about the role of the clitoris, for example, often leads to satisfying changes in technique and more relaxed attitudes towards oral or manual caresses.

Many men worry that their penis is too small. But such worries usually vanish when they learn

Erotic sculpture
on Indian temples is part of Hindu Tantric tradition. The Kamasutra remains the most famous Indian treatise on civilised living and loving. Some of its beautifully illustrated sexual couplings, however, appear impractical if not impossible.

Cross references
Anxiety neurosis 170
Good stress 167
Sexual desire 73
Sex hormones 71

Exhibitionism and voyeurism can stimulate equal sexual excitement in both men and women. Neither is necessarily deviant or perverted.

Sex education is very important for the development of a mature and informed attitude towards sex, which in turn helps to build loving and lasting relationships.

that the range of penis size is less in the erect than in the relaxed state, and that women are no less satisfied by a small penis than a large one.

Another major source of misinformation has to do with what is considered 'normal', in terms of frequency of sexual activity, techniques, fantasy, differences between men and women, unconventional practices such as anal intercourse, making love in funny places, and so on. The guilt and fear associated with wanting or having unconventional sex probably does far more harm than the acts themselves.

Revealing the mechanisms of anxiety During therapy each individual must come to understand both in a general and a personal way how anxiety diminishes sexual response.

Therapy almost always includes 'homework' assignments carried out between sessions with the therapist. The first assignment often requires each partner to take turns in caressing the entire body of the other, excluding the genitals, and telling each other what is most and least pleasant. The purpose of this assignment is to diminish the pressure to perform, and with it anxiety.

In fact, many couples fail to comply with their assignments most of the time, and it is the discussion of their failure and their resistance to breaking down established habits which provides most of the substance of sex therapy.

Specific techniques Masters and Johnson and other sex therapists have identified several techniques, besides improving communication and increasing experimentation, which can help with specific sex problems. For example, erection can be prolonged, preventing premature ejaculation, by the 'squeeze technique' (applied by the woman when the man feels he is close to coming) or by the woman ceasing to stimulate the man, thus allowing his erection to subside for a few seconds.

Another useful technique was developed for women who experience orgasm during masturbation but not during intercourse. First, the woman teaches her partner how she stimulates her vulva to produce intense excitement and orgasm. Then her partner learns to duplicate this manual stimulation. Then either she or he provides manual stimulation during intercourse. After a number of repetitions manual stimulation is gradually decreased. It is quite normal for a woman not to achieve orgasm during thrusting activity alone.

Another technical suggestion is often given to the man with erectile difficulty. First, the couple is forbidden to have intercourse and encouraged to engage in frequent erotic caressing. Usually, the man will begin to have erections during this activity, although if he thinks about intercourse the erection subsides. However, he learns the important message that erections come and go, and that should one begin to lose an erection during sexplay, there is no need to panic.

The existence of specific treatments for sexual problems dates only from the last decade, and we can expect much change in how such problems are viewed and treated in the future.

Skeleton: a system of struts and levers

Skeleton and muscles

Bones constitute the general framework of the body, supplemented by cartilage, the softer material covering the ends of many bones. Bones support the body's weight, provide the levers needed for movement, and protect the soft internal organs. The bones are moved by muscles which are inserted into them by fibrous structures known as ligaments. All muscle can contract, either under voluntary or involuntary control.

Joint damage

due to various types of arthritis is very common. In rheumatoid arthritis permanent damage is caused to both cartilage and bone.

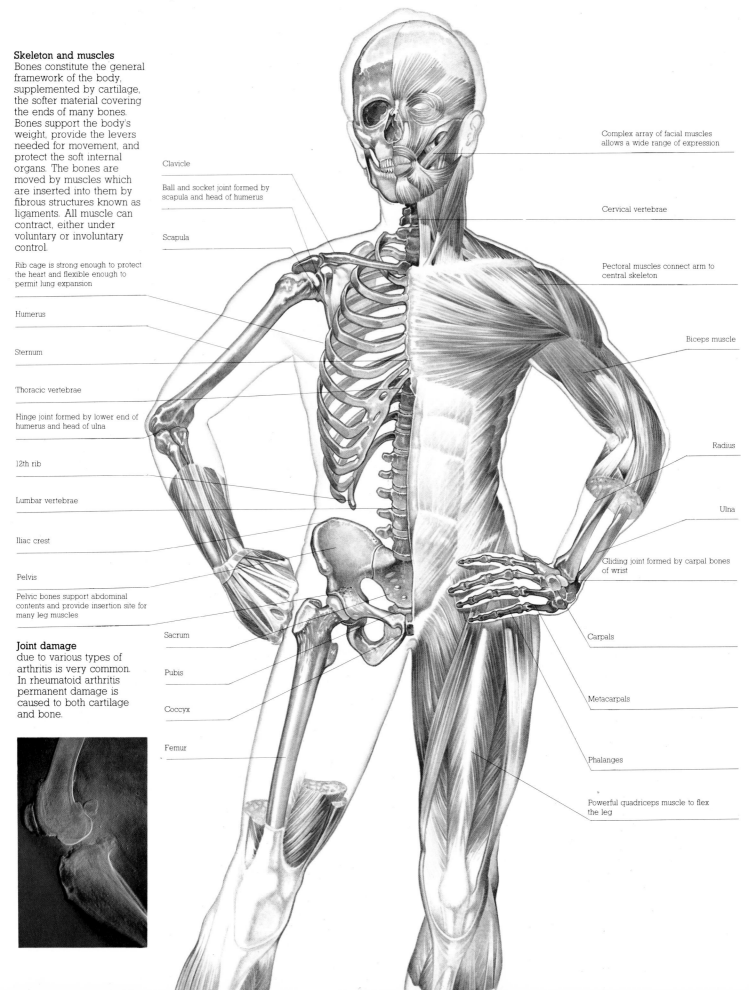

Clavicle

Ball and socket joint formed by scapula and head of humerus

Scapula

Rib cage is strong enough to protect the heart and flexible enough to permit lung expansion

Humerus

Sternum

Thoracic vertebrae

Hinge joint formed by lower end of humerus and head of ulna

12th rib

Lumbar vertebrae

Iliac crest

Pelvis

Pelvic bones support abdominal contents and provide insertion site for many leg muscles

Sacrum

Pubis

Coccyx

Femur

Complex array of facial muscles allows a wide range of expression

Cervical vertebrae

Pectoral muscles connect arm to central skeleton

Biceps muscle

Radius

Ulna

Gliding joint formed by carpal bones of wrist

Carpals

Metacarpals

Phalanges

Powerful quadriceps muscle to flex the leg

The skeleton is the body machine's structural support system onto which the muscles are anchored. Although the skeleton derives its name from the Greek word meaning 'dried up', live bone is anything but dry. Bone is one-third water and one of the most biologically active tissues. The body's mineral banks are stored in the bone, and millions of red blood cells are manufactured every minute in the marrow, the soft core of bone.

As a chassis the skeleton is unique. It twists and bends to permit a wide range of movement unequalled by any man-made machine. Equipped with highly sophisticated shock absorbers and a remarkable lubrication system, the skeleton is also more durable than any man-made creation.

There are 206 bones in the normal adult body. Though the longest and toughest are as strong as reinforced concrete, bone accounts for only 14 per cent of the body's total weight. Steel bars of comparable size would weigh some four to five times as much. We do not start life with our adult complement of bones; in fact newborn babies have as many as 300 bones, some of which fuse together early in life.

The internal structure of bone is made of a tough protein fibre called collagen (from the Greek words *kolla* meaning 'glue' and *gen* meaning 'forming'). On this structure are deposited calcium and mineral salts for hardness and strength, making the final structure as tough as reinforced concrete. If collagen is removed from bone it crumbles; if the salts are removed, it becomes as flexible as rubber.

Bone formation and distribution is determined genetically and by the stresses and strains imposed on the bones, especially during childhood. In consistency, shape and thickness, individual bones are custom-built for specific tasks and they incorporate the same kind of structural support system designed into machines and buildings to withstand stresses and strains. The thigh bone, the longest and strongest of the bones, follows the basic engineering principle that a hollow cylinder is an excellent design for ensuring maximum strength with minimum bulk. Measuring some 20 in (50 cm) in length and 1 in (2.5 cm) in width at maturity, the thigh bone is designed to withstand a pressure of 1,200 lb per sq in (3,500 kg/cm^2) when we walk.

Physical activity can increase both bone volume and density; conversely, inactivity results in loss. Cavalrymen, for example, have been known to develop new bones in the thighs and buttocks as a result of horsework. This is an extreme instance but it does show how the bones sculpt the body machine to meet various physical demands.

Space exploration has shown how remarkably sensitive bone is to environmental change. It seems that a permanent, weightless existence in space would reduce the human legs to purposeless stumps. X-ray studies of the Gemini and Apollo space mission pioneers revealed a loss of bone structure amounting to about 1/7 oz (4 g) of calcium per month, about 0.3 to 0.4 per cent of the body's total calcium. Evidence from the 84-day Skylab mission was particularly disturbing. The heel bones of two of the three crewmen decreased in density despite vigorous exercise and a special diet.

The thin and brittle structure of the crewmen's bones resembled those of the victims of osteoporosis. This condition, which makes sufferers prone to fractures, especially in the hip bones, is so widespread that it is regarded as an inevitable part of ageing. New knowledge arising from the experience of the American and Russian astronauts whose bone loss has been limited may prove helpful in the treatment of osteoporosis among the elderly. In women osteoporosis accelerates after the menopause.

It would also seem that, during a lifetime, the skeleton itself records time by calcium loss. This idea has been developed by Professor Wilton M. Krogman of the Department of Physical Anthropology at the University of Pennsylvania, USA. Also a noted forensic scientist, Professor Krogman has X-rayed decalcified areas of skeletons to assess age at death. He found that bone from dried-up skeletons can also reveal sex, race and medical history.

The structure of bone
Bone has an outer fibrous coating (periosteum) well supplied with blood vessels and nerves. The hard structural part of bone consists of many tiny parallel canals (Haversian canals); these run the length of long bones and have blood vessels inside them. Enclosed by this shell of compact bone is a looser mesh of bone tissue or a cavity filled with blood-forming marrow.

Parallel Haversian canals formed by concentric rings of bone tissue

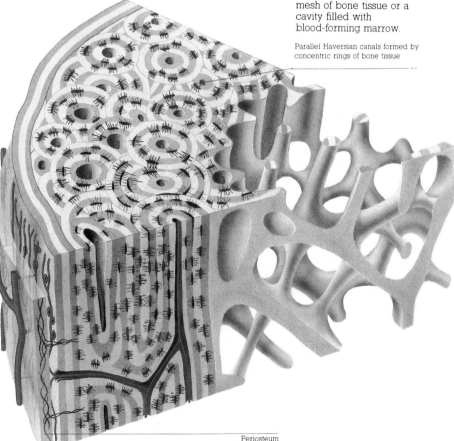

Periosteum

Bones and joints

Bone distribution The skull, the most important protective mechanism in the body, contains 29 different bones: 14 in the face, eight in the cranium or brain box which are fused together, two in the jaw and three in each of the ears. Buried deep within the middle ear, these bones are the smallest in the body. They convey sound vibrations to the inner ear, where they are converted into nerve impulses and transmitted to the brain for rapid interpretation.

The skull is supported by the spine. The spine or spinal column which contains the tail and extension of the brain, is built up of 26 bones called vertebrae. These have to withstand all the stresses and strains of a lifetime of bending and stretching while at the same time supporting the weight of the body. Each vertebra is linked to the one above and below by joints and by flat, biscuit-shaped discs of cartilage, a flexible white tissue or gristle. These discs act as shock absorbers, softening the impact of jolts on the spine and allowing the spine to bend and rotate.

There are seven vertebrae in the neck or cervical region, the head being supported by the top vertebrae. Next come 12 thoracic vertebrae which support the ribs, the cage protecting the heart and lungs; the five lumbar vertebrae coincide with the small of the back; and at the base of the spine is the sacrum and coccyx or tail, a vestigial reminder of

Agile antics
The remarkable agility of the human body is exemplified by this young gymnast. With dedicated training and practise it is possible to reach an astounding pitch of suppleness and coordination.

Rheumatoid arthritis
shown here causing swelling of the knuckle joints and characteristic 'swan neck' deformity of the fingers. There is also wasting of the muscles and disruption of their ligaments.

Man in space
conjures up exciting visions of the future, but the human body was not evolved in a gravity-free environment. One of the effects of weightlessness appears to be bone loss. On returning to earth most astronauts have shown a certain amount of thinning of their bones, despite the precautions taken.

Cross references
Chassis **32**
Muscles **36**
Hearing **60**
Ageing **156**
Transplants **236**

The complex anatomy
of the hand. The vast range of intricate movements performed by the hand is achieved by the 20 intrinsic muscles of the hand and the 14 muscles connected to the arm.

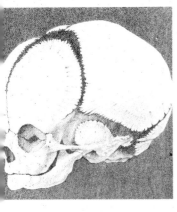

The foetal skull
looks rather strange because the jaw bone is relatively slow to develop. The bones of the vault of the skull do not fuse completely until two or even three years after birth.

A joint for every job
Some joints permit a wide range of movement where it is advantageous, as at the shoulder, or relatively little movement, as in the spine, where stability is the most important requirement.

our past. The coccyx is the only bone in the human body without a function.

The lumbar region of the spine receives the most punishment because of our upright posture. For us to be able to stand up our lumbar spine has to be curved which, together with the weight of the upper body, puts it under considerable mechanical stress. Consequently the lumbar region is the seat of much back pain.

The skull, the spine and the ribs are known as the axial skeleton, as distinct from the appendicular skeleton, which supports the limbs. A person can survive without limbs but not without the support of an axial skeleton.

We have 32 bones in each arm and 31 in each leg, a total of 126. But 112 of these are in our hands and feet, wrists and ankles. This means that half the bones in the human body support our intricate extremities.

Joints Muscles and bones are held together by tendons; joints between bones are made by ligaments. Our joints are oiled by a substance called synovial fluid—this reduces friction between moving parts in much the same way as oil lubricates the moving parts of an automobile engine. The bearing surfaces of joints have a lining of cartilage, which is almost frictionless. Our ears and the tip of our nose are made of cartilage, rather than bone, which is why they are so flexible. Initially the foetal skeleton also consists of cartilage rather than bone.

There are various sorts of bone joint. Ball-and-socket joints, as in the shoulder and hip, permit maximum range of movement. In the hip the top of the thigh bone is nearly spherical and slots into a semi-circular socket in the pelvis. Hinge joints, which are found in the fingers, toes, elbows and knees, allow movement in one direction only.

Saddle joints allow movement in two directions; we have a saddle joint in our thumb. Without it we would be unable to pick up small items like needles or tiny screws. Even a large object like a cup is extremely difficult to pick up with the fingers alone. Without its opposable thumb, the hand is little better than a claw.

All movable joints, whether in man-made or biological machines, are prone to wear and tear, but the biological ones have a longer guarantee. Modern surgical techniques, combined with newly developed materials, mean that many of the major joints can be replaced by metal or plastic ones, though these never last as long as a good original.

Arthritis This is caused by inflammation of the joints. After repeated attacks a joint may become severely deformed; today hip, knee and even finger joints can be replaced with artificial substitutes. There are several forms of arthritis, the most common being osteoarthritis (osteoarthrosis) and rheumatoid arthritis. Caused by wear and tear of the joints and loss of some of the almost frictionless cartilage linings, osteoarthritis is usually at its worst immediately after use of the affected joints. The most commonly affected sites are the neck, hands, hips and knees. Although it is not usually a progressively crippling disease, osteoarthritis can be extremely debilitating.

Rheumatoid arthritis is a condition involving the immune system and is usually at its worst in the morning. The immune system attacks the fibrous connective tissue around the joints and causes the muscles around the joints to stiffen, in time distorting and even dislocating them.

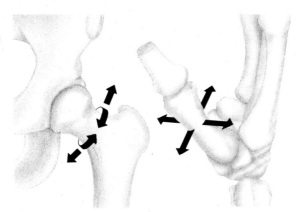

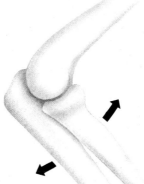

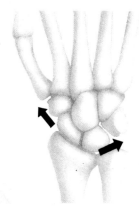

Hip joint—the ball-and-socket principle allows movement in virtually any direction

Thumb joint—the development of the saddle joint in the thumb was a major evolutionary breakthrough; an opposable thumb greatly increases dexterity

Elbow joint—a hinge joint, allowing movement in one plane only, absolutely vital for lifting

Gliding joint in the wrists—the carpal bones slide relative to the end of the radius bone

Muscles in close-up

Main superficial muscles
(front view). In the average
person muscle tissue
accounts for just over a third
of body weight. The
maximum force a muscle
can generate depends on its
mass. The force of its
contraction is concentrated
on a restricted area of bone
by tendons, which have a
tensile strength similar to
that of bone and about half
that of steel.

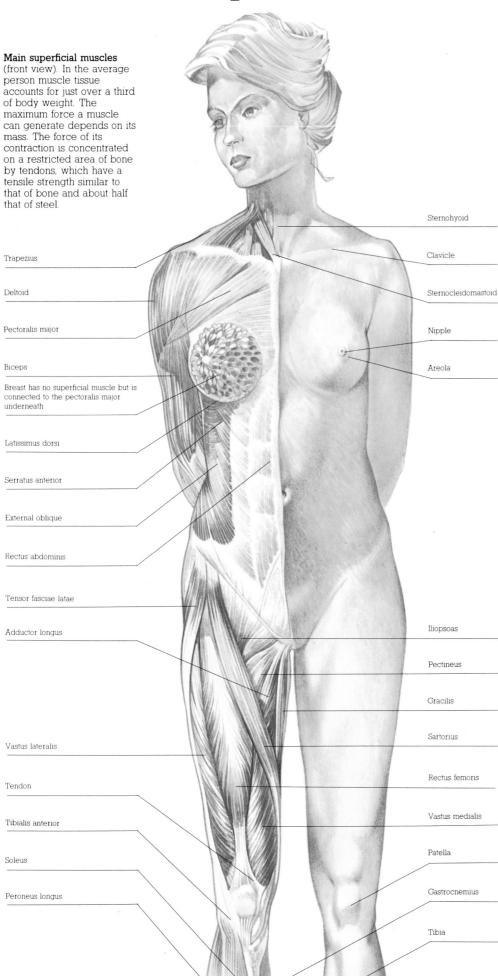

Trapezius

Deltoid

Pectoralis major

Biceps

Breast has no superficial muscle but is
connected to the pectoralis major
underneath

Latissimus dorsi

Serratus anterior

External oblique

Rectus abdominis

Tensor fasciae latae

Adductor longus

Vastus lateralis

Tendon

Tibialis anterior

Soleus

Peroneus longus

Sternohyoid

Clavicle

Sternocleidomastoid

Nipple

Areola

Iliopsoas

Pectineus

Gracilis

Sartorius

Rectus femoris

Vastus medialis

Patella

Gastrocnemius

Tibia

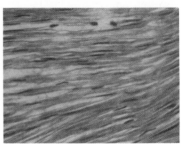

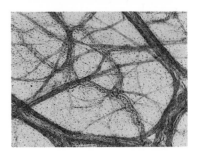

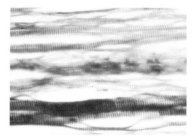

Variations in muscle
cells have developed to
perfom different functions
within the body. Short thick
cardiac muscle fibres (top)
occur only in the heart and
ends of the major blood
vessels. Their rhythmic
contraction does not depend
on their nerve supply; this
only modifies the rate of
contraction. Smooth muscle
(middle) is made up of
spindle-shaped cells and is
found in the walls of the
digestive and urinary tracts,
blood vessels, the male and
female sex organs and other
hollow organs. Striated
muscle (bottom) is
cylindrical in shape and
unlike smooth muscle is
under voluntary control. This
type of muscle moves the
bones but also takes part in
some reflex actions.

The muscles are the body machine's engines. They account for some 40 per cent of body weight and convert chemical energy into force and mechanical work. The release of energy exerts force on the tendons and, through them, on the bones and their joints.

Muscle types There are three different sorts of muscles: skeletal or voluntary muscle, used for locomotion; heart or cardiac muscle, consisting of linked fibres that contract in unison; and smooth or involuntary muscle, which automatically regulates movement in the urogenital, circulatory, digestive and respiratory systems.

Movement Muscles work by contracting and relaxing. During contraction they shorten their length by as much as 40 per cent to bring closer together their points of attachment on two different bones. In this way every movement is a pull, not a push, even when we are pushing against something; the effect of the muscle on the bone is to pull it.

Voluntary muscle The skeletal muscle system consists of some 650 muscles anchored to the skeleton. It powers all actions ranging from the delicate threading of a needle to the lifting of great weights. It also powers the visible expression of our feelings and emotions—our vast repertoire of facial expression is controlled by only 30 muscles, some of them less than an inch (2.5 cm) long.

Made up of numerous short cylinders of tissue, under the light microscope voluntary muscle is seen to be divided by bands or striations into sections rather similar to stacked piles of plates. Movement is initiated by nervous impulses or signals from the central nervous system (CNS). The gap between nerve fibre and muscle surface is part of a specialised unit, the neuromuscular junction. This amplifies the tiny current running down the nerve fibre by releasing a chemical called acetycholine which crosses the gap and passes to the muscle surface, causing the muscle to contract.

Each muscle is made up of filament-like structures called fibrils of which there are two sorts, actin and myosin, which face one another like two combs with partly interlocked teeth. As contraction occurs, the 'teeth' move closer together, shortening the length of the muscle. Then, unless another impulse arrives, these interlocking fibrils relax. The capacity for repeated contractions depends upon health and fitness, but any muscle used repeatedly, without rest, ultimately stops contracting altogether. Conversely, muscle shrinks and wastes away if it is not used at all. Muscles thrive on exercise but only within reasonable limits.

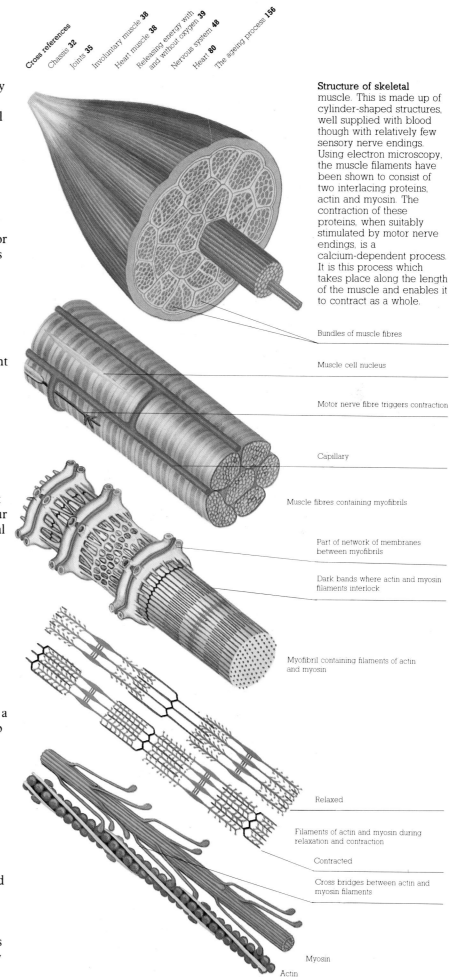

Structure of skeletal muscle. This is made up of cylinder-shaped structures, well supplied with blood though with relatively few sensory nerve endings. Using electron microscopy, the muscle filaments have been shown to consist of two interlacing proteins, actin and myosin. The contraction of these proteins, when suitably stimulated by motor nerve endings, is a calcium-dependent process. It is this process which takes place along the length of the muscle and enables it to contract as a whole.

Bundles of muscle fibres

Muscle cell nucleus

Motor nerve fibre triggers contraction

Capillary

Muscle fibres containing myofibrils

Part of network of membranes between myofibrils

Dark bands where actin and myosin filaments interlock

Myofibril containing filaments of actin and myosin

Relaxed

Filaments of actin and myosin during relaxation and contraction

Contracted

Cross bridges between actin and myosin filaments

Myosin

Actin

Muscles at work

Yifter 'the Shifter' wins at the 1980 Olympics. The success of runners like Yifter (from Ethiopia) and Bikila (from Kenya) has been attributed to, amongst other factors, a slightly more efficient line of pull of the tendons in the calf. Running involves virtually all the muscles of the legs, trunk and arms, some providing thrust, others working as fixators or stabilisers.

Involuntary muscle Smooth or involuntary muscle reacts much more slowly to stimulation than skeletal muscle does. It is under the control of the autonomic nervous system, which is composed of an accelerator, the sympathetic nervous system, and a brake, the parasympathetic nervous system.

The opposing actions of the sympathetic and parasympathetic nervous systems create peristalsis, the strong waves of gravity-defying muscular contractions that squeeze food along the coils of the 25-foot long (7.6 m) digestive tract. Smooth muscle lined with mucous membrane runs through the digestive tract almost from beginning to end. Smooth muscle also makes up the wall of the bladder, regulates the width of the small air passages in the lungs, controls the flow of blood through the blood vessels and determines the ever-changing size of the pupil of the eye.

Heart muscle During rigorous exercise the sympathetic nervous system stimulates the heart, increasing the rate and force of the beat. Subsequently, parasympathetic stimulation inhibits the heart, decreasing its rate and force of contraction. The heart has, however, a built-in mechanism to maintain rhythmical contractions which is independent of nervous control. A turtle's heart, if removed from the turtle's body, may keep on beating for a long time by itself. Similarly, human heart muscle stored in certain solutions may also continue to contract rhythmically outside the body for some time.

Muscle capacity Many, indeed most, of the machines we build—automobiles, cranes, bulldozers—are designed to compensate for our limited strength and stamina. It has been estimated that the muscle of a 35-year-old European labourer can be expected to generate 0.49 horsepower over an eight-hour day for a 40-hour week. But only 0.1 per cent of this is actually available for useful productive work. No machine is 100 per cent efficient, as will be explained later, and the body machine is no exception. A 20-year-old man can be expected to produce about 15 per cent more horsepower over the same period and a 60-year-old man about 20 per cent less. Well-trained athletes can produce 1.5–2.0 hp in bursts lasting from five to ten seconds, or up to 6 hp in bursts of less than a second. But this compares poorly even with early automobiles such as the 1905 Adams (9–10 hp), let alone the 1,760 hp Jameson Concorde with which we cannot really compare ourselves at all. Furthermore, automobiles can run for hours on end, unlike humans.

The body design of humans actually limits power. It has been estimated that if a man could drive his legs as quickly as an ant, he would be able to run at speeds of more than 100 miles (160 km)

Cross references
Muscles 36
Heart 80
Digestive system 124
Nervous system 48

per hour. However, built as we are, if we could run at this speed, something would give—bones would snap and muscles tear. An engineer cannot increase power output by simply designing a larger model of an existing machine. The maximum speed of the Wright Brothers' aeroplane, for example, could not have been bettered by building a larger model of the same design—the airframe would have broken under the strain.

Efficiency The efficiency of machines is assessed by calculating how much of the energy they produce is absorbed in useful work, and here again the body can usefully be compared with the automobile. Much of the energy generated in both the automobile and the human body is wasted but studies have shown that the average human body is about 25 per cent efficient, usually better than the average automobile. Efficiency varies with fitness and ability, in other words with balance, agility, power, co-ordination and speed of movement. A finely tuned body machine can be as much as 50 per cent efficient. In contrast, a reciprocating steam engine is about 17 per cent efficient, a finely tuned automobile engine about 30 per cent, a steam turbine about 40 per cent, and an electric motor about 80 per cent.

If the body were a perfect machine it would use, regardless of its rate of work, the same amount of energy. But in the same way as the automobile, the faster we work the more energy we use. We all know that at 90 miles (144 km) per hour an automobile consumes more gas than at 45 miles (72 km) per hour. Similarly, sprinting consumes more energy than jogging the same distance.

Energy conversion Automobile fuel is refined before it reaches the tank. In the body the raw sources of energy are refined 'on the open road', so to speak, through the wonder of metabolism, the biochemical processes by which the body breaks down basic food materials to provide energy and then builds them up into living tissue.

Almost all the sugars in our food are converted into glucose, which is then converted into glycogen (chains of glucose molecules) and stored in the liver and muscles. Fat, stored all over the body but mainly under the skin as a useful thermal insulator, is similarly converted, into glycerol (which can then be converted into glucose) and free fatty acids (the form in which fat is distributed as fuel in the blood). Step by step cells break down glucose molecules and fatty acid molecules, extracting energy at each step. This energy is stored in the cell in a compound known as adenosine triphosphate (ATP). When ATP releases a phosphate group it is converted into another substance called adenosine diphosphate (ADP) and energy is released. In muscle cells, which store plenty of glucose as

glycogen, the breakdown of ATP is caused by nervous stimuli, and the energy released causes the muscles to contract.

Releasing energy with and without oxygen The most usual and efficient way for muscle cells to generate energy is by low temperature combustion of 6-carbon atoms of glucose with oxygen. This process is known as aerobic glycolysis and involves first the production of a 3-carbon substance, pyruvate, which, in the presence of an oxygen supply, is further degraded to water and carbon dioxide by a cycle of enzymes in the mitochondria, the Krebs Cycle.

Lifting weights involves two kinds of muscular exertion. During the lifting phase muscle contraction is isotonic (employing the full range of movement in the back and arm muscles); in the holding phase contraction is isometric (applied continuously against a fixed resistance).

Muscles in health and sickness

The Krebs Cycle cannot work without oxygen, i.e., in a muscle in spasm which prevents blood flow. In this case the pyruvate is converted to lactic acid which is removed later when normal circulation is re-established.

For short periods, and only for short periods, anaerobic glycolysis (sugar splitting without the presence of oxygen) is a highly efficient means of harvesting energy. Although it extracts only five per cent of the energy from glucose, it yields 20 per cent more energy in a given time because it can process glucose molecules more rapidly. Unfortunately all energy processes within a cell cease if lactic acid accumulates locally, tiring the muscles and causing cramp. The acidity of lactic acid, which arises when the whole body is short of oxygen (oxygen debt), makes us puff and pant after short, sharp sustained bursts of physical effort.

Athletic events such as the 100 and 200 metre sprints are usually performed anaerobically, or without much oxygen being carried into the muscles. The 5,000 and 10,000 metres, however, are mainly aerobic events with anaerobic final spurts. However, as faster speeds are being achieved anaerobic capacity is becoming increasingly important in longer races such as the marathon. Modern training programmes are designed to boost the quantity of enzymes (catalysts) which enable anaerobic glycolysis to take place, and also the quantity of certain buffer substances and other enzymes which alleviate the effects of lactic acid build-up and help to eliminate lactic acid from the blood.

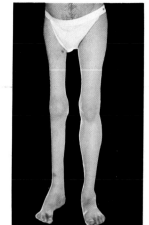

The polio virus specialises in destroying cells in the front part of the spinal cord, and with them the motor nerves which operate the skeletal muscles. Unused muscles weaken and waste away.

Life in a wheelchair need not mean the end of enjoyable physical activity. Many disabled people train for national and international sporting events with all the enthusiasm of the able-bodied.

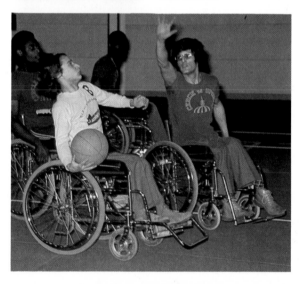

Cellist Jacqueline du Pré, a victim of multiple sclerosis, a chronic degenerative condition of the central nervous system which takes the form of random loss of myelin around nerve fibres and loss of muscular coordination. Women are more prone to MS than men. Prognosis is always difficult and uncertain—in many cases disability does not drastically worsen after onset.

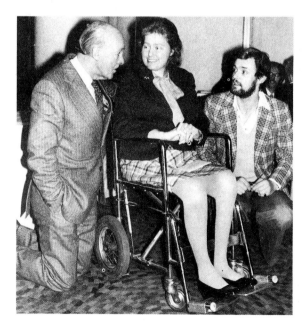

Dreaming of Pavlova? Classical ballet relies on footwork which places enormous strain on the muscles and bones of the foot. Most dancers suffer from fractures, dislocations and torn ligaments fairly early in their career.

A woman's muscles
do not have the same potential for development as a man's, and for several reasons. A woman has fewer muscle fibres to start with, and their ability to store and convert glycogen into useful energy is less. Her bones also tend to be slighter and shorter, with less attachment area for ligaments.

Muscular hypertrophy
as displayed by Mr America. Bodybuilding increases the size of individual muscle fibres. As size increases so does contractile strength. And the tighter muscles contract the harder they feel.

Massage Japanese-style
Massage can be good for relaxing tense muscles and toning up lazy ones. As a method of reducing both physical and mental stress it has clear advantages over tranquillisers. Massage uses several basic techniques, including friction, smoothing, percussion and kneading.

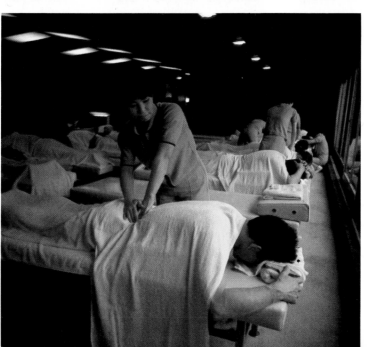

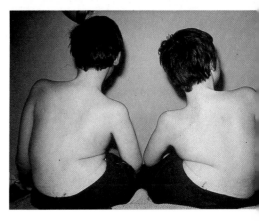

The Duchenne form
of muscular dystrophy affects only boys. By the age of eight or nine there is often severe curvature of the spine, the back muscles being too weak to support it.

Skin: the living barrier

An aborigine boy
Body art is a major part of
artistic tradition among the
aborigines of Australia.

Multi-layered skin
Skin consists of three
principle layers. The
epidermis, perforated by
hairs and by the openings of
sweat and sebaceous
glands, has no blood
vessels. Beneath it is the
dermis, containing the hair
roots and the sebaceous and
sweat glands. The dermis is
well supplied with nerve
endings and blood vessels,
and contains a lot of elastic
connective tissue. Deeper
still is a layer of fat.

Dermis
Fat layer
Sebaceous gland
Keratin coating
Nerve endings
Blood vessels
Hair follicle
Hair root
Muscle
Sweat gland
Fascia of dense fibrous tissue

Beauty treatment
The appearance of the face
has always been considered
to be very important. The
idea of improving skin
quality by applying a mud
pack goes back many
thousands of years. All a
mud pack does is lift off
superficial grease and dead
skin, and tighten the skin as
it dries.

Dark skinned peoples
throughout the world inherit
the capacity to produce the
skin pigment melanin in
large amounts. In the
pygmies of Zaire (right), who
live in remote areas of
tropical forest, sun-resistant
skin is somewhat redundant.

An albino Xhosa boy
(South Africa) with normally
pigmented companions.

Cross references
Blood **100** Cancer **228** Skin diseases **44** Fingerprints **44**

In spy stories, man-made machines are frequently programmed to self-destruct. The body machine also has self-destruct mechanisms to regulate internal security. One of them is the outer layer of the skin, the body's almost waterproof leather jacket, the frontier between the outer and the inner world. If we touch either ourselves or another person, we feel warmth and life. But the skin that we touch—the scales of the outer layer of the epidermis, one of two principal layers of skin—is actually dead.

Dead skin is not instantly discarded like self-destructed spying devices. Instead it acts as the body's first line of defence against harmful radiation and foreign agents. The self-sacrificing cells of the epidermis prepare for this sandbag role by producing a hard horny substance called keratin, the main constituent of hair and nails. And it is this process which triggers the self-destruct mechanism, not exposure to air. As the cells are shed, they are replaced by those beneath them.

Keratin waterproofs the skin. Nevertheless skin wrinkles if it is submerged in water for long periods; in these circumstances water penetrates the keratin barrier and leaks into the softer cells below, making them buckle. Keratin enables the body to present a tough, horny front to the outside world but there are highly delicate regions where toughness gives way to softness. The body's orifices lack heavy keratin coating and need to be both elastic and moist, so their boundaries are lined with sheets of mucous membrane. These contain mucus-secreting glands to lubricate and protect the soft membrane.

Just like a leather jacket, the skin not only needs considerable care but is also tough and heavy; the average adult's skin weighs almost 6 lb (2.7 kg), almost twice as much as the brain, and covers more than 18 sq ft (1.7 m²).

Cooling system The skin is as much an organ as the brain or the kidneys and it is much more than just a protective jacket for the body. The skin plays a major part in sustaining the body; it is the first organ to respond to pain or touch; it is the principal organ of sexual attraction; and it is also an agent of secretion and excretion. And, most important of all, it operates the cooling system which keeps internal temperature constant.

The dermis plays a major part in these functions. Lying beneath the epidermis, the dermis is the second principal layer of the skin. It contains a mass of blood vessels, three million sweat glands, the follicles which house the hair roots, erector muscles for each hair root, and the sebaceous or grease glands which pour a fatty substance, sebum, into the hair follicles to oil the hair and skin. Both sebum and sweat are mildly antiseptic, and both contribute to the suppleness of the skin.

The body's cooling system is 'switched on' when temperature rises. Blood vessels in the outer dermis dilate to increase the rate of blood flow and sweat production is stepped up. When the temperature falls, the blood vessels respond by constricting and sweat production decreases. Activated by its erector muscles the hair stands on end to increase the amount of trapped air insulating the skin.

A layer of fat cells between the dermis and the muscles stores energy and insulates the body.

Skin colour Deep within the epidermis, in all people except albinos, are brown granules of a special pigment called melanin, a word derived from the Greek word for 'black'. This natural cosmetic gives skin its colour and it is produced by cells called melanocytes, which are equally distributed in white and black people. The difference between, for example, a black African and a white European lies in the productive capacity of their melanocytes, this productive capacity being determined by genes. The key role of melanin is graphically illustrated by albinos, who have white hair, bright pink skin and pink eyes (due to the small blood vessels showing through) because they lack an enzyme needed to manufacture melanin. Melanin is present in the eyes, hair and skin of all non-albinos.

Suntans Melanin-producing cells are activated by ultraviolet light from the sun. Freckles are formed when the distribution of these cells is irregular; moles originate from masses of cells containing unusually high melanin concentrations; and suntans arise from sustained exposure to the sun, which stimulates melanin production.

Suntans are widely recognised today as symbols of good health and fitness, to the delight of the package holiday industry. And of course the sun is good for us because skin cells absorb the sun's rays to produce Vitamin D.

But lazing on the beach in the hot summer sun, either scantily clad or even entirely naked in order to obtain a rich brown tan, is not always a health tonic. Turning brown is the body's protective response to the hostility of the sun's rays. People who don't tan well and expose themselves excessively to the sun can suffer premature wrinkling and, if exposure is continued for many years, skin cancer. The white, sun-loving Australians have one of the world's highest skin cancer rates; California too is high in the skin cancer league. Usually cancer of the skin is less dangerous than most other forms of cancer, partly because it is usually noticed at the early stage and partly because it does not metastasise (spread elsewhere). This is one form of cancer which is fairly easily dealt with, but prompt treatment is nonetheless important.

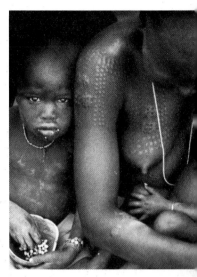

Woman of the Dinka tribe (Sudan) with a much admired scar pattern on her skin. Tattooing is an equally indelible form of adornment; the skin is punctured and pigments inserted into the punctures.

Fair hair and fair skin evolved for climates with long winters and short mild summers. It is the ultraviolet or tanning component of sunlight which can cause cancerous changes in the skin. People with fair skins are most at risk, because their capacity to produce protective melanin is low.

Skin disorders, fingerprints

Modern sun worship
Sunburn and suntan are
caused by the sun's
ultraviolet rays, with the
shorter UV rays doing the
burning and the longer ones
the tanning. An effective
suntan lotion cuts out the
burning effects but lets the
tanning rays get through.
General purpose lotions
often prevent the skin
getting burnt but do not stop
it going red.

Skin diseases Medical literature describes literally
hundreds of different skin diseases, many of which
are unexplained but many of which are aggravated
by anxiety. Some skin diseases cause severe
anguish because they are irritating and
embarrassing and because they appear and
disappear for no apparent reason. A classic example
is psoriasis, named from the Greek *psoros*
meaning 'scaly'. This normally appears as red
plaques covered with silvery scales but there are
many other forms of this common condition, which
affects men and women equally. It is estimated that
2 out of every 100 people in the Western world
suffer from psoriasis, meaning that there are seven
million sufferers in the USA and one million in
Great Britain. Although psoriasis can appear at any
time it is less common in the elderly and the young.

The condition may break out anywhere on the
skin but it frequently afflicts the elbows and knees.
There are three major complications: a flare up
affecting the whole skin surface; development of
local or widespread pustules, which look like
pimples and contain sterile pus; and affliction of

the joints, resulting in a form of arthritis.

Psoriasis often provokes unpleasant remarks and
cold stares from non-sufferers, usually because of
the totally misguided fear that psoriasis is
contagious. Although suffering can be aggravated
by emotional distress, the cause of psoriasis is not
fully understood, but it does seem to involve a
gross acceleration in the turnover of epidermal
cells. In normal skin the number of cells lost is
exactly balanced by the number of new cells.

Contact dermatitis or contact eczema is another
common skin disease. It can arise from an allergy to
a substance the sufferer may have been using for
many years without apparent ill effects. A doctor or
dermatologist may be able to pinpoint the
offending substance, perhaps from the patient's
history, from the site or sites affected, or by testing
the areas affected. Other common skin complaints
include acne, which can intensify the
embarrassments and awkwardness of adolescence,
and eczema. The latter seems to run in families,
especially in those with a history of complaints such
as asthma or hayfever.

Cross references
Ageing **156**
Immune systems **110**
Allergy **112**
Putting bacteria to work **238**

All the above complaints merit medical investigation. In fact, any persistent skin complaint should be seen by a doctor.

Fingerprints By the third or fourth month of foetal life the body machine has a sort of 'serial number' in the form of fingerprints and palm prints. Fingerprints are formed by the friction ridges on the finger bulbs and they comprise a rich assortment of whorls, forks and loops which cannot be altered except by the complete destruction of the skin. Not even plunging your finger tips into boiling water or hot oil will obliterate the distinctive pattern of your fingerprints.

There are, of course, exceptions to most rules. Leprosy can permanently modify the ridge patterns of fingerprints. Some other conditions, including poliomyelitis, change the distances between the ridges, but without changing the basic design and structure of the pattern.

Most people know that careless criminals risk conviction by leaving fingerprints at the scene of the crime but no so well known is that pore patterns can also clinch the case for the prosecution. In some countries pores are used to identify blurred or partial fingerprints. There are between 9 and 18 pores on each millimetre of a ridge and pore patterns vary from person to person. Some are so close together that the distance between them is less than the diameter of the opening; in others it is eight times larger.

In one noted criminal case two thieves were convicted on the strength of prints left on a rosewood box. In the case of the first man there were more than 900 similarities between the pore impressions of his left middle finger and those found on the box. This was in addition to 74 other points of similarity. In the case of the second man, who had left a small area of his palm imprints on the box, there were more than 2,000 pore similarities, in addition to 94 other similarities detectable on the prints.

Prints not only help to detect criminals but also point towards congenital abnormalities in newborn babies. Some 14 per cent of normal babies have abnormal prints, known as 'accidentals' because they do not conform to the four normal groups. But the figure has been found to be as high as 50 per cent among congenitally abnormal babies whose mothers contracted German measles during their pregnancy.

Any similarities in print patterns between one generation and the next, and some have been found, are believed to be coincidental. Even so it has been suggested that fingerprint patterns be used in cases of disputed paternity.

Prints from the soles of the feet are just as individual as hand prints, but how many criminals are caught burgling houses in their bare feet?

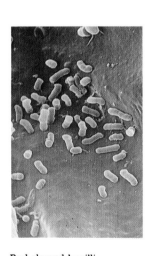

Rod-shaped bacilli, of which there are many different species, cause diseases such as anthrax, dysentery, tetanus and tuberculosis. Being slightly acid the skin is an ideal haven for them. Soap, which is alkaline, temporarily reduces their numbers. Regular washing is a vital ingredient of personal and public health. Millions of bacteria colonise every inch of the skin, and also the intestines. Most are harmless, a few are postively useful (certain bacteria in the gut, for example, break down a sugar called fructose), and a few are troublesome only if they get trapped in grease-clogged pores (acne) or in a wound.

Past her salad days With age the skin loses its elasticity, mainly due to atrophy of the elastic fibres in the dermis. The adipose cushion beneath the dermis also thins. The result: bags and wrinkles.

Severe skin infections are often associated with poor nutrition. Here a man from a remote Mexican village receives treatment from a doctor working with LIGA, an American organisation which airlifts medical teams into this impoverished region.

Hair: growth and loss

A very hairy orangutan
Though man has been called the 'naked ape' the average human has just as many hairs as his ape relatives, only so short as to be virtually useless in cold climates.

Section through a hair root (left) and through hairy skin (right). Hairs grow from follicles embedded in the dermis, with each hair root ending in an enlargement known as the hair bulb. The conical area inside the hair bulb is the papilla; this contains many capillaries, which feed the developing hair, and also many nerve endings. Sebaceous glands exude sebum into the hair follicle to keep both hair and skin supple. Dead cells on the surface of the skin constantly flake off; when trapped by hair, as on the scalp, they tend to collect as dandruff.

Robbie Burns, the eighteenth-century Scottish poet, has been much maligned as a man who drank himself to death; now scientists believe that he may have died not from drink but from mercury poisoning—because of his hair.

Hair is, in addition to being a protective coating and a means of self-expression, one of the body's garbage cans. In much the same way as a waste disposal unit draws off polluting by-products from an assembly line, the hair withdraws traces of toxic metals from general circulation.

Research today into the hair of people alive hundreds of years ago, including the hair of Napoleon Bonaparte and King Charles II of England, would have been impossible but for one endearing tradition: the use of locks of hair as keepsakes. Locks of hair were once kept much as photographs are kept today, Napoleon being extremely liberal with the distribution of his locks. Scientists today use hair to assess levels of exposure to industrial pollutants. Because hair grows slowly, about $\frac{1}{30}$ in (1 mm) every three days or 5 in (12.5 cm) a year, it creates a memoir which can be read just as layers of ancient remains are read by archeologists. As a source of scientific information about industry, hair is easier and cheaper to handle than the traditional bodily source materials—blood and urine samples. There is also plenty of it: about 100,000 strands on the average head, each one of which grows, on average, for three years before being pushed out by a new hair below.

Three kinds of hair Hair is made from the tough protein keratin (which also waterproofs the skin), and it goes through three growth phases: lanugo, vellus and terminal.

Foetal lanugo hair is seen on some premature babies, often to the alarm of parents. Soft, silky, long and furry, lanugo, which is an inheritance from our wild ancestors, sprouts on the face as well as on the body and head. Usually it disappears by the seventh or eighth month of pregnancy, to be replaced by vellus hair but in exceptional cases growth is maintained. There are more than 20 reported cases of furred adults.

Terminal hair is the hair of later life. In some ways it is inappropriately named because vellus hair also frequently grows in old age. Less commonly, lanugo hair can also recur as a result of disease late in life, an occurrence that gives substance to the idea that people become baby-like in old age. Perhaps the ageing body seeks comfort from the cycles of growth associated with the warmth and security of the womb.

Although humans have been described as 'naked apes', we have more hair per unit of surface area than other primates. Our shorter, finer hair not only protects us from the elements but also increases our sensitivity to touch. You can test this for yourself by moving a finger lightly over your forearm hair without touching the skin; you will feel a very slight tingling sensation.

Hair as a body defence Hair protects the body in various ways: hair in the nostrils and ears traps foreign bodies; the eyebrows prevent sweat from dripping into the eyes; and hair, or more correctly its erector muscles, responds to cold or alarm by standing up to trap air pockets on the skin surface, creating an insulating layer in much the same way that double glazing does. The distinction between a hair and its erector muscle is an important one because visible hair, like visible skin, is dead and it is the sensory nerves beneath the skin which respond to touch, not the hair itself. The root is the only living part of the individual hair and it is

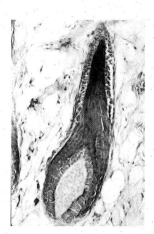

Absence of hair
may be unavoidable or, if fashion dictates, artificial. Getting rid of 'unwanted hair' is an obsession among many women, done here by electrolysis.

tucked within the follicle, or protective sheath. Although hair is dead, it has to be kept in good condition to maintain its protective power; the natural conditioning agents are the sebaceous glands which grease or oil the skin.

Individual hairs come and go but the follicles, formed in the womb when the foetus is between two and five months old, last much longer, and have resting, active and moulting phases. The resting phase lasts for a few months, after which the follicles enter the active phase which may last from one to six years. Hair growth appears to be constant and regular because different follicles follow different time cycles, giving the impression of uniform growth.

Hairs permitted to grow to full length rarely exceed 3 ft (0.9 m) although it was reported that the hair of a certain Jane Burford, worn in two plaits, was more than 8 ft (2.5 m) long and reached down to her ankles. Disease can also cause abnormal hair growth. Swami Pandarasunnadhi, head of the Tirudaduturai Monastery, Tarjore district, Madras, India, was reported in 1949 to have hair 26 ft (nearly 8 m) long; it is believed that he was suffering from a rare disorder.

Hair disorders Disease, emotional shock and pregnancy can cause hair loss, but stories of this happening overnight, or severe shock turning the hair white overnight, are apocryphal. This latter trauma is said to have been experienced by Sir Thomas More before his beheading in 1535 and by General Gordon before the siege of Khartoum in 1885. But dead tissue like hair cannot respond to shock or disease. Hair loss or baldness, known medically as alopecia, is a medical mystery. Nobody knows why body hair increases with maturity, while head hair decreases, or why hair on the front of the head should stop growing, while hair at the back and sides should continue sprouting vigorously.

Alopecia areata or 'spotty' baldness This is often found in children and young adults of both sexes and manifests itself as hair loss in sharply defined patches. Nowadays it is regarded as a defect of the auto-immune system, and drug treatment is usually effective.

Toxic alopecia This is caused by serious illnesses such as typhoid, malaria, syphilis and other infectious diseases; it is usually only temporary.

Involutional alopecia This is a comparatively uncommon sort of balding which affects women after the menopause. The probable cause is an imbalance created by loss of female hormones during the menopause. Unhappily there is no effective treatment.

Postpartum alopecia This usually occurs a few months after a woman has given birth. During pregnancy hormone changes can cause the normal hair cycle to cease. When the cycle resumes, all the hairs which should have fallen out during pregnancy do so within a comparatively short period of time.

Male pattern baldness This is the most common sort of baldness. Hair clinics make fat profits from a wide range of 'hair replacement' treatments but there is no cure. If a man becomes bald at an early age, it is quite likely that his son will too. There is no evidence that such baldness is triggered off by too much or too little washing, by wearing hair long, by dandruff or by hats. Male pattern baldness does not affect libido. The best treatment is philosophical acceptance.

Remarkable lengths
some hairs will grow to get into the *Guiness Book of Records*! However it appears that some brew other than Guiness worked this minor miracle.

Nerve cells and what they do

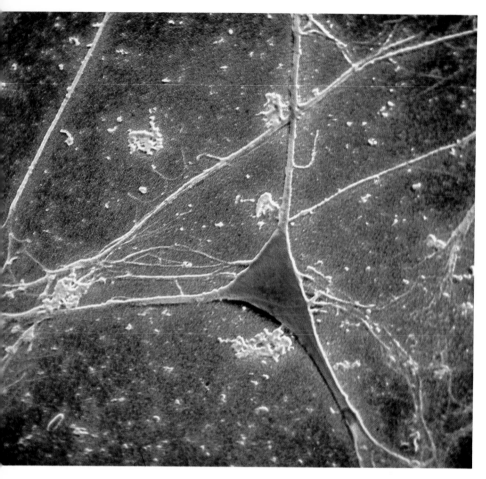

A typical neuron,
the basic functional unit of
the nervous system. There
are 28 billion neurons in the
human body. The main
body of a neuron, containing
the nucleus, has two sorts of
extensions: dendrites and an
axon. The dendrites receive
impulses and the axon
passes them on.

Me

I think that I shall never see
A calculator made like me.
A me that likes Martinis dry
And on the rocks, a little rye,
A me that looks at girls and
such,
But mostly girls, and very
much,
A me that wears an overcoat
And likes a risky anecdote,
A me that taps a foot and
grins,
Whenever Dixieland begins.
They make computers for a
fee,
But only moms can make a
me.

Hilbert Schenk Jr

In the poem below, Schenk is talking about the first
wonder of the world, the human brain, the chief
executive of the nervous system and the organ with
which the computer is so often compared. The
comparison is reasonable because a computer is
similar to the brain and in some ways it is better: a
computer never forgets; it will carry out logical
operations faster and more reliably than the brain;
it can probably beat 99.5 per cent of the world's
chess players; and it is consistent. But a computer
does not feel emotion; it has no sense of humour;
no aesthetic sense; no values; and it cannot
re-program itself in the same way as the human
computer. In fact it is the reprogramming facility
which puts the human brain in a class of its own.

The nerve cell

The nervous system is made up of billions of nerve
cells or neurons which detect and process
information from outside and regular movement
inside the body. Thus neurons are communication
specialists. They are also the most delicate and
helpless of living cells. Dr Peter Wingate has
described the neuron as "like the legendary genius,
pre-eminent in his chosen speciality, but incapable
of looking after himself".

All people are born with a full quota of neurons,
progressively larger numbers of which die as they

age. Loss of neurons, whether from ageing or from
severe head injuries or chronic poisoning by alcohol
or other drugs, is permanent and irreversible.
Neurons are also more vulnerable than other cells
to oxygen deprivation; they die within a few
minutes if they are deprived of blood and the
oxygen and glucose it contains.

It would seem that neurons have become highly
vulnerable in the cause of specialisation. The
extensions from some nerve cell bodies extend for
several feet and the circuitry is immensely
complex. There are probably 10,000 million nerve
cells in the brain, each one of which is connected to
several thousand other cells. It may be that new
cells simply could not be incorporated into the
existing circuitry.

Neurons vary widely in size and shape, as the
illustrations show. For example, the granule cells
in the cortex are only $1/200$ mm in diameter, while
the spinal cord motor cells are about $1/8$ mm across,
or about 27 times as big. But all neurons share one
common characteristic: they transmit impulses or
electrical signals, which carry messages to, from,
and inside the brain. Impulses are generated by a
change in the body's internal or external
environment. Computer and telephone systems
work in much the same way: when a telephone
number is dialled, a series of impulses travels along
the telephone wire to the exchange which connects
the caller automatically to the number dialled.

The transmitting part of the nerve cell is a thin
projection known as an axon or nerve fibre. Axons
vary in length from about $1/10$ in to about 3 ft (a few
millimetres to about 1 m) and from about
0.5–20 microns in diameter (a micron is $1/1000$ mm
or about $1/2500$ in). The receiving apparatus is a
shorter projection called a dendrite. Each cell has
as many as a dozen dendrites.

Insulation Although a potential William
Shakespeare or Albert Einstein is born with all the
neurons he will ever have, he will not be able to
write a sonnet or understand algebra by the age of
one; in fact a one-year-old can hardly walk, let
alone run. He may know innately that walking is
better than crawling and may want to imitate his
parents but the learning progress is held up. One
obstacle is the premature state of little layers of fat
that insulate many nerve fibres and promote the
conduction of impulses from neuron to neuron.

These fat layers are called myelin sheaths and are
wrapped around the nerve fibres in segments
several millimetres long. The junction between one
segment and another, known as a node of Ranvier,
speeds up the conduction of nerve impulses by
allowing them to hop from node to node. A
breakdown of the biochemical processes involved
in myelin formation can lead to disease, the most
feared of which is multiple sclerosis. About one

Cross references
The ageing process **156**
Voluntary muscle **31**
Involuntary muscle **38**
Blood **100**
Brain **50**
The developing nervous system **146**

Motor neurons

send their axons out from the central nervous system to the muscles which operate the skeleton. Most axons have an insulating sheath of myelin which speeds up the rate at which impulses travel. In the tip of each axon terminal are tiny sacs of transmitter chemicals (e.g. acetylcholine). When an impulse arrives these sacs empty their contents across the nerve-muscle junction, causing the muscle to contract and thus moving the bones.

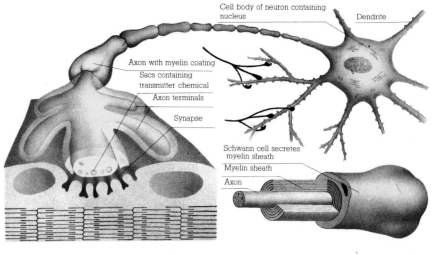

Cell body of neuron containing nucleus
Dendrite
Axon with myelin coating
Sacs containing transmitter chemical
Axon terminals
Synapse
Schwann cell secretes myelin sheath
Myelin sheath
Axon

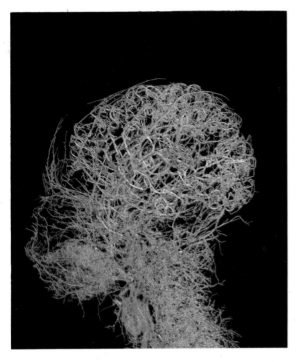

A child's brain,
showing the dense network of blood vessels on which the brain depends. Brain cells suffer permanent damage if their blood supply stops for more than two minutes. The consequence of ruptured or blocked blood vessels in the brain can be a stroke. The seriousness of paralysis or loss of mental faculties following a stroke depends on how much brain tissue has been starved of oxygen.

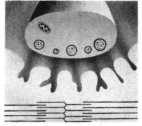

Resting phase
No electrochemical connection between the axon terminal and the highly folded surface of the muscle fibre.

Transmission phase
An impulse arrives and the sacs in the axon terminal empty their contents into the synaptic cleft, increasing the permeability of the muscle.

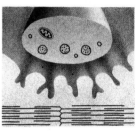

Muscle contraction
Sodium ions enter the muscle fibre, and the actin and myosin filaments contract. The transmitter chemical is then inactivated.

person in every 2,000 in the USA suffers from multiple sclerosis. The cause is believed to be either an allergy or the late effects of a virus.

In healthy people the speed at which nerve impulses are conducted is determined by the thickness of the myelin sheath insulating the fibre. The thicker the sheath, the faster the impulse. The biggest fibres have the thickest sheaths and conduct impulses at about 325 miles (523 km) per hour, whereas the smallest fibres, which are not myelinated, conduct impulses at the speed of about 1½ miles (2.4 km) per hour.

Most people know that nasty split second between the recognition of injury and the onset of pain. This occurs because impulses arising from tissue damage travel at only 2¼ miles (3.6 km) per hour. But an impulse from a pin prick travels at 27 miles (43.4 km) per hour, and that generated by a loving or threatening touch speeds along at 135 miles (217 km) per hour.

Electrical impulses Although nerve impulses are electrical waves, a nerve fibre does not resemble the continuous wire in a man-made electrical system which carries impulses at nearly the speed of light. Nor is what travels along a nerve fibre similar to ordinary electricity. The electrical activity of neurons is determined by electrically-charged particles or ions of potassium and sodium found in the fluid inside and around the cells. In a resting nerve cell the ratio of potassium inside and outside the cell is about 30:1. The interior is negatively charged and the exterior positively charged. A cell becomes active when sodium ions on the outside flow in and potassium ions on the inside flow out. This reverses the electrical charge and forms a current, so that a nerve impulse is really a wave of depolarisation. This wave depolarises the next segment, then the next, and so on.

Communication between different nerve cells occurs at specialised sites called synapses. Unlike the electrical current in a man-made system, electrical impulses conducted along neural pathways do not travel in a continuous, uninterrupted flow. The axon, the transmitting apparatus, stops short of the dendrite, the receiving apparatus, of the neighbouring neuron. When a nerve impulse reaches the end of an axon, it triggers the release of chemical transmitters which diffuse across the tiny gap (the synapse) between the two neurons to carry the impulse across.

There are many of these transmitters, including acetylcholine, noradrenaline (norepinephrine in USA), serotonin, and dopamine. Dopamine deficiency is associated with the neurological symptoms of Parkinson's disease.

Brain and spinal cord

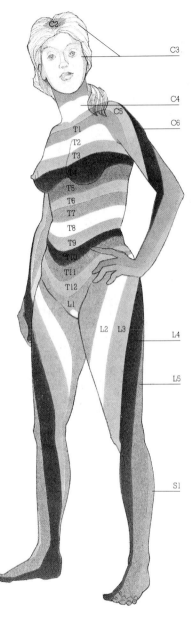

Nerves serving the skin
Each segment of skin is served by a specific spinal nerve. The head and part of the arms are supplied by cervical nerves (C2–C6), the trunk and part of the arms by the 12 thoracic nerves (T1–T12) and the lower limbs and buttocks by the lumbar nerves (only S1 shown). This segmental distribution is fundamental to the muscular and nervous topography of all vertebrates.

Input and output If you trap your finger in a door, a *sensory* nerve pathway relays the sensation to the central nervous system, which consists of the brain and spinal cord. The brain's response (an order to withdraw the finger from danger) is conducted through a *motor* nerve fibre.

Sensations such as pain, vibration, heat, cold, touch or pressure are registered by sensory receptors connected to sensory nerve fibres. These receptors include light-sensitive cells in the eye, and pain receptors and onion-shaped structures in the skin which react to pressure or small movements. The latter act as transducers, converting mechanical input into electrical output in much the same way as a gramophone pick-up or a microphone. But, not all inputs are mechanical; in the case of temperature or extreme pain, the input may be physico-chemical, but the end result is still a message to the central nervous system.

The reflex response Reflexes are unconscious actions in response to sensory stimuli. Examples include the sudden withdrawal of the hand if the fingers touch a red hot object; the quick closing of the eyelid if something threatens the eye; a sudden coughing attack if a particle of food is caught in the throat; and the fast recovery of balance to prevent a fall.

The simplest example of a reflex response is the 'knee jerk'. If you tap someone just below the kneecap, the sensory receptors in the knee (in this case muscle spindles) transmit a nerve impulse via the femoral nerve in the thigh to the spinal cord. The impulse is then transmitted to the motor nerve cells and down their fibres to what is known as the effector organ, in this case the thigh muscle, which contracts and causes the lower leg to jerk into the air. This response does not involve the brain.

Many other reflexes control body functions. Examples include the dilation of blood vessels in the skin in response to heat; sweating; respiration rate; secretions from glands; and movements of the stomach and intestine. Urination and defaecation by infants is carried out reflexly at first but impulses from the bowel and bladder can be controlled as the sensory nerve tracts develop. This is an example of how conditioning, social taboos, emotions and training can override reflex responses. Ultimately, however, the reflex is stronger than the will—we cannot prevent ourselves from breathing for very long.

Central nervous system

The central nervous system consists of the brain and the spinal cord, with the spinal cord acting as the nervous link between the brain and the rest of the body. Motor pathways, as they are known, which carry stimuli from the brain to the various organs of the body descend through the spinal cord, while sensory pathways from the skin and other organs ascend through the spinal cord carrying messages to the brain.

The spinal cord weighs only 1½ oz (42 g), yet all limb movement depends upon it. About 17 in (43 cm) long and ¾ in (2 cm) thick, it lies within the neural canal of the vertebral column and stretches along about two-thirds of it; 31 pairs of nerves spring from the spinal cord, each pair serving a specific part of the body. Therefore if the cord is injured, it is possible to detect which part is affected by examining functions in various parts of the body.

The spinal nerves are part of the peripheral nervous system, which also includes the autonomic nervous system and the cranial nerves. The peripheral nervous system comprises sensory nerve fibres which carry impulses from organs such as the ear and the skin to the brain, and motor nerve fibres which carry impulses from the brain to effector organs such as skeletal muscle. The autonomic nervous system in turn is divided into two parts: the sympathetic system and the parasympathetic system.

These two systems alter the body machine's overall activity to adapt it to changing circumstances. The effect of one system counterbalances the effect of the other. For example, sympathetic stimulation dilates the bronchi, permitting more air and more oxygen to enter the body. Parasympathetic activity constricts the bronchi, reducing air and oxygen intake. Similarly, sympathetic stimulation increases heart rate, while parasympathetic stimulation reduces it.

Brain

Human beings are not physically well-endowed compared with other creatures. Our muscle strength is unimpressive and we have only a poor sense of smell, a thin skin and weak jaws and teeth. However, while other animals adapt to the environment, we adapt the environment to our needs and have done so ever since the first animal skin was worn for protection and the first fire was lit. And this is the marvel of the human brain.

A major difference between the human brain and that of other species is its size. The most brainless giant reptile of the Mesozoic, *Stegosaurus*, had a body weight of 13–14 tons (tonnes) and an estimated brain weight of 2½ oz (71 g), a brain to body ratio of 1:250,000. In contrast, the average human brain weighs just over 3 lb (1.4 kg), a brain to body ratio of 1:50. A dog, a gorilla and a man of the same body weight would have brains of about ½ lb (225 g), 1 lb (450 g) and 3 lb (1.4 kg) in weight respectively.

Post-mortem studies of great men have led to speculation that brain size is related to genius. Measurement of Lord Byron's skull, for example,

Cross references
The nerve cell **48**
Muscles **36**
Involuntary muscle **38**
Touch and pain **58**
Seeing **56**
Hearing **60**
Ageing **156**

This electrode helmet
monitors activity in various parts of the brain during tasks involving more than one sense. This man is responding to auditory stimuli by typing responses onto a keyboard; the three senses involved here are hearing, touch and sight. Experiments with apparatus such as this have helped to map the functions of various parts of the brain.

The spinal cord,
well protected inside the vertebral column, runs from the midbrain down to the level of the first lumbar vertebra, and then diverges into various branches. Both the brain and the spinal cord are enveloped by three membranes, the meninges. Descending tracts of nerve fibres, carrying messages from the brain to the body, appear grey because they contain many cell bodies belonging to motor neurons. Ascending tracts, which appear whitish, relay sensory messages from the body to the brain.

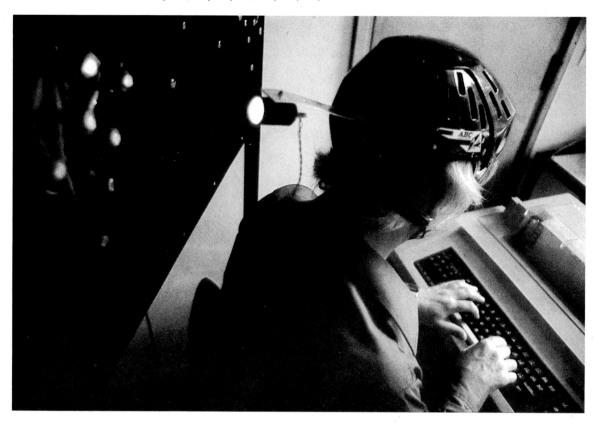

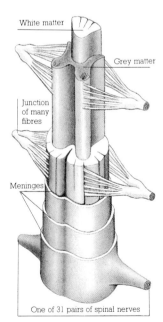

White matter

Grey matter

Junction of many fibres

Meninges

One of 31 pairs of spinal nerves

indicated a brain weighing 4.4 lb (2 kg). However, there are many gifted people with small brains and lots of very ordinary people with large brains, and there is no anatomical means of distinguishing the brain of a person with an IQ of 80 from that of a person with an IQ of 180. Paradoxically, brain size does not affect human intelligence, but it is the very essence of our superior intelligence. But then, if the human brain were simple enough to be easily understood, human beings would be far less complex creatures.

Inside the computer Our biological computer contains about 11,000 million cells, 10,000 million neurons and 1,000 million supporting cells, or glia, a name which means 'glue'. Surrounded by three membranes known as the meninges, the brain and spinal cord are bathed in cerebro-spinal fluid, which acts as a cushion and shock absorber. Although the central nervous system works as an integrated whole, the brain is classified into three parts: forebrain, midbrain and hindbrain. These three divisions emerge in the embryo from bulb-like structures in the spinal cord. In the mature brain the forebrain and the hindbrain are extensions of the midbrain or brain stem, which is in turn an extension of the spinal cord. Human evolution has been marked by a gradual increase in the size of the forebrain. This is also known as the 'new brain'.

Forebrain This is the largest part of the brain and it is made up largely of the cerebral or 'outer covering' of the brain. The cerebral cortex interprets sensory information and is the site of intelligence, thought and memory. It divides into two hemispheres which are sub-divided into four lobes. The right hemisphere controls the left-hand side of the body, and vice versa. The two hemispheres are joined by the corpus callosum, a thick bundle of nerve fibres. Cutting them surgically has been used as a method of confining epileptic seizures to one side of the brain. This does not seriously impair mental faculties and successfully limits convulsions which could otherwise prove fatal.

The forebrain also includes an egg-shaped mass of cells, the thalamus, which relays sensory information to the cortex and is also believed to be responsible for our powers of concentration. Beneath the thalamus is the minute hypothalamus. Sometimes described as 'the brain within the brain', the hypothalamus regulates physiological drives such as eating, drinking and sex; heat production and loss; and emotions such as pleasure, rage and terror. It also controls the endocrine system, a collection of hormone-secreting glands scattered throughout the body. Hypothalamic damage may cause reduction in sexual activity and an increase in the frequency of emotional outbursts.

Structure of the brain

Midbrain This is the intermediate zone between the forebrain and the hindbrain, and it began its evolutionary history with the first segmented worms some 500 million years ago. The midbrain carries ascending sensory nerves and descending motor nerves from the spinal cord and includes centres in the medulla oblongata that control automatic functions such as respiration and heartbeat. Lying in the central core of the brain stem is a dense network of neurons called the reticular activating system. This controls our sleeping–waking cycle and arouses us to attention-demanding stimuli. It accomplishes these crucial functions because it has connections that fan out to all areas of the cerebral cortex. In other words, the level of activation of the cortex depends on this more primitive part of the brain. Consciousness is mediated by the reticular activating system. Without it, we would be in a state of impenetrable somnolence or coma.

Hindbrain Lying behind the brain stem is the cerebellum, the non-stop monitor of all movements commanded by the motor area of the cortex. The cerebellum gives precision and smoothness to body movements. Well-learned motor skills such as playing tennis demand minimal conscious attention because of the detailed movement information stored in the cerebellum. Damage to the cerebellum can account for unsteady gait and clumsy, uncoordinated muscle movement. Nerve impulses from the semicircular canals of the ear go to the cerebellum to help maintain the position of the head, telling us whether we are the right way up or upside down.

Studying the brain The brain is locked in a casket of bone and protected by the meninges and cerebrospinal fluid. As such it is a difficult organ to study, but much has been learned from electrical stimulation during brain operations performed under local anaesthetic—it is because the brain is insensitive that such operations have been performed under local anaesthetic. Researchers can place electrodes, or tiny electric wires, in the area under investigation and pass electric currents through them. The current stimulates the area in just the same way as an impulse from a neuron. If one part of the cortex is stimulated, the patient feels a tingling sensation in his leg. If the electrode is moved, the site of the sensation moves, and the patient utters a sound or moves an arm. He or she is quite aware of what is happening, but has no control over his or her responses. Work like this has enabled scientists to isolate the types of cells which coordinate groups of muscles, for example, and thereby to 'map' certain areas of the brain.

Researchers can also record the electrical activity of the brain by applying electrodes to the scalp and

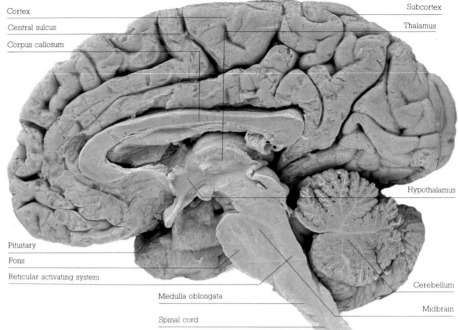

Cortex
Central sulcus
Corpus callosum
Pituitary
Pons
Reticular activating system
Medulla oblongata
Spinal cord
Subcortex
Thalamus
Hypothalamus
Cerebellum
Midbrain

The brain: a double organ
This section through the midline of the brain clearly shows the corpus callosum, the upper junction point between the two hemispheres. The many folds and furrows of the cortex represent an information storage capacity far superior to that of our living ape relatives.

1 Pre-motor area
2 Eye motor area
3 Speech motor area
4 Hearing area
5 Body sensory area
6 Speech understanding area
7 Reading centre
8 Eye sensory area
9 Body motor area

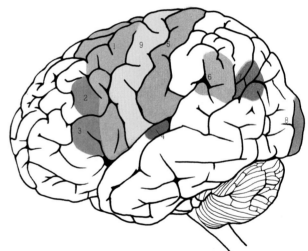

measuring the minute voltage fluctuations that represent the synchronized electrical activity of millions of neurons. These are known as brain waves and are recorded on an electroencephalograph (EEG). For convenience, brain waves are rather arbitrarily divided into four wave or frequency bands: alpha, beta, theta and delta.

Alpha waves are the most striking feature of the normal adult EEG and are observed when the subject is relaxed with eyes closed. When a person opens his or her eyes or starts to think hard about something, alpha rhythm is 'blocked' and replaced by fast, irregular activity. Practised meditators can maintain alpha activity even with their eyes open, but this is very unusual.

Beta activity is characteristic of unrelaxed, wakeful states and, paradoxically, is induced by tranquillisers and some sleeping pills.

Mapping the cortex
Many mental functions appear not to correspond with marked activity in any specific area of the cortex. Shown above are the areas whose function we are reasonably certain of. Motor areas control movement, and sensory areas process information from sensory organs and from various receptors in the body. The pre-motor area works in conjunction with other motor areas.

Cross references
Mental abnormality **168**
Mind medicines **175**
Sleep **192**
Dreaming **192**

All our emotions
are the result of complex
interactions between
sensory information
relayed through the
thalamus and intellectual
processes—remembering
and evaluating—which take
place in the higher centres
of the brain. Similar
situations can elicit different
feelings, fear in one person,
anger in another. Physical
reactions may be the same
in both. What we feel is
overwhelmingly determined
by the labels we put on
external events and body
sensations.

Aggression
is one of the least
controllable emotions,
perhaps because it has
sound survival value.

A chess problem,
like any problem requiring
sustained, sequential
thought, correlates with very
fast brain waves in the beta
waveband, reflecting a high
level of activity in the
cortex. But the
concentration required to
solve such problems
appears to be maintained
by the hippocampus, a
structure which is part of the
subcortex.

There is a strong correlation between abnormal
personality and 'immature' EEG patterns
containing increased theta activity. In one study
two-thirds of murderers and 85 per cent of
aggressive psychopaths showed theta patterns, as
compared with only 15 per cent of the
normal population.

Delta activity is characteristic of deep sleep.

The study of the brain has shown that certain
parts perform specific functions, but the brain
cannot be neatly divided into parts each solely
responsible for one sort of behaviour or response.
Nor, for that matter, is it possible to point to a
particular component of an automobile and say that
it alone is responsible for hill-climbing ability or
fast acceleration; many components interact to
produce a single aspect of performance.

The new brain The outer part of the forebrain, the
newest part of the brain in evolutionary terms, is
known as the cerebral cortex, and is composed of
ridges and grooves called gyri and sulci. Because
these are highly folded—in the manner of a
compressed concertina—the surface area of the
cortex is increased some 30 times. The folds are
about as thick as 30 pages of this book; laid out flat
they would cover an area of 5 sq ft (0.5 m^2). The
major landmarks of the cerebral cortex are the
oblique fissure of Sylvius, a groove which divides
the temporal lobes from the frontal and parietal
lobes above them, and the vertical fissure of
Rolando separating the frontal lobes from the
parietal lobes.

For more than 100 years, following the tragic
case of Phineas Gage, scientists have believed that
the frontal lobes are the seat of personality. In 1868
Gage, the foreman of a road gang, was severely
injured when a crowbar penetrated his frontal lobe
in a dynamite accident. He survived, but there was
a marked change in his personality; he became
childlike, had fits of temper when he did not get his
own way, and swore very violently.

Perception, concentration and specialisation

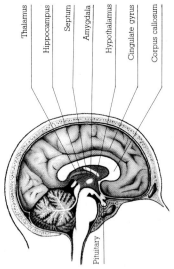

Thalamus Hippocampus Septum Amygdala Hypothalamus Cingulate gyrus Corpus callosum

Pituitary

Deep in the brain core are the areas controlling many of our basic functions and drives. The thalamus is the relay station for all impulses from the sense organs to the cortex. The hypothalamus controls hunger, thirst, aggression, sex drive and the activity of the pituitary gland. Then there is the rather complex limbic system, complex because it integrates the activities of several structures, namely the hippocampus, cingulate gyrus, septum and amygdala. The limbic system regulates moods, emotions and concentration.

Frontal lobe damage arising from accident, disease or from surgery for the treatment of some mental disorders, can affect judgement and insight. Self-confidence may increase and ability decrease. Concentration also suffers, and emotions may be blunted; this is because the prefrontal lobes are connected with other cortical regions and with deeper brain structures such as the thalamus and the hypothalamus which are responsible for regulating emotion.

Frontal lobe damage may express itself in violent fits of temper, extreme cheerfulness or loss of self-control. In a typical case of this kind, a previously well-behaved citizen may start shouting obscenities at passers-by. However, such disturbances are not necessarily restricted to localised damage to the prefrontal lobes; they can also be the result of damage elsewhere in the cerebral cortex. The hearing area in the brain lies in the temporal lobe, which also contains centres for speech and for memory and learning.

The parietal lobes, lying behind the frontal lobes, are the primary reception areas for all sensations of touch and are also involved in our sense of body position. But the way we respond to touch shows how other parts of the brain are also involved in our responses to simple sensations. For example, if you scratch your stomach lightly, the stimulus is much the same as when a child tickles you, but your brain interprets the stimulus in a different way—one input can produce several different outputs.

Switching on and off Wearing a bandage on your wrist activates 'touch neurons'—for a while you know there is something round your wrist, but after that you stop feeling it. This is because the human body contains more inhibitory neurons than that of any other species, and these 'off-switches' probably account in part for our superior intelligence and powers of concentration. A person deeply engrossed in conversation in a crowded room may not notice the rain outside or the efforts of someone trying to attract his attention because stimuli from these inputs are suppressed.

Perception We may be completely unaware of some potential inputs to the brain—not because they are suppressed, but because they are not registered. If a kitten spends the first six weeks or so of its life in a cage with vertical bars and is not exposed to any horizontals, it grows up unable to register horizontals because the visual cortex does not develop the cells for doing so. If a piece of string is held horizontally in front of the kitten, it does not raise a paw to it, as other kittens would.

Humans are much the same; we see what we are accustomed to seeing. Early research suggested that the human eye was usually better at

discriminating horizontal and vertical lines than slanted ones. This was assumed to be a genetic peculiarity until an investigation with the Cree Indians in James Bay, Canada, suggested otherwise. Cree infants are brought up in slanted wigwam-like structures and are far more sensitive to slanted shapes than children who have been raised in a world where verticals and horizontals are predominant.

So the relationship between external reality and internal perception is a complex one; inputs are shuffled around to match our preconceptions. In other words reality is filtered.

Concentration When an elevated railway line in New York ceased to operate, the police received calls from people complaining that something peculiar was happening to them. The calls usually coincided with the times when trains used to pass by and marked the absence of a familiar and perhaps reassuring sound. This became known as the 'El-Bowery phenomenon'.

Deep in the brain is a sausage-shaped structure, the hippocampus. It is composed of folded layers of cells stacked like a pile of micro-circuit boards and is connected to the sensory organs and to the reticular formation. The reticular formation, which monitors all incoming sensory information, is part of what James Old, an eminent researcher, described as 'the hot brain' as distinct from 'the cold brain', the cerebral cortex. The hot brain is impulsive, wanting everything now. The cold brain considers the future, and weighs things up. The hot brain and the cold brain are therefore in conflict with each other, but, in the same way as the two cerebral hemispheres, they also complement each other. They are divided by a middle man, called the hippocampus.

The hippocampus is part of the cold brain and is believed to compare sensory inputs with a learned pattern of expectations. So long as these expectations are met, the hippocampus remains active and dampens down the activity of the reticular formation. It may be that the peculiar feelings experienced by the New Yorkers when the trains stopped running marked a change of hippocampal activity: instead of damping the inputs from the reticular information, the hippocampus stopped 'firing', thereby permitting a free flow of inputs from the reticular formation to the higher sensory centres.

Humans have the largest hippocampus of any species. In an open-plan office, for example, the brain has to contend with the sound of banging typewriters, ringing telephones, conversations from neighbouring desks and people passing by. The hippocampus screens out inputs of nil interest, enabling us to concentrate. Mild hippocampal damage can affect recall of stored information.

An electroencephalograph (EEG) records electrical activity in different parts of the brain. The procedure is entirely painless and is therefore invaluable for diagnostic and monitoring purposes. An EEG can detect brain tumours and epilepsy; it can monitor sleep patterns, post-operative progress, and levels of concentration or emotional arousal; and it can confirm death.

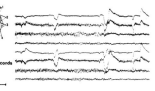

A normal EEG readout
The eight traces seen here correspond to electrical activity in the cortex at eight different points. The key indicates the frequency and voltage of the wave patterns.

Memory The Russian psychologist, A. R. Luria, once came across a poor unfortunate man who could not forget anything, S, as Luria called him. S could recall lists of words or numbers of any length and could recite them backwards as well as forwards. All his experiences were accompanied by vivid sensory inputs: every number, name or letter evoked very strong feelings, colours and sounds which fixed them in his brain. But S could not think on an abstract level. He could not organise, classify or evaluate his sensations, and was therefore unable to hold down a job. So he became a professional mnemonist, earning his living by demonstrating his extraordinary feats of memory.

Pleasure and pain Scientists have discovered the existence of 'pleasure centres' and 'punishment centres' in the brain. When stimulated a pleasure centre gives such intense satisfaction that it takes precedence over all other feelings and drives, even to the point of becoming life-threatening. This has been shown with experiments in which electrodes are implanted in the brains of rats; provided with a bar to press, which controls the current stimulating the pleasure centres, the creatures may starve to death before relinquishing control of the bar.

Conversely, with electrodes implanted in the neighbouring punishment or pain centres, rats struggle to avoid stimulation. Depressed patients treated with pleasure centre stimulation have experienced feelings ranging from supreme bliss to deep relaxation.

Right brain—left brain The left and right halves of the brain have fundamentally different roles. The left hemisphere is the 'logical' or 'verbal' brain and the right hemisphere is the 'artistic' or 'visual' brain, and also the navigator. So when you speak to someone you are communicating primarily with the left half of their brain. Spend a day painting with that person and you will get to know, so to speak, their other half. Most of the time the activity of the two hemispheres is complementary, which is important because each hemisphere is responsible for different sensory functions. Joining the two hemispheres is a thick band of nerve fibres, the corpus callosum, the bridge which enables the right-hand side of the brain to know what the left-hand side is thinking and doing.

In most people the left hemisphere specialises in intellectual, logical, analytical and verbal activity, while the right hemisphere is predominantly intuitive, spatial, musical and emotional. If the connections between the two are severed, each continues to function independently as if it were a complete brain in itself. But, of course, the right-hand side no longer knows what the left-hand side is doing, and vice versa. Normally, if you are blindfolded and asked to identify a coin placed in

your left hand, the right hemisphere distinguishes it and then, because it has no verbal activity of its own, communicates this information to the left hemisphere via the corpus callosum so that you can describe it out loud. Discussions like this demonstrate that it is remarkably difficult to describe right and left hemisphere functions in a way which is instantly intelligible, so deeply is the unitary function of the self built into our language and the way we think.

The role of the corpus callosum became apparent after operations severing the links between the two brains were carried out to prevent epileptic seizures from spreading from one hemisphere to the other. The surgery achieved the desired results and the patients appeared to be living ordinary lives, but studies by psychologist Roger Sperry and his colleagues in the USA showed that surgery left patients with a 'split brain' or 'split mind'. In one investigation Sperry tested response to verbal stimuli by showing the word HEART on a screen. The patients were positioned so that HE was to the left of their noses and ART to the right.

The ordinary reaction would be to report seeing the word HEART, but Sperry's patients said they saw only ART, the part projected to the left hemisphere which contains the centre for speech. Under normal circumstances each side of the brain would communicate with the other, compare what had been perceived, and link the two together into a whole.

A person without right-hemisphere function acts more normally than the person without left-hemisphere function. The left hemisphere enables him or her to speak, write with his right hand, and describe sensation but he is artistically poor and has bad visual memory. In most people left-hemisphere damage impedes speaking ability, sometimes totally. However, more than ten per cent of left-handed people and some two per cent of right-handed people have 'speech' in the other hemisphere, or the function is shared. Early in life each side of the brain carries the potential for speech and language so that if the left side of the brain is damaged, the right side cultivates a language facility. By the age of ten this facility, and others, is usually established in one hemisphere and little if any transference can take place from one side of the brain to the other.

In these ways the right and the left sides of the brain complement each other to impose a sense of order and meaning on an avalanche of sensory inputs. It has been estimated that in a lifetime the brain absorbs as many as one quadrillion (100,000,000,000,000) pieces of information.

One of the most remarkable features of the brain is its ability to adapt to change by using its circuitry to compose new programmes, or find solutions to problems not encountered before.

Eyes and eyesight

Vision, our single most important sense, not only enables us to see but is also an important source of information for the brain. In fact, the eyes are really part of the brain and one of its contacts with the outside world.

To a limited extent the eye is like a camera. The retina in the eye, which is comparable to a photographic film, receives light or visual signals and transmits them to the brain for interpretation. The lens, working with the cornea, focuses the picture on the retina, and the iris controls the amount of light let in, rather like a camera's iris diaphragm. When the iris contracts, the pupil, the aperture through which light enters the eye, reduces in size. The iris, named after the Greek word for 'rainbow', also gives the eye colour (blue or brown) and distinction in the form of rich patterns of rays, rings and spots which are as individual as fingerprints.

Our eyes take two simultaneous pictures: one in colour, the other in monochrome or black and white and shades of grey. The colour images are registered by the cone cells and the monochrome ones by the rod cells. Surprisingly, although we are mainly daytime creatures, we have many more rods, designed principally for night use, than cones. There are about seven million cones and some 125 million rods in each human eye. In contrast, daytime birds have more cones than rods, while nocturnal birds and mammals such as the owl and the bat have a greater proportion of rods.

The rods are about $\frac{1}{400}$ in (0.06 mm) long and about $\frac{1}{100}$ in (0.25 mm) thick. The cones are shorter and thicker. It seems there are three different types of cone cell, each sensitive to one of three colours: red, blue or green. Other colours are produced by combinations of these. Surprisingly, yellow is a mix of red and green.

Colour blindness, an inherited condition, occurs when certain types of cone are missing or are in short supply. Most colour-blind people are unable to identify red or green, and in rare cases blue.

The cones contain a pigment known as visual purple or rhodopsin which, it is believed, is broken down and bleached by light. This breaking-down process sets off an electrical charge which transmits the light in the form of nervous impulses to the brain by way of the optic nerve. These impulses are in a code and are interpreted by the visual cortex to give us the sensation of sight. The rods function in the same way.

Seeing red or green before the eyes after looking at the sun indicates a temporary shortage of visual

Science and medicine advanced rapidly with the invention of the microscope. Here a surgeon uses a special microscope to see inside the ear. An instrument like this magnifies up to 30 times; an electron microscope can magnify things up to 500,000 times, which has led to great advances in microbiology.

An expert braille typist hard at work. There are three main causes of blindness in developed countries: cataract (clouding of the lens), glaucoma (excess pressure in the fluid of the eyeball) and senile degeneration of the retina. About 90 per cent of registered blind people have some vision.

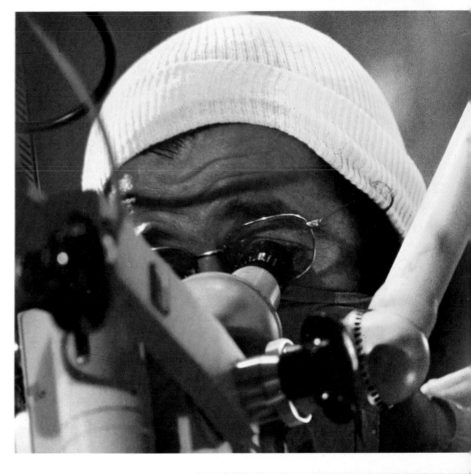

Shortsightedness (myopia) With age the ligaments which alter the focusing power of the lens become slack, giving permanently short focus.

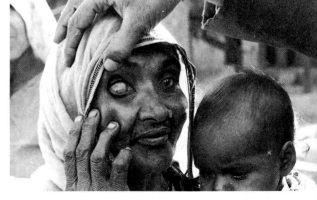

Trachoma A major cause of blindness in the tropics, trachoma is a contagious virus which thrives in conditions of extreme poverty. The conjunctiva erupts in hard red nodules which turn to scar tissue, the eyelid shortens and turns inwards and the conjunctiva and cornea dry out.

Structure of the eye

The eye really contains four refractive (light-bending) elements: the cornea, the fluid in the chamber between the cornea and the lens, the lens itself, and the gel which fills the inner chamber. On entering each of these transparent media light rays change direction in such a way that they converge at a central point on the retina, the fovea.

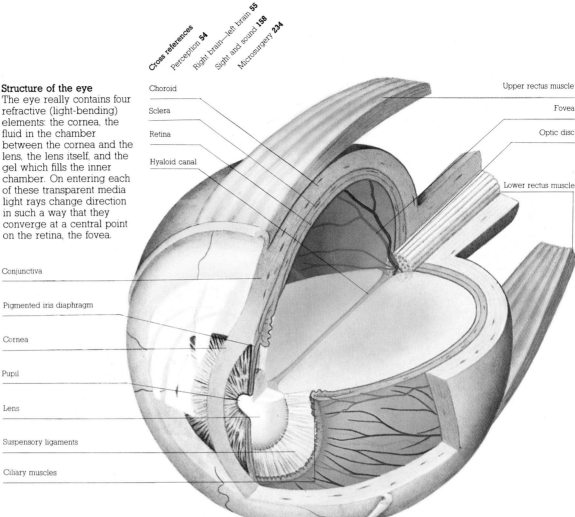

Choroid

Sclera

Retina

Hyaloid canal

Conjunctiva

Pigmented iris diaphragm

Cornea

Pupil

Lens

Suspensory ligaments

Ciliary muscles

Upper rectus muscle

Fovea

Optic disc

Lower rectus muscle

No known sight defect requires the wearing of these strange looking spectacles! These are inverting spectacles which turn everything upside down; they are used in psychological experiments to study how habit and learning affect perception.

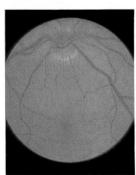

An ophthalmoscopic view of the inside of the retina. At the top is the optic disc where the optic nerve enters. The larger blood vessels are arteries which go to feed the retina and the slightly darker area is the fovea or focal point of the retina.

purple. In fact, we lose visual purple throughout the day, although usually we are unaware of this because only a few cells are exhausted at any one time. Visual purple is replaced at night, a process for which Vitamin A is needed.

For half an hour of every day we are, in effect, blind. This half an hour is the time we spend blinking. Lasting 0.3 to 0.4 seconds, the human blink occurs once every two to ten seconds. Blinking stimulates the tear ducts to produce a sterile fluid which keeps the eye surface moist and lubricated. Because the surface of the eye is slippery it has considerable freedom of movement: the eyeball can tilt 35 degrees up, 50 degrees down, 45 degrees out and 50 degrees in towards the nose.

Experiments with animals have shown that some cells in their visual cortex respond only to certain visual stimuli but not to others. For example, some cells register horizontal lines but not vertical ones and vice versa; some are sensitive to specific shapes but not to others. The human visual cortex is believed to work in the same way.

The way we see the world, however, varies from culture to culture and from person to person; it also varies depending on whether we are male or female. Abilities, background, attitudes, knowledge, motives and belief play a part in shaping our visual perceptions. One team of researchers demonstrated that a man's pupils open

by as much as 30 per cent when he sees an attractive woman. Magazine publishers have learned that men prefer pin-ups of women whose pupils have been enlarged by retouching. Far more interesting scientifically are the things we do not see. We tend to respond only to what we can recognise. For example, we see only the colours that we can name. Most people can recognise six or seven colours in a rainbow, but Australian aborigines cannot. They 'see' only the three or four colours for which they have names.

The tendency to see what we want to see has been demonstrated many times. In many studies people have reported seeing things which were not there at all. In one investigation volunteers deprived of food for 24 hours were shown a series of blurred images on a screen. As the experiment progressed they increasingly reported 'seeing' food.

Despite the importance of vision, blindness of varying degrees is common. In older people this is usually due to some degenerative disease associated with ageing. Among young adults the commonest causes are diseases of the retina (most of which are poorly understood), diabetes and glaucoma. The latter is a condition in which abnormally high fluid pressure builds up inside the eye.

Touch and pain

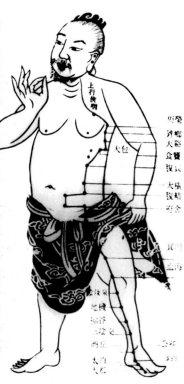

Ming period engraving
Showing one of 14 acupuncture meridians or routes around the body. The tso-tae-yin meridian has 21 acupuncture points on it, most of them distant from the systems (genital, urinary, digestive) they affect.

Sensations of touch, temperature and pain are perceived in the sensory cortex of the parietal lobe. Each part of the body has receptors which transmit messages to a relatively well-defined area of the cortex. 'Mapping' experiments have shown that the toes are represented by an area at the top of the brain adjacent to the fissure between the left and right hemispheres. Pathways from the internal organs and from the tongue, throat, trunk, legs and arms terminate at sites lower down and to the sides.

It is perhaps not surprising that the most sensitive areas of the body command the largest areas of sensory cortex; our lips, fingers and thumbs account for as much space in the sensory cortex as the rest of the body put together.

Although fingers and thumbs are especially sensitive to touch stimuli, we may become oblivious after a time to, say, a ring or a pair of gloves. Neither represent a threat, and if we were to spend much time thinking about them we would be unable to focus our attention on more important things. The messages which say 'gloves on' or 'ring on' are switched off, as it were, by inhibitory neurons. As we mentioned earlier the human brain has more of these off-switches than the brain of any other species. The sensory receptors themselves also decrease the amount of information they send to the brain.

There are various types of nerve ending in the skin. The outer layer or epidermis has free nerve endings for registering pressure and temperature, Merkel's discs for continuous pressure, and receptors called 'end bulbs of Krause' believed to be for registering sensations of cold. The dermis, the underlying layer of the skin, contains Meissner's corpuscles which register the texture of touched objects, Pacinian corpuscles for pressure, and Ruffini corpuscles for temperature change.

Touch also determines in part how we respond to other human beings. Some kisses are more pleasurable than others. Some handshakes make us warm towards a stranger, or make us feel suspicion or revulsion.

As a means of communication touch has been found to have a marked effect on mother-baby relationships. Mothers whose premature babies were placed in an incubator immediately after birth had 'attachment problems' with their babies later on. No such problems were found among mothers who experienced periods of mutual touching in the first few days of their babies' lives. Later these women were also found to have more satisfying relationships with their children.

Interpreting pain Have you ever felt pain and struggled to find the word to describe it? Our concepts of bodily sensations are very crude—we have a parallel lack of words to describe phenomena like snow, but the Eskimoes have 16 words for it. We talk about a stabbing pain or a pricking pain, but when does a 'prick' become severe enough to be a 'stab'? Similarly, how do we distinguish a light pain from a moderate pain?

Interpretation of pain varies from culture to culture. Levels of heat stimulation described as 'warm' by Northern Europeans were 'painful' to people of Mediterranean origin. Similarly, electric shocks easily tolerated by Anglo-Saxon and Jewish women greatly distressed Italian women—they would not or could not tolerate the 'pain'.

Research has also shown that Jewish women respond better to suggestion than Protestant women. After being told that their religious group had a low tolerance of pain, their tolerance levels increased, while the Protestant women's tolerance remained the same. And from all over the world there are well-documented accounts of men inflicting serious injuries on themselves during religious rituals apparently without feeling pain. Recovery is usually quick and scarring minimal.

A number of Swedish studies have shown that pain in childbirth tends to be more pronounced in women who have marital problems, feel negative or ambivalent about pregnancy, and who are late in seeking antenatal advice. Such women often use unreliable contraception and passively 'let themselves get pregnant'.

Physiology of pain The position of pain receptors has been plotted experimentally by using a needle and a hot or cold stylus. In the fingers it is possible to distinguish sensations only $\frac{1}{10}$ in (0.25 cm) apart, but on the thighs sensation points must be some 3 in (7 cm) apart before they begin to be distinguished separately.

Drs Robert Melzack and Patrick Wall have suggested that the input from pain receptors reaching the brain is regulated by a nervous mechanism which opens or controls a 'gate'. If the 'gate' stays partly open for some time or opens wide, then enough sensory input reaches the brain to cause a sensation of pain. Psychological processes affect the operation of the gate. Worry fear or negative attitudes can determine how much pain is felt.

Pain control Variations in response to pain stimuli may be accounted for by small brain proteins known as endorphins. The first of these, known as the enkephalins, only discovered in 1975, rush to sensory receptors to block pain signals. Spinal fluid of patients connected to pain-relieving electrical stimulators has been found to contain increased amounts of enkephalins. Scientists are now developing synthetic enkephalins for use in pain control. The curative potential of enkephalins for drug addicts is also under investigation.

Cross references
Brain **50**
Skin **42**
Nerves **48**
Drugs **199**

Acupuncture Research with enkephalins may provide a biochemical explanation for the 5,000-year-old medical art of acupuncture. Insertion of acupuncture needles into various sites in the skin relieves pain in regions quite distant from the needles. Presumably acupuncture causes pain gateways to close, preventing signals from reaching the pain perception areas of the brain.

Experimenting with enkephalin production and acupuncture, Dr David Mayer of the University of Virginia School of Medicine, USA, administered electric shocks to the feet of a number of brave volunteers. He found that acupuncture significantly reduced the pain of the shocks. Then he administered shots of naloxone, a chemical which counteracts the effects of enkephalin, and shocked his volunteers again. This time acupuncture did not block the pain, and his volunteers screamed and jerked. On the basis of this it seems that acupuncture may stimulate the brain to release enkephalins.

Endorphins Other brain chemicals may be involved in pain perception. In one study 'remarkable results' were achieved in treating patients with beta endorphins. With one injection doctors eliminated pain for up to two or three days in a group of patients for whom treatment with conventional pain killers gave only partial relief.

Initially, beta endorphins were injected into the bloodstream with no noticeable effect. But in this particular trial they were injected into the spinal cord, the tail end of the central nervous system. Fourteen patients with very severe pain were treated in this way and all reported complete pain relief. Treatment caused no discomfort, though most of the patients became drowsy for a while and some slept. Pain relief lasted on average for 33 hours, with one patient remaining free of pain for up to three days.

The raw agony of bullet wounds at an Israeli frontier kibbutz. Sudden injury can cause reflex overactivity of the vagus nerve, possibly causing the heart to stop. Losing a lot of blood lowers blood pressure, and pulse rate increases to compensate. Pain and anxiety often increase bleeding and blood loss.

Top: self-flagellation with knives during the Muslim festival of Moharram in Lahore, Pakistan. Women, not allowed to expose their bodies, pierce their faces and tongues. Does ecstasy shut out the pain? Experienced meditators show no response to painful stimuli once they reach the deepest state of meditation, characterised by alpha brain rhythms.

Body awareness Touch is generally under-used in the West to express emotion and affection. Improving body communication, in a non-sexual context, is one of the aims of several forms of group psychotherapy pioneered by the Encounter Movement.

Ears: hearing and balance

Imagine a keyboard the size of a pea with some 20,000 notes laid out with the treble notes at one end and the bass notes at the other; and an amplifying system built up from the body's three smallest bones; and a drum which vibrates like a loudspeaker cone—these are some of the more remarkable features of the human ear which enables the brain to transform the vibrations of sound waves into the sounds of language and music. The ear also includes the organ of balance.

The ear consists of three parts: outer, middle and inner. The outer ear is the visible flap that we call the ear. It is divided from the middle ear by a passage lined with stiff hairs at the outer end to keep out foreign particles. It also contains glandular cells which secrete a bitter-tasting yellow wax to protect the ear from invading insects. This passage leads to the eardrum which responds to high-pitched sounds by vibrating faster, and to low-pitched ones by vibrating more slowly. These vibrations are transmitted to the amplifying system of the middle ear, which has three main components: the eardrum (tympanic membrane), an oval window sealing off the fluid contained in the inner ear, and three little bones, the ossicles. Named after their respective shapes, namely the malleus (hammer), incus (anvil) and stapes (stirrup), these are the smallest bones in the body.

Vibrations from the eardrum are passed on to the malleus, which is attached to it, and from there to the incus and the stapes. The ossicles have a lever-type action which intensifies the force of the vibrations. The stapes vibrates at the same rate as the drum but with a force that is approximately 20 times greater.

This vibratory motion makes the fluid inside the inner ear vibrate, producing changes in pressure which are picked up in the organ of Corti. This is the actual organ of hearing and is contained within the cochlea, a fluid-filled coil named after the Latin word for 'snail shell'. The vibrations are converted into nerve impulses by the auditory keyboard and signalled to the brain (where they are interpreted as sound) by means of hair cells. These cells are arranged on a layer of fibres, the basilar membrane, which is divided into two spiral compartments.

Different notes travel different distances along the spiral or keyboard. A note of any given pitch, or sharpness of sound, always dies out at the same point on the spiral. It seems that in interpreting any given sound, the brain identifies the distance that it travels along the spiral. The innermost turn of the spiral contains the cells which register the deepest bass notes.

The human ear can distinguish notes with wave frequencies ranging from about 16 cycles a second (16 Hz), the sound of the lowest register of an organ pipe, to 20,000 cycles (20 kHz), the high-pitched

Inside the ear
The delicate and complex mechanism of the ear analyses sounds into frequency components and feeds them to the brain in coded form. The ear is also a feedback system, enabling us to monitor our own speech, and a direction and range finder. The pinna or ear flap channels sound waves into the eardrum.

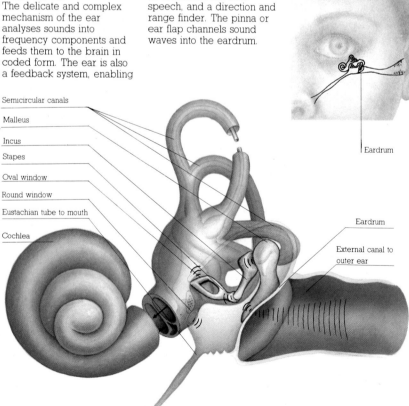

Semicircular canals
Malleus
Incus
Stapes
Oval window
Round window
Eustachian tube to mouth
Cochlea

Eardrum

Eardrum

External canal to outer ear

Inside the cochlea
Vibration of the oval window causes vibration of the fluid in the vestibular canal; this in turn vibrates Reissner's membrane, displacing fluid in the middle canal and causing movement of the basilar membrane; as this moves the hair cells projecting up to the tectorial membrane are distorted and send impulses to the cochlear nerve.
Displacements in the fluid of the tympanic canal are taken up by stretching of the round window.

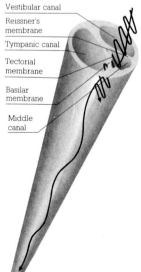

Vestibular canal
Reissner's membrane
Tympanic canal
Tectorial membrane
Basilar membrane
Middle canal

Keeping your balance
The three fluid-filled semi-circular canals of the middle ear detect movement of the head in any plane. Vision and pressure cells in the soles of the feet also help to orient us in relation to gravity.

Cross references
Skeleton **32**
Ageing **156**
Right brain—left brain **55**
Sight and sound **158**

Hearing at risk

The human ear is not really designed to withstand prolonged, high-intensity man-made noise. It takes about 36 hours to regain normal hearing after 100 minutes' non-stop exposure to 100 dB. During recovery time all sound frequencies have to be louder than usual to be heard. High-intensity noise can cause giddiness and nausea because of resonance in the semicircular canals, not to mention irritability, fatigue and poor concentration. And pure tones are potentially more damaging than broad spectrum noise. The ear has two built-in protection mechanisms. The first is the aural reflex, which enables us to tense our eardrums; this pulls the eardrum outwards and the stapes inwards, stiffening the lever action of the middle ear bones and lowering sensitivity. The other mechanism comes into operation with noises louder than 140 dB; these cause the ossicles to rock from side to side rather than backwards and forwards; the result is a sudden drop in loudness.

scraping of a grasshopper. This ability is not exceptional. In fact, in terms of the range of frequencies perceived, it seems that man has the most limited range of all the mammals. Bats and porpoises have hearing ranges encompassing an additional two octaves to frequencies as high as 100,000 Hz.

It seems that the auditory characteristics of each species have evolved in ways most suited to their specific requirements. For example, rats have been shown to have particularly acute hearing in a very narrow band of frequencies inaudible to us but which corresponds precisely to the frequency spectrum of sounds made by their young. The purpose of this, it seems, is to enable mothers and offspring to locate one another in the dark.

In contrast, human hearing is uniquely suited to the reception of speech sounds, so much so that there is little doubt that speech communication has been its main evolutionary aim. However, since the loudest sound we can hear is more than a million times louder than the quietest, we can afford to concede the rat's superiority without alarm.

Less easy to accept, perhaps, is the fact that babies can distinguish a greater range of sound from a good stereo system than a middle-aged person can. Such systems can produce frequencies up to 20,000 cycles a second (20 kHz), but by about the age of 60 we are fortunate if we can still hear

sounds of 12,000 cycles (12 kHz). This deterioration is believed to arise from loss of sensory hair cells.

The loudness or intensity of sounds is measured in decibels. The human ear can hear sounds ranging in loudness from 10 decibels to 140 decibels—a whisper is some 20 decibels loud, normal conversation 60 decibels, and a jet aircraft about 140 decibels. Loudness becomes increasingly painful, and harmful, above 100 decibels.

Just as important as being able to hear is being able to locate the source of sounds, especially in dangerous situations. The distance between the ears means that there is a minute time lapse between their receiving the same sound. By interpreting this time lapse the brain can plot the direction and sometimes the location of the sound source. This is why we often turn our heads if sound is beamed at us either from directly in front or behind. The plotting mechanism cannot work if both ears are receiving an identical message at exactly the same instant in time.

Since sounds are vibrations, we can feel as well as hear them. Actually vibrations travel faster through solids and liquids than through air, a fact recognised hundreds of years ago when people put their ears to the ground to listen for the approach of galloping horses—the vibrations could be heard in the ground well before they could be heard in the air.

A sense of smell

Each one of us has an individual smell, an odour tag as distinctive as our fingerprints. The chemical sequences of these odour tags are, however, common to every member of the same family. So if a bloodhound loses your scent, it will happily plod after your brother.

How we smell is another example of our never really being happy about the way we are. Many people use perfumes and deodorants to hide or suppress natural odours. But such smells are important for many reasons. Also we tend to remember odours. We often forget names or places, dates or faces—less so smells. Even the slightest whiff of a characteristic smell can evoke a sharp memory from long ago.

Smell is the most basic and most primitive of the senses, some 10,000 times more acute than our sense of taste. Most food flavours are smelled, not tasted, as anyone with a heavy cold will verify. Nasal congestion prevents the little eddies of air, stirred up by the action of chewing and swallowing, from reaching the receptors in the roof of the nasal cavity. Professional wine or tea tasters cannot work if they have a severe cold.

Human smell receptors can distinguish several thousand different types of smell and detect some airborne chemicals at a dilution of only one part per million parts of air. Some people have a better sense of smell than others—what one person

regards as a strong smell may not be noticed at all by someone else. Some South American Indians track game entirely by smell, which suggests that the demands of survival may sharpen perceptive capacity. This animal-like capacity is surprising because the smell receptors in a human being occupy only a tiny area, 100 times smaller than the equivalent area in a dog. But sensitivity to odours is not determined solely by the area taken up by the receptors. Good smellers such as wasps, bees and moths show that the location of the receptors is also important.

We can usually perceive only one smell from any one flower, but these insects locate the different parts of a flower by their different smells. Their organs of smell are on their antennae, which they can push right up against the source of a smell. Our smell organs are high up in the nasal cavity, and so we have to sniff deeply to confirm the presence of a smell, and often we inhale a mixture of odours. Fish also have a highly developed sense of smell. Salmon use it to find their way back to the rivers in which they were born. The smell of an injured fish repels its own kind but attracts predators. Examples such as these show that the sense of smell is far more important to other species than it is to us. We have come to depend more on other senses for information about the environment. Nevertheless, we are able to exploit the smelling

The 'nose' or 'bouquet' of a wine is always sampled before the taste. Every good gastronome suffers from synaesthesia, a crossing-over of the senses. Wines are described as 'velvety', 'fruity', 'sonorous' . . .

Abolishing body odour . . . a social courtesy, or brain-washing by the cosmetic industry? Medically and hygienically a daily soap-and-water session is usually adequate. Vaginal deodorants, popular in the early 1970s, created more 'personal problems' then they solved. Most antiperspirants contain salts of aluminium and zinc, which quite frequently cause skin allergies.

Cross references
Studying the brain **52**
Pheromones and taste **64**
How we breathe **117**

power of animals like dogs to track people or detect explosives or drugs. We have, so to speak, the best of both worlds.

Smell receptors A smell is a chemical reaction between substances drawn to the smell receptors and moisture secreted by the nasal membranes. A completely dry nose would be unable to smell anything effectively.

The smell receptors are in a small patch of tissue—about ½ sq in (1 cm²)—in the ceiling of the nasal cavity. Each receptor cell terminates in tiny hairs called cilia, which protrude from a thin covering of mucus. The cilia are attached to columns of cells which support the smell receptors. When odorous substances activate the cilia—quite how they do so is not known—the receptors respond by firing off a series of nerve impulses to the brain for analysis. There are some 50 million nerve fibres leaving the olfactory mucosa (smell membranes) on each side of the nose; these link with a further 50,000 nerve fibres which carry messages to the frontal lobes of the brain.

The pathway along which these impulses travel comes into direct contact with the limbic system, the part of the brain associated with memory and emotion. This may explain why the effect of smell may be subtly different from that of the other special senses. The pathways for hearing and vision go through the thalamus, which acknowledges cruder sensations such as heat and pain.

Axons leading from the nerve endings in the olfactory epithelium pass to the small olfactory bulb, an extension of the cortex lying immediately above the nasal cavity. Fibres from the olfactory bulb pass into the olfactory tract which ramifies to various structures on or near the ventral surface of the cortex, notably to areas which play a part in emotional responses.

Each different type of smell probably does not have a specific kind of smell receptor. More likely smells are mixed, rather like colours. We can see all the colours in the spectrum even though the eye's three types of colour-sensitive cells contain only three different colour pigments.

One theory is that the olfactory receptors are sensitive to some 30 primary smells and that other smells are made up of mixtures of some or all of these. Another theory postulates seven primary scents: mothball-like, ethereal (nail polish), floral (rose-like), musky (angelica root), peppermint, pungent (lemon-like), and putrid (rotten eggs). Secondary smells occur when these primaries are mixed in varying concentrations and proportions. It seems that, in effect, each primary smell has a chemical identity card with which it gains access to a corresponding nasal receptor. Using another analogy, smell particle and receptor fit together like two pieces in a jigsaw puzzle.

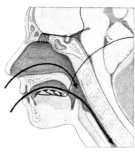

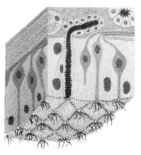

The linked airways of the nose and throat. The smell receptors are not in the main line of normal breathing, so we have to sniff and push air forcibly up towards them. The mucous membrane which lines the nose is continuous with that of ducts leading to the tear glands; very strong concentrations of noxious airborne chemicals (ammonia for example) irritate this sensitive membrane causing a stinging sensation, extra mucus secretion and tears.

Smell receptors in the nose cavity. Airborne molecules impinge on the clusters of tiny hairs at their tips. The cells lining the duct shown on the left secrete mucus to keep the nasal cavity moist.

A pungent protest from the fishermen of Calais and Boulogne in 1975 when the French government refused to raise fish support prices. Smell is a powerful weapon: prisoners go on 'dirty' protests, refuse collectors work to rule, sewage workers go on strike . . .

Pheromones and taste

We tend to think of smells as sensations we are aware of, but there are also subliminal smells, smells which we do not perceive consciously but which nevertheless influence behaviour. These are known as pheromones. American studies have shown that a virgin female moth can attract a male moth more than ¾ mile (1 km) away by secreting pheromones. Ants recognise ants from their own colonies by pheromones; an alien ant will be admitted to the fold only if it smells right. As a result, other creatures such as beetles and wasps can also gain access to the ant colony by acquiring this disguise. In its larval stage the beetle *Atemeles pubicollis* lives like a VIP in the nest of the European wood ant *Formica polyctena*. It steals food from and even eats the young of its hosts, yet is treated with amazing hospitality. The ants feed, groom and rear the beetle's larvae just like their own—all because of the way they smell. The power of this pheromone is so strong that a piece of filter paper soaked in the secretion and left outside the nest will be carried into it by the ants and treated with tender loving care.

Human beings also produce pheromones. A woman who has just ovulated and is in the fertile phase of her menstrual cycle secretes a different scent from one who is menstruating. It may be that this post-menstrual scent attracts males. Scientists are examining chemical substances in the urine and from the apocrine glands to establish just what does happen.

It has been found that women who live together over long periods gradually begin to menstruate at the same time. In an investigation of 135 resident college students, the American psychologist Martha McClintock found that the menstrual cycles of room mates and close friends started to coincide as the school year progressed. Her idea that the sweat odour was responsible was confirmed in a subsequent study. In one experiment one group of women had cotton pads placed under their arm. A second group rubbed the pads against their upper lips. The periods of the second group began to occur at the same time as those of the first.

In another intriguing pheromone study 22 babies aged two to seven days old had two breast pads applied close to their noses for two minutes. One pad was clean, the other had been against their mothers' breasts for 3½ hours. The babies tended to turn their heads towards the pads from the mothers' breasts. The pads were reversed half way through the experiment so that the right-side pads were applied to the left side, and vice versa. The babies showed far less interest in the clean pads, presumably associating the other ones with food.

In another investigation of 32 babies it was found that at two days of age the babies showed just about equal interest in pads that had been applied to their own mothers' breasts and the breasts of strangers.

Pigmeat stall in a Chinese market. Muslim and Hindu taboos against pork have less to do with taste than with *Taenia solium*, a tapeworm which parasitises pigs and also man if pigmeat is not properly cooked. Meat inspection in Western countries and in the United States has largely eliminated this danger.

Half the pleasure of eating is in the combination of smell and taste, but both sensations fade after the first mouthful. You can taste garlic when you eat it but you cannot smell it afterwards.

At six days of age, however, the head-turning showed that significantly more babies try to bury their noses in their own mothers' pads. This trend was even more pronounced four days later.

Taste

It seems that we may be born with a sweet tooth; certainly we demonstrate a clear preference for sweet foods early in life. If babies of two or three days old are offered liquids of varying sweetness, they suck hardest and longest on the sweet-tasting solutions. Some countries seem to have more of a sweet tooth than others. The average Briton eats more sweets than anyone else in the world.

One explanation is that the body needs sugar with which to make glucose. But this may be only part of the answer. In the jungle, bitter tasting plants and berries tend to be poisonous, whereas sweeter ones are usually safe to eat. In other words,

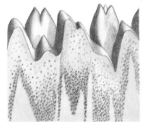

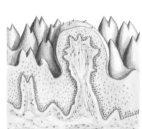

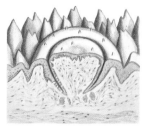

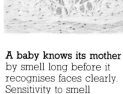

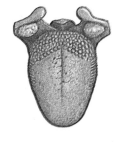

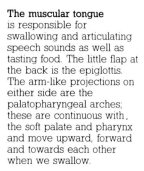

The muscular tongue
is responsible for
swallowing and articulating
speech sounds as well as
tasting food. The little flap at
the back is the epiglottis.
The arm-like projections on
either side are the
palatopharyngeal arches;
these are continuous with
the soft palate and pharynx
and move upward, forward
and towards each other
when we swallow.

Papillae on the tongue
are not the taste buds as
such. These occur in
greatest number around the
base of the various types
of papillae.

Top: the peak-shaped
(filiform) papillae found
more or less all over the
tongue, except at the back.

Middle: the mushroom-
shaped (fungiform)
papillae found at random
mostly in the middle of
the tongue, with a few
occurring at the sides
as well.

Bottom: a vallate papilla, one
of only 8 to 12 which form
the V-shaped border at the
back of the tongue. Vallate
papillae are much larger
than the others.

Anyone for fruitbats?
These are a delicacy in
Singapore and other parts of
Southeast Asia.

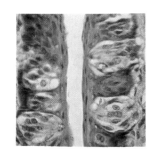

A baby knows its mother
by smell long before it
recognises faces clearly.
Sensitivity to smell
decreases as one
grows older.

Taste buds in close-up
In this stained section
through the trench area of a
vallate papilla, each cluster
of taste buds appears pale
by comparison with the
surrounding cells. The buds
open into the trench through
tiny taste pores.

our sweet tooth might be the residue of a safeguard
built into primitive man to ensure survival.

Most of our taste receptors are concentrated on
the upper surface of our tongue, but a few are
located on the soft palate and on the epiglottis, the
thin piece of cartilage in the throat that prevents
food from being inhaled into the lungs. The four
different types of taste bud (salt, sweet, bitter and
sour) lie on different parts of the tongue. Salty and
sweet sensations are tasted best at the tip, bitter
ones at the back, and sour ones at the sides. There
is little sensation in the middle.

The taste buds are located in minute protrusions
called papillae. There are four different kinds of
papillae, but these do not correspond with the four
senses of taste. Each papilla responds to a mixture
of tastes (except for the vallate papillae which form
a V across the back of the tongue and which
register only bitter tastes).

An adult has some 9,000 taste buds, a good deal
fewer than a baby. As we get older, many taste
buds disappear and with them the appreciation of
flavours, which may help to explain why adults
tend to disbelieve children's complaints about
foul-tasting medicine.

The tongue also contains nerves that register
temperature, pain and touch. These also influence
the way things taste. For example, most people
agree that a hot cup of tea or coffee tastes better
than a cold one. Consistency, texture and even
appearance also influence our attitudes to food and
its appeal to us.

You can prove to yourself how vital smell is to
taste by sampling some gastronomic delicacy,
savouring it and the holding your nose. The
reduction in 'taste' is dramatic. A bad head cold, in
which the mucous membranes of the nasal sinuses
are inflamed, has the same effect.

Endocrine system: chemical communication

Why are some people giants? Why are some people more violent than others? Why do animals, including humans, mate more in spring and summer than in winter? Why are some women fertile and others not?

To begin with, we need two basic definitions: endocrine, from *endon* meaning 'within' and *kinein* meaning 'to separate'; and hormone, from *hormon*, meaning 'to stir up'.

Almost everything we do bears a hormonal stamp. Among other things, hormones regulate basic drives and emotions such as sexual urges, violence, anger, fear, joy and sorrow. They also promote growth and sexual identity, control temperature, assist in the repair of broken tissue and help to generate energy.

The body thermostat

Although the endocrine system is not fully understood, we know that it employs what is known as a negative feedback system. Central heating works in much the same way; if the temperature in a centrally-heated house drops below a certain preset limit the thermostat 'instructs' the boiler to pump out more heat to push the temperature back up to the desired level. Likewise, the boiler reduces its output if the house gets too hot.

When body temperature drops, blood temperature drops, resulting in a flow of colder blood to the brain. This activates the thermostat within the hypothalamus, an area of the brain we describe later. The thermostat then releases hormones which permeate through the bloodstream to other glands. These initiate a host of functions directed towards creating energy and reducing further heat loss by cutting off blood supply to the skin, particularly to feet and hands.

No man-made regulator is as versatile. Perhaps the most sophisticated human application of negative feedback is that found in guided missiles; these are equipped to track and even predict evasive action by the target and to twist and turn accordingly. But the design is gross compared to that of the endocrine system and is required to operate once only. The thermostat in the human brain has to continue functioning for at least 60 years. Sometimes it deteriorates earlier than the human 'pipes'. An old person may feel the cold but be unable to respond normally. Some people lose both the ability to respond normally and to feel a cold environment, and the result can be fatal hypothermia. Neither bodies nor machines are immune to the wear and tear of ageing.

Hypothalamus

This consists of a tiny cluster of nerve cells at the base of the 'old' brain, that part of the brain which deals with body control and instinct, as distinct from the 'new' brain which is the centre of voluntary action, intellect and memory.

The function of the hypothalamus is to integrate and ensure appropriate responses to stimuli. It receives impulses or messages from both the conscious and subconscious parts of the brain and then sends out signals via *both* nerves and hormones.

The central nervous system (CNS) is a high-speed communication system which transmits messages in the form of coded electrical impulses through a network of fibres. But messages from the slower endocrine system travel as hormones in the blood and are directed at specific cells or targets. In much the same way that a radio is tuned to a specific frequency, so target cells are 'tuned' to specific chemical messengers. In other words, target and messenger slot together like two pieces in a jigsaw. The part of the target cell which receives the message is known as a receptor.

Hormonal communication involves a series of chain reactions. In most cases it begins when the hypothalamus responds to a message from the CNS by sending a message to the master gland, the pituitary. The pituitary then releases another messenger to a target gland which in turn sends yet another messenger to the specific tissue or organ that it regulates. At the same time the target cell despatches a message back to the hypothalamus and/or pituitary so that production of the hormone concerned can be decreased or increased as required, just as happens in a thermostatically-controlled central heating system.

Pituitary

The pea-sized pituitary is linked to the hypothalamus by a short stubby stalk. It hangs from the undercarriage of the brain in a small bony hollow, the Turkish saddle, behind the nose and between the eyes. The pituitary is two separate glands: the posterior (rear) lobe and the anterior (front) lobe.

The anterior lobe is known as the controlling gland because all its hormones, except growth hormone, regulate the function of other endocrine glands. These hormones are known as trophic hormones, that is hormones that 'feed' or 'nourish'. They include:
1 Growth hormone (GH);
2 Prolactin, which stimulates milk secretion (also maternal behaviour in non-humans);
3 Thyroid stimulating hormone (TSH) or thyro-trophin, which stimulates thyroid growth and secretion;
4 Adrenocorticotrophic hormone (ACTH), which stimulates the adrenal cortex, an energy-generating gland;
5 Follicle stimulating hormone (FSH), which stimulates ovarian follicle growth in the female and

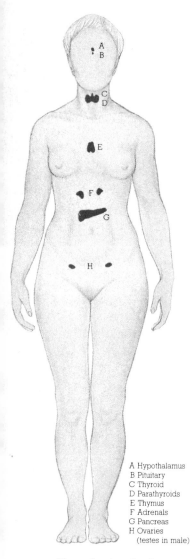

A Hypothalamus
B Pituitary
C Thyroid
D Parathyroids
E Thymus
F Adrenals
G Pancreas
H Ovaries
(testes in male)

The endocrine glands
The hormones produced by the pituitary, parathyroids and pancreas are proteins or peptides (parts of protein). Those manufactured by the thyroid and adrenal glands are either aromatic compounds or steroids (complex compounds made of interlocking rings of carbon atoms).

The moment of truth . . .
The hypothalamus at work, orchestrating emotions, gestures, exclamations. In some animals electrical stimulation of the rear part of the hypothalamus causes a rage reaction.

The Austrian giant
Wintrelmeier, all 8 ft 1 in of him, as photographed in 1887. Too much growth hormone in childhood leads to overgrowth of bones, muscles and internal organs. Too much GH in later life causes acromegaly.

sperm production in the male;
6 Luteinising hormone (LH), which provokes ovulation in the female and stimulates the sex hormone testosterone in the male.

The posterior lobe of the pituitary secretes oxytocin, which causes contraction of the uterus during pregnancy and acts on certain muscle cells which squeeze out milk during suckling; and also vasopressin, which acts on the kidney tubules to regulate body fluid and sodium and potassium concentrations.

Another hormone, melanocyte stimulating hormone (MSH), controls the quantity of melanin in the skin. This dark pigment, which gives skin its colour, regardless of race, arises from a cleft of tissue wedged between the anterior and posterior lobes of the pituitary.

The hormones listed opposite underline the diversity of the endocrine system. Hormone levels differ from person to person, accounting for differing abilities and characteristics as well as differences in physiological function. Hormones have literally hundreds of therapeutic uses. Many disorders can be treated by the administration of hormone compounds, including sterility, allergies, rheumatism, and various types of inflammation. They are also used as contraceptives and body builders; they can also prevent some effects of ageing and localise the action of anaesthetics.

The Hormone Show
Short and tall, male and female, brown and white—all done by hormones switching on and switching off at precise times . . . or never switching on at all.

Pituitary, thyroid, parathyroid

The gift of concentration Just as some individual hormones play more than one role, the constituents of hormones—many hormones are built up from small proteins or polypeptides—have many tasks.

Research suggests that the gift of concentration is partly determined by a protein shared by two pituitary hormones, ACTH and MSH. Investigations in the USA funded by the Veterans Administration Medical Center and Tulane University School of Medicine have shown that the ACTH/MSH protein enhances visual retention and concentration.

In studies with mentally retarded patients Drs Abba Kastin and Curt A. Sandman found that the protein resulted in greatly improved comprehension—patients were able to think more clearly. In studies with students Drs Kastin and Lyle H. Miller found that shots of ACTH/MSH made them feel able to study more effectively for longer periods. So maybe the gift of concentration is determined in part or wholly by ACTH/MSH levels in the blood.

Growth: dwarfs and giants Growth hormone from the pituitary works in tandem with the sex hormones and other hormones during childhood and adolescence to promote growth and development. It fosters the growth of bones and the production of proteins, the body's building blocks.

An untreated GH deficiency causes a marked slowing of growth, resulting in dwarfism. Two of the world's most famous dwarfs were Charles Stratton, otherwise known as Tom Thumb, and his bride Lavinia Warren. They were less than 3 ft (0.9 m) tall but perfectly proportioned and intelligent. Over-secretion on the other hand can lead to a condition called gigantism. The best known victim of this condition was Robert Wadlow of Alton, Illinois. Towering 8 ft 11 in (2.7 m) tall, Wadlow weighed more than 35 stone (220 kg) and had feet almost 20 in (50 cm) long. He died in 1940.

The principle for treating hormonal deficiencies is a simple one. Under-secretion is treated by administering extra hormones and over-secretion by suppressing hormone production. Deficiencies can be treated with hormonal extracts from non-human species (pig or ox) but GH is 'species specific'; that is, a child with GH deficiency can be treated only with human GH.

GH deficiencies are rare, as are cases of excess growth. In Great Britain, for example, with a population of 56 million, only 50 such cases are reported every year. Some adults with pituitary tumours secrete large amounts of GH. They cannot grow any taller but their bone structure becomes distorted. Hands and feet enlarge and become thicker and the face assumes a lion-like look as the

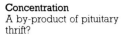

Concentration
A by-product of pituitary thrift?

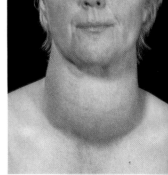

Goitre
Swelling of the thyroid gland in the neck. This can be due to overactivity of the thyroid gland itself or to excess TSH from the pituitary, or to underactivity due to little iodine in the diet. Just 1 mg of extra thyroxine a day can increase an adult's energy requirement from 2,500 to 3,500 calories; so if only 2,500 calories are eaten weight loss will follow. This is why thyroxine has been used as a treatment for obesity.

Cross references
Sex hormones **71**
Hormones and sexuality **72**
Skeleton **32**
Infancy **142**

skin becomes coarser and fleshier; the brow becomes more prominent, the face broadens, the lower jaw enlarges, and the nose widens.

The tumour may be removed surgically or be subjected to radiation treatment to suppress GH secretion. The drug bromocryptine may also be used to regulate GH secretion. Where a child is exceptionally tall, however, it does not mean that he or she has a tumour affecting the GH-secreting gland. It is worth stressing that these tumours are rare although tall children are very common.

The maternal male In all animals health and behaviour is affected by the hormonal levels in the body. Though male rats have a sharply defined masculine role, given prolactin injections they will defy their masculine stereotype and assume a less aggressive, nest-building maternal role. Similarly, human males with high prolactin levels secrete breast milk.

Thyroid gland: energy control The complex process of growth depends not only on GH but also on thyroxine from the thyroid gland. This gland weighs about 1 oz (28 g) and is situated in the neck. A baby born without a thyroid gland will be severely retarded because intellect does not develop without thyroxine. Thyroxine also controls reflexes and dictates the rate at which the body produces energy and transforms food into body components. One of the key constituents of thyroxine is body-building iodine. Babies cannot grow properly without iodine; a deficiency in infancy or early childhood causes cretinism. In older people, iodine deficiency causes hair loss, slowed speech and drying and thickening of the skin; our iodine requirement is only about a millionth of an ounce (0.00003 g) per day but it is vital and highlights the delicate balance between sickness and health.

Thyroxine also controls temperature. If the thyroid gland is removed from a rat it will build a thicker, bigger nest. People with over-active thyroid glands tend to feel uncomfortably hot in that they tend to wear thin clothes in mid-winter. Conversely, people whose thyroid gland is under-active are liable to wear thick clothes on the hottest of days.

Too much thyroxine speeds up metabolism, an occurrence which can be compared to a driver pulling out the choke of his automobile and forgetting to ease it back again—the engine races. Conversely, too little thyroxine prevents the body machine from firing healthily on all cylinders.

Parathyroid glands: calcium balance The parathyroid glands, which are embedded within the thyroid, regulate calcium concentration in the blood by secreting parathyroid hormone or parathormone. If the concentration falls,

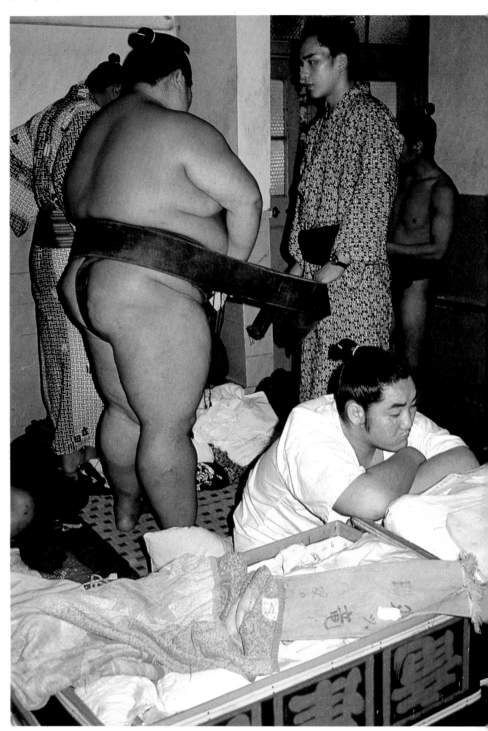

parathormone is released to bring calcium out of the bones. Calcium plays a crucial role in many metabolic processes; too much or too little can disrupt the normal function of muscles and nerves.

It is known that calcium concentration is influenced by the biological clock which regulates our lives. Eskimos have been found to excrete eight to ten times more calcium in their long dark winter than in their short light summer. In winter they are prone to a bewildering emotional disorder known as 'winter madness' or 'Arctic hysteria'.

Belting up for Sumo wrestling. More energy input than output equals fat, even if the output involves heaving one's opponent out of the ring. Hormone imbalances may help to maintain obesity but are seldom the cause of it.

Thymus, adrenal glands, pancreas

The adrenal medulla is activated by a wide variety of stress conditions. Cold weather, low blood pressure or low blood sugar levels trigger the same reaction from the adrenal medulla as fear or anger. The medullary hormones adrenaline and noradrenaline constrict arterioles and veins, and can be added to a local anaesthetic to localise its action.

Thymus: fire fighter Situated directly below the thyroid and parathyroid glands is the mysterious thymus gland. Very little is known about the thymus but recent evidence suggests that it helps the body to recognise and reject foreign substances, including bacteria and viruses. The thymus secretes a hormone known as thymic humoral factor (THF).

Adrenal glands: alarm system The adrenal glands, the cortex and medulla, each weigh about $\frac{1}{4}$ oz (7 g), and sit above the kidneys in the abdomen. Although they are anatomically linked, the adrenal glands serve different masters. The medulla is an agent of the sympathetic nervous system and is therefore activated by nerve impulses, not by blood-borne hormones. The cortex is an endocrine gland triggered by adrenocorticotrophic hormone (ACTH) sent out from the pituitary.

The cortex hormones, cortisol and aldosterone, are known as the corticosteroids and are essential to life. Cortisol is an energy generator, fire fighter and the quartermaster in charge of energy storage. It masterminds the conversion of carbohydrates into glucose and directs reserves to the liver. In its fire fighting role it also suppresses inflammation. As inflammation is part of the body's response to infection and injury, this could be potentially beneficial but unchecked inflammation would

spread like wildfire, ravaging normal tissue. Cortisol works by cordoning off the afflicted areas of the body and preventing the inflammation from encroaching upon healthy tissue.

Aldosterone prevents excessive loss of water through the kidneys and maintains the crucial balance between sodium (salt) and potassium, thereby oiling the mechanism which maintains the contractility of muscles.

The adrenals are part of the body's reaction to stress—one of the major preoccupations of modern life. Stress is examined later in this section.

Pancreas: sugar regulator The pancreas, a large parcel of tissue lying behind the lower part of the stomach, is the second largest gland in the body and takes its name from two Greek words meaning 'all meat'. The pancreas is a sugar regulator, and without it food cannot be digested properly.

The pancreas secretes two hormones into the blood, glucagon and insulin, produced respectively by alpha and beta cells in special areas of tissue called the islets of Langerhans. Insulin (from the Latin word for 'island') is so named because it originates from these islets.

Diabetes occurs when the pancreas fails to secrete enough insulin and so fails to control sugar or glucose levels in the blood. All sugary and starchy foods such as bread, potatoes, cakes and puddings, are broken down into glucose. In this form they can be absorbed by every cell in the body, including the cells of the liver, one of whose major roles is to store glucose. Cells absorb glucose and 'burn' it in structures called mitochondria, the cellular powerhouses, using the energy it contains and producing carbon dioxide and water as by-products. This burning up process is the body's principal source of energy and it cannot take place without insulin.

Insulin works like a key, making cell membranes permeable to glucose. Without insulin, glucose accumulates in the blood, which results in various kinds of biochemical mayhem. If glucose overflows into the urine, for example, it takes body water with it, resulting in acute thirst, one of the first signs of diabetes; or, starved of glucose, cells may start to burn up fat instead, causing weight loss, or start to burn protein, weakening muscle and other tissue. If insulin deficiency is serious and prolonged, the diabetic sinks into a coma and eventually dies.

Insulin also regulates glucose storage by the liver as well as regulating glucose levels in the blood. It may seem strange, therefore, that glucagon has the opposite effect of increasing glucose release by the liver. However, it is as much a guardian of health as its fellow hormone insulin and is produced and sent into the bloodstream to increase the sugar level in circulation.

One of the most dramatically successful hormone treatments is insulin isolated from pigs and cattle. It is estimated that the lives of some 25 million diabetics have been saved since two Canadians, Frederick G. Banting and Charles H. Best, extracted insulin from the pancreas during the early 1920s.

Sex hormones The gonadotrophins released by the pituitary are the same in both sexes and they act in essentially the same way. One of them, follicle stimulating hormone or FSH, controls the formation of ova or eggs by the ovary and sperm by the testes, so it is principally responsible for propagation of the species. The other is luteinising hormone, LH, which stimulates the production of sex hormones.

There are three groups of sex hormones; androgens, oestrogens and progestogens. All three exist in both sexes, their differing proportions determining gender. Male characteristics such as a deep voice, facial hair and muscular physique develop if androgens predominate. The oestrogens on the other hand promote female characteristics such as breast development. The progestogens prepare for and maintain pregnancy. The sex hormones also trigger the onset of puberty, when sexual identity is given sharper definition.

Putting the shot,
East Germany's I. Slupianek at the 1980 Moscow Olympics. Natural testosterone or anabolic steroids, synthetic hormones derived from testosterone, are increasingly used by the 'big girls' of international athletics to build up their muscle power. If sufficient time elapses between taking them and having a femininity test before a sporting event, they are not directly detectable.

Dr Renée Richards,
(formerly Dr Richard Raskind) a transsexual seen here playing in a women's tennis tournament. Genetic sex (a question of X and Y chromosomes) cannot be altered; a 'sex change' involves a combination of surgical and hormonal treatments.

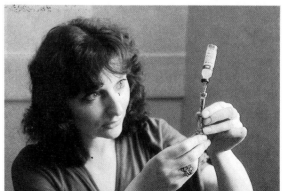

Insulin restores the ability
to use glucose and fats. Being a protein, insulin is inactive by mouth so has to be injected in carefully measured amounts.

Hormones and sexuality

Waiting for a client
A male prostitute in downtown New York. There is no reliable evidence that deviant sexual behaviour is controlled by one's hormones and genes.

Right: three generations.
The ovaries of a baby girl contain about 400,000 primitive eggs. During her reproductive years a woman may release up to 5,000 mature eggs. When the ovaries cease to produce oestrogen, ovulation ceases, because it is oestrogen which signals the pituitary to produce the hormone which causes the eggs to mature.

Puberty The dramatic process of adolescence, initiated by the hypothalamus, follows a set cycle. In boys, for example, it begins with enlargement of the testes; in girls it begins with the budding of the breasts and in both sexes pubic and underarm hair develops. The onset of puberty varies so much that it cannot be considered to have been delayed by a faulty biological clock until in girls the menarche (the first menstrual period) has failed to occur by the age of 17 or in boys the testicles have failed to develop by the age of 15.

Sexual development before the age of ten is thought of as premature. So-called sexual precocity is more common in girls than in boys and is usually attributable to a 'slip' of the biological timer. In a few rare cases precocious puberty occurs in infancy. In one well-documented case a girl developed pubic hair and started menstruating by the age of 17 months. She had well-developed breasts by the age of three and a half.

Fortunately, synthetic hormones can hold puberty in check until an appropriate time; these suppress the release of gonadotrophins from the pituitary gland. Sexual precocity among boys is usually associated with a tumour in the region of the hypothalamus.

Recent research has shown that the menarche occurs at a slightly younger age in blind girls than in fully-sighted ones. The significance of light in the maintenance of the life cycle is discussed later.

Premenstrual tension (PMT) Theories abound as to the cause of this distressing aspect of the menstrual cycle but no one theory seems to apply to all cases.

It might be that thoughts and fears about PMT compound any problems which occur. Thoughts can and do trigger the secretion of hormones just as they can and do suppress secretion. Tests have shown that women who score high on 'neuroticism tests' tend to suffer more menstrual distress than women who score low. Furthermore, the responses that women receive from the people around them interact with their individual tendencies. Research suggests that premenstrual women are more susceptible to conditioning by others and are, on the whole, more likely to conform to the behaviour expected of them. Therefore if women expect to suffer from PMT, they are more likely to do so.

Investigations support this conclusion. Catholic, Protestant and Jewish women have the same hormonal mechanisms but research has revealed marked differences in their psychological response to menstruation. The psychologist Karen Paige believes that the differences arise from the different cultural and religious approaches to women and the human body.

Menopause As the menopause or 'change of life' approaches, oestrogen levels begin to fall, while levels of gonadotrophic hormones from the pituitary begin to rise. This process of preparation by the body can begin some while before changes in the menstrual pattern. As egg production ceases and hormone levels fall, menstruation becomes less frequent, eventually stopping altogether. Alternatively, periods can be totally unpredictable and sometimes very heavy.

Many women experience the menopause without problems or regrets; some find it extremely trying, either psychologically or physically, or both. The change can bring hot flushes, or hot flashes as they are known in the USA, dizziness, aches and pain in the joints and discomfort during intercourse. Penetration can be difficult as the vaginal lining becomes drier.

Later effects of lowered oestrogen levels include weakening of the bones. However, these effects can

Onset of menstruation
At the first sign of menstrual blood Mechinacu Indian girls are cloistered in a special 'fattening house' for six months. Many primitive and some not so primitive cultures surround menstruation with taboos which have no foundation in medicine or hygiene.

Behaviour differences
between male and female homosexuals reflect those between male and female heterosexuals. Like heterosexual women, lesbians tend to look on sexual aggressiveness and promiscuity as offensive and unfeminine.

be controlled by small doses of sex hormones. Hormone replacement therapy in middle age is comparable with giving insulin for diabetics.

Sexual desire Many people believe that sex hormones have important effects on sexual desire but extensive research only partly supports this view. Hormone injections will often alter sexual desire but so will injections with water. This is the mysterious placebo effect at work, belief alone making a treatment effective. If aphrodisiacs have any effect it is through the placebo effect.

Most endocrinologists estimate that well over 90 per cent of impotence problems are psychological rather than hormonal in origin. Fear of failure after one disappointing performance is often to blame.

Homosexuality

Attempts have been made to detect hormonal differences between homosexuals and heterosexuals and to see if transsexuals—people who request sex change surgery—are hormonally abnormal. Results from these studies, however, are inconclusive.

Research has shown that people with low hormone levels sometimes, but not always, have diminished levels of sexual interest; and that people with abnormal hormone levels sometimes, but not usually, have unconventional sexual interests. So the only observation that can be made with any certainty is that the role of sex hormones, except for their direct effect on the functioning of the genitals and sexual development, is unclear.

Responding to emergencies

Stress hormones We distinguish between various types of threat. If we are attacked by muggers, we would say we were 'afraid'; marital or financial problems, however, would be summed up as 'worry' or 'anxiety'. But the body's thermostat makes no such distinctions; the biological response to fear and anxiety is the same. For our primitive ancestors this response was ideal since their emergencies tended to be a question of crude survival. But it is less well-suited to the complexity of the modern age. Many problems today tend to persist and so accumulate, yet our response to fear and anxiety is designed to withstand only short-term emergencies.

If the hormonal accelerators are pressed down hard for weeks on end, the engine suffers, overloading the servicing department and causing breakdown. Even worse, the hormones respond to imagined fears in much the same way as they respond to real ones. Irrational fears are common and are more likely to last than real ones. The crisis in the life of the footballer who can no longer score goals usually passes quickly enough; either he improves and keeps his place in the team or he is sacked. But the company executive with continuous and unfounded fears for his job may suffer a sustained crisis that culminates in one of the stress diseases.

The body responds to acute stress by preparing for war and it is the hormones which mobilise the troops. The adrenal medulla pours adrenaline and noradrenaline (epinephrine and norepinephrine, USA) into the bloodstream for this purpose. The heart steps up its activity, providing more blood for the brain and muscles; blood vessels close to the skin constrict and clotting time shortens, making severe bleeding from wounds less likely; breathing is faster and deeper, providing more oxygen; saliva and mucus dry up, increasing the size of the air passages to the lungs; and increased perspiration cools the body.

Many muscles tense and tighten to prepare the body for rapid and vigorous action. Even the pupils dilate, making the eyes more sensitive. William Shakespeare gives a good description of these external changes in the Harfleur scene in *Henry V*: "Stiffen the sinews, summon up the blood, … lend the eye a terrible aspect."

More white corpuscles are produced to help fight infection while low priority functions, such as eating and digesting food, are postponed to conserve energy. In these ways all the forces of the body are prepared either to attack an enemy or flee to safety.

There are, of course, various responses to stress. This can be demonstrated by the story of the three sober strangers of comparable strength and physique who were confronted by an aggressive drunk in a bar. The first man retreated discreetly;

The modern equivalent of doing battle against woolly mammoths and sabre-tooth tigers? Using skill and anticipation to outwit an animal of much greater speed and strength.

the second man cracked a lighthearted joke in an attempt to cool the atmosphere; and the third man knocked the drunk to the floor. The three men in the story had three totally different responses to the same threat.

On the strength of recent research it seems that response to a threat such as this could be determined partly by what is known as the 'adrenaline/noradrenaline ratio'. This could also explain violent criminal histories involving unprovoked assaults on defenceless strangers.

Let's go back to the three men in the bar. All three men were afraid, yet only one responded violently. If current theories are correct, the noradrenaline levels of the third man—the violent one—would have been higher than those of the other two, while his adrenaline levels would have been lower. It seems that adrenaline has a restraining influence. The adrenal medullae secrete adrenaline and noradrenaline in the ratio of four to one. Adrenaline concentrations rise when we are

Cross references
Stress **162**
Coronary heart disease **96**
Blood pressure **106**
Mental abnormality **168**

Getting the noradrenaline flowing to order. But what if your opponent just isn't dislikeable enough to KO? All physical contact sports depend on controlled aggression.

Children under stress in Northern Ireland. Political uncertainty, sectarian violence, death of friends and relatives, poor housing, inflation and unemployment . . . these can all be coped with, but at the cost of establishing patterns of aggression and instability that persist into adulthood.

afraid and noradrenaline concentrations rise when we feel aggressive. Research suggests that aggressive people have higher base levels of noradrenaline than other people and are therefore more inclined to lose their temper impulsively.

Evidence also points to a correlation between adrenaline/noradrenaline ratios and social class. It seems that a person who is lower down the social order is more likely to have high base levels of noradrenaline. This is a statistical relationship of course; it does not necessarily mean that a well-spoken, plausible lawyer will secrete less noradrenaline and be less aggressive than a rough, unskilled labourer. Nevertheless, it is well established that children from poorer backgrounds have a harder life and take more physical punishment than children from wealthier backgrounds; and that children subject to harsh parental discipline are more aggressive outside the home—violence really does breed violence.

It has yet to be established whether violence inflicted routinely on children in the form of physical punishment sets off changes in base noradrenaline levels but it is known that if newborn mice are taken from their mothers, put in isolation for a month, and then placed together again, fighting breaks out. In normal well-adjusted mice, noradrenaline is converted into adrenaline by enzymes or catalysts and this is believed to have a restraining influence on their behaviour. In mice isolated at birth, however, these enzymes do not function normally; the result is a shortage of adrenaline and an overall imbalance in the adrenaline/noradrenaline ratio so that noradrenaline, the anger hormone, predominates, causing aggressive behaviour.

While it is not known if people under stress behave in the same way, it is known that hormone levels change in mental illness, especially in depression. Depressive states are believed to be associated with noradrenaline deficiency.

Two British investigators, Dr D. D. Woodman, a biochemist, and John Hinton, a psychologist, set out to test the relationship between aggressive personalities and the catecholamines, the group of hormones which includes noradrenaline and adrenaline. They conducted a study in Broadmoor, a British maximum security hospital for the mentally abnormal, in which they compared the Broadmoor patients' hormonal levels with those of healthy volunteers and other mental patients. All three groups, totalling 115 subjects, were subjected to a wide range of everyday stresses including criticism, frustration, mental tests and pictures of human suffering. The stress programme was taped so that each subject was identically stressed.

Reporting the results in the British journal *New Society*, Dr Woodman said that about a quarter of the Broadmoor patients showed less physiological response than others in their own or the other two groups, so demonstrating higher noradrenaline to adrenaline ratios. Not until after the study had been completed did Woodman and Hinton examine the case records of those who had participated. They found that the patients with abnormally high levels of noradrenaline relative to adrenaline were also those with case histories indicating murderous intent in physically violent crimes. These patients accounted for well over half the patients convicted of crime resulting in death and for many more attacks on total strangers. Sixty-four per cent of their victims were strangers, compared with only 20 per cent of the victims of the physiologically responsive group.

At intervals between 4 and 25 months after the initial study, the Broadmoor patients were tested again. They showed approximately the same noradrenaline/adrenaline ratios seen originally, suggesting that base levels of these two hormones probably remain fairly constant.

Biological clocks

An appointment to keep
Times of arrival and
departure are virtually the
same every year for
hundreds of species of
migrating birds. What
internal timer enables them
to judge day length?

*Love everything in the universe because sun and earth
are but one body* Ancient Chinese maxim

The clock is another example of a man-made
machine built in the human image. The hands and
face of the clock follow a 12- or 24-hour cycle; the
body machine follows a 24-hour cycle, coinciding
with the rising and setting of the sun.

It is fashionable to talk about the 'biological
clock' as a single entity, yet the term may be
misleading because there are probably many
internal timers clicking in unison like metronomes,
forcing one another to keep time. The skeleton
punches a time clock from the moment of birth,
while our cellular death warrants, the fibroblast
cells, determine the length of the human lifespan.
Fibroblasts are, in effect, pre-set timers which tick
off the allotted lifespan of each cell and thereby the
lifespan of the whole body, provided no other fatal
disease or injury intervenes. These cells divide
regularly about 50 times before dying.

Heart beat, blood pressure and temperature
—under the influence of hormones—are regulated
by daily cycles. The most obvious daily cycle is
sleep, during which heart rate, blood pressure and
temperature fall. Another example is the female
monthly cycle in which hormones prepare a lining
in the womb ready for pregnancy; if an egg is not
fertilised the lining is shed and a period begins.

Procreation The changing ratios of light and dark
marking the seasons are believed to set off a chain
of hormonal reaction originating in the pineal

gland, the so-called 'third eye' in the brain. This
probably accounts for animal migration, moulting,
hibernation and preparation for the mating season.

Before discussing human procreation and the
biological clock, it would be sobering to stop and
wonder at the migratory and navigational talents of
birds. This book has stressed that man-made
machines and instruments are built in the human
image, but although the body machine is the
supreme machine in terms of overall performance,
many amazing natural patents are incorporated in
other species. Either consciously or unconsciously
we then exploit the greater power of the species
concerned—the smelling power of the bloodhound,
for example—or we exploit the principle upon
which the patent is based.

For hundreds of years the unerring navigational
skill of birds such as the homing pigeon intrigued
scientists. Now research suggests that the
homing pigeon has tiny magnetic particles in its
head which enable it to plot its position and set a
course for home. In other words it does not rely
solely on the position of the sun to decide which
way to go. It has a built-in compass, many times
more compact than the smallest man-made
compass. This probably explains why experienced
homing pigeons do not lose their way when the sun
is obscured by heavy cloud.

On a clear summer day migrating birds maintain
a constant course by flying at different angles to the
sun according to the time. And it is their biological
clock—the same mechanism which urges them to
start nest-building as increasing day length signals

Cross references
Search for immortality **242**
Sleep need **194**
Menstrual cycle **21**
Clockwork routine **78**

An Arctic winter
Well adapted as they are to the cold, have the Eskimos really adapted to prolonged low light intensities? Loss of plasma calcium causes tetany, abnormal excitability of the nerves resulting in muscular spasms and convulsions.

the end of winter—which tells them the time.

Electric light and central heating have not made man immune to similar primitive seasonal urges. The old saying that 'in spring a young man's fancy turns to thoughts of love' is perfectly true. People do mate more in the spring and summer judging by seasonal birth rates.

In Great Britain in the last 150 years, the first half of the year has usually seen more births than the second half, and since 1840 the second quarter, corresponding to summertime conceptions, has consistently topped the poll. The birth rate is usually at its lowest in November. It rises sharply until the late winter month of March, remains high until the early summer months of May and June, and then falls again. However, there is a minor rise in September, corresponding with a high number of Christmas time conceptions.

Animal experiments have shown that the secretion of a hormone, melatonin, from the mysterious pineal gland helps to maintain daily and seasonal breeding cycles in animals. Also known, somewhat sinisterly, as 'the third eye', the pineal gland hangs from the centre of the brain and has nerve connections to the retina and other parts of the brain. A recent study at the USA National Institute of Health in Maryland suggests that melatonin helps to maintain daily cycles in humans as well as in other species. Several earlier attempts to show the same effects in humans failed, possibly because the intensity of light to which the subjects were exposed to was too low.

The four men and four women in the Maryland

study spent two nights sleeping in a dark room. On the first night they were woken up and exposed to fluorescent light of about the same intensity as domestic artificial light; and on the second night they were woken up and exposed to incandescent light of an intensity similar to indirect sunlight on a clear spring day. Their melatonin concentrations, measured in blood samples through a fixed catheter, were unaffected by the fluorescent light, but fell quickly in response to the incandescent light. Within an hour their concentrations reached almost daytime levels, suggesting that humans do indeed respond to fluctuations of light and darkness in the same way as other animals.

The Eskimo experience described earlier also suggests that we use light levels to reset our internal timers. Eskimos excrete eight to ten times more calcium in their long dark winter than in their summer, and during winter are prone to an emotional condition known as Arctic hysteria or winter madness.

Is there a connection between prolonged darkness and calcium loss? Certainly, it is known that hormones regulate calcium concentrations and that calcium influences nerve function. It is also known that sight-restoring cataract operations can restore normal hormonal cycles in blind people. Further, if a person is isolated in a room with no windows, allowing them no glimpse of the natural cycle of light and day, their internal timer goes haywire. The body lapses into longer cycles of 26 or 28 hours; it has trouble pacing itself, no longer knowing what the time is.

Use and abuse of body rhythms

Jet lag The negotiations that culminated in the United States' Declaration of Independence in 1776 were dogged by complaints about King George III's choice of venues for 'summit meetings'. One observer wrote: "He has called together legislative bodies at places unusual, uncomfortable and distant . . . for the sole purpose of fatiguing them."

Today, preparation for top-level meetings has changed to take account of the effects of travel fatigue; modern statesmen break their journeys with 'stop-overs'.

Eastbound flights have a more marked effect than westbound ones. The faster a passenger travels westwards, the quicker he or she approaches yesterday; the faster he or she moves east, the quicker he or she moves into tomorrow.

The urination patterns of British troops flown from Britain to Singapore (seven hours ahead of British time) remained consistent with British time for three days, compounding the effects of travel fatigue. The men were tested to assess the effects of the journey on marching, staged assaults, weapon handling and shooting. Their efficiency in precise work such as aiming and shooting was impaired, but tasks demanding less skill were less affected.

However, soldiers are younger and fitter than most travellers. Recent interest has centred on the effects of jet lag on the typical jet-setting executive.

Crossing time zones is part of an international airline pilot's job, but as yet no civil aviation authority enforces longer rest periods after travelling forward in time. For a long-haul pilot the effects of jet lag are overlaid by the effects of flying through the night after a normal waking day, eating at irregular hours, and having to fit in with local time, wherever 'local' may be. Minimum rest periods between flights and between periods of duty are compulsory.

A study was carried out in which 14 people were flown from London to San Francisco and back. They were examined for a week before leaving London, for ten days in San Francisco and for a further week on their return. Reporting the results to the Royal Aeronautical Society, Dr George Christie, a consultant to a pharmaceutical company, said: "Physiological adaptation, which took longest, required no less than seven to ten days to adjust to the new time zone after the westbound flight (from London), and again seven days eastbound. Biochemically, from blood tests, the westbound flights required at least four days for adaptation and the eastbound more than seven."

It was in the area of performance that the most revealing results emerged. The first and most significant feature was the wide variation in the degree to which different individuals were affected, some showing the biggest decrease in performance immediately, others taking as long as five days to show the full effects. Some showed only a small decrease in ability, but others performed with only half their usual efficiency.

Correlation of the results with personality tests showed that it was the older, individual go-getters who suffered most. Disturbingly, it seems that after crossing several time zones, they had a tendency to be inarticulate, hesitant and twice as likely to make mistakes. Concentration and memory also suffered. Unfortunately, there is no pharmacological panacea which converts the jet-lagged executive back to his normal bushy-tailed condition.

Clockwork routine We do not expect peak performance from an automobile when we turn on the ignition early in the day, especially on a cold winter day. Cold engines do not run smoothly. It is much the same with the body machine. We are at our coldest and most inefficient early in the day.

As our engines warm up, and the cardiovascular motor changes gear to prepare for the open road, performance and feeling of well-being improved markedly. This familiar daily pattern is accompanied by small but crucial changes in body temperature, one of the most reliable indicators of body time. The significance of these fluctuations was illustrated by two British scientists, Dr Robert Wilkinson and Dr Peter Colquhoun, in a study of naval recruits.

The vigilance and mathematical ability of the recruits was assessed shortly after waking from sleep. During the first three hours their body temperature rose on average by 0.56°F (0.2°C); thereafter it was relatively stable, changing by only 0.4°F (0.15°C) during 60 per cent of the day. Peak efficiency coincided with peak body temperature. As body temperature fell, so did the efficiency of the recruits. These changes might seem small but it is worth remembering that we survive within a narrow range of temperature. Normal healthy temperatures range between 96° and 99°F (35.6°–37.3°C).

Dr Lawrence Scheving and his colleagues at the University of Arkansas followed 12 healthy volunteers around the clock for three days to relate temperature to mood and memory. At 7am when the volunteers woke up their temperatures hovered around the 97°F (36.1°C) mark. As their body temperature rose both their mood (self-rated on a scale of 1 to 7) and memory (the number of digits remembered per second) improved.

Studies like these demonstrate that as our temperature changes, we become more skilled in some areas and less skilled in others. The implication is that intellectually demanding tasks like budgeting should be handled early in the day, while business meetings requiring tact and diplomacy should be left until later—the better you feel, the more able you are to cope with a potentially stressful situation.

Mind should take precedence over matter, but faced with an unreasonable boss or a tight deadline, it often doesn't. Nevertheless, it is better to keep in time with the biological clock than try to beat it.

The same principle applies to the treatment of disease. It has been found that mice with leukaemia are eight times more likely to survive than other leukaemic mice if they are treated with drugs at certain times in the daily cycle. Human cancer patients are now being treated with 'cycle specific drugs' administered at times which coincide with certain phases in the cycle of cell division.

One explanation for this could be that drugs which temporarily stop cells from making DNA, which contains the code of instructions for building the body, kill cells at certain stages in their rhythms. It has been known for many decades that body cells do not divide at an even rate throughout the day. For example, skin cells divide mostly between midnight and 4am when we are asleep. So, if such drugs are administered when cells in healthy organs are not making new DNA, only the proliferating cancer cells die because these cells are multiplying at faster rhythms than the normal non-malignant cells.

Suicide Suicides, attempted suicides, depression and many other types of illness also go in cycles. A statistical analysis in Minnesota, USA, demonstrated a peak in deaths from atherosclerosis (the underlying condition of coronary heart disease) in January, the coldest time of year. Suicides peaked in the spring and early summer, and accidental deaths in July and August, the holiday season. Criminal offences by women have been shown to occur in the pre-menstrual and menstrual phase of their cycles.

One down and one to go
President Ford comes a cropper, Henry Kissinger keeps his cool. How fit are statesmen to take major decisions after long flights?

Heart: romance and reality

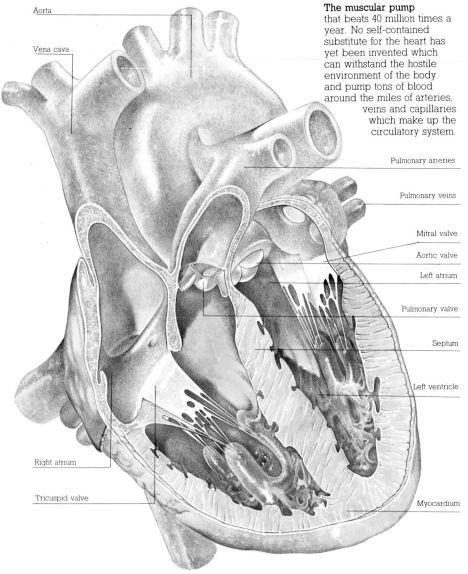

Aorta

Vena cava

Pulmonary arteries

Pulmonary veins

Mitral valve

Aortic valve

Left atrium

Pulmonary valve

Septum

Left ventricle

Right atrium

Tricuspid valve

Myocardium

The muscular pump
that beats 40 million times a
year. No self-contained
substitute for the heart has
yet been invented which
can withstand the hostile
environment of the body
and pump tons of blood
around the miles of arteries,
veins and capillaries
which make up the
circulatory system.

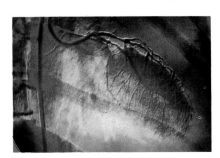

Arterial blood supply
to the heart revealed by
coronary angiogram. Dye is
injected into the coronary
arteries through a fine tube
passed into the heart
through a peripheral artery.
The dye shows up on an
X-ray. Note the dangerous
narrowing (stenosis) of the
arteries just before they
enter the heart.

In classical poetry, romantic fiction and popular
song the heart is unequalled as a symbol of
romantic feeling. No other organ of the body
commands so many quotations: there are heroic
hearts, stout ones, kind ones, pure ones, hearts of
oak, hearts of stone, hearts of steel. If this entire
section was devoted to quotations about the heart,
it would cover very few of them. Generations of
poets and writers have earmarked the heart, which
has no power over feeling, for this special treatment

in preference to the brain, the source of all
thoughts and actions. Logically the brain would be
a better choice, but logic does not lend itself to
romance, and the brain does not easily lend itself to
symbolism. The shape of the heart is far more
attractive than that of the brain—it does vaguely
resemble the Valentine emblem. And more
important, we can feel our hearts responding to the
thrill of love or fear. We never feel the brain.

However, in affairs of the heart, feeling can be
misleading in more ways than one. Most people
believe that the heart is on the left hand side of the
chest because that is where they feel it beat. In fact,
about a third of the heart lies on the right hand
side. In normal circumstances, the beats are felt on
the left hand side because of the heart's sharp apex
which points downwards and outwards towards
the left nipple.

Mistaken beliefs like these are of no real
consequence, but they do reflect a basic lack of
understanding about the heart, and need for
understanding has never been greater. Coronary
heart disease is the number one killer in
industrialised countries. Sadly, and paradoxically,
it is a disease of affluence and technological
progress. We exercise less today than at any other
time in history. We no longer have to chase prey or
run from predators; instead, today, we save our
legs at the expense of our hearts by using
escalators, automobiles and other labour-saving
devices. The result is a head-on collision between
progress and evolution. The human lifestyle has
changed, but the human body has remained
basically the same; it still thrives on the stimulus of
exercise in exactly the same way that it did a
thousand years ago.

Exercise strengthens muscle and thereby
strengthens the heart, which consists almost
entirely of muscle. The sole function of the heart is
to pump blood around the body to feed the tissues
with oxygen and other nutrients, and to pump
blood to the lungs where waste products like
carbon dioxide are removed. The speed at which
the heart does this is remarkable. At rest, the
body's entire blood content is circulated around the
body every minute. During exercise the same
process can take as little as ten seconds. With every
heart beat 1/20 pint (28 ml) of blood is pumped out.
The heart beats, on average, 70 times per minute;
100,000 times a day; 36 million times a year;
2,500,000,000 times in 70 years. As a result, during
the course of a day some 2,000 gallons (7,500 l) of
blood pass through the heart at a rate ranging
from between 10–50 pints (4.5–24 l) per minute,
enough to fill a small road tanker within a day.

Structure

In structure and shape, the heart is a very
uncomplicated organ. It consists of a hollow,

muscular structure that is clearly divided into two halves, known for convenience as the left and right sides of the heart. The right side receives blood from the body and pumps it to the lungs, where carbon dioxide is removed and the blood receives a fresh supply of oxygen. This oxygenated blood then returns to the left side of the heart to be pumped to all the tissues of the body.

Each side or half of the heart has to function as both a receiver and deliverer of blood, and two chambers are provided for each of these functions. The receiving chamber, known as the atrium, is a thin-walled cavity separated from the thick-walled, more powerful delivering chamber known as the ventricle. In this way the heart has a left atrium, a left ventricle, a right atrium, and a right ventricle. The tubes conducting the blood away from the heart are known as arteries. Blood flows from the right ventricle into the pulmonary artery to the lungs and from the left ventricle into the aorta, the body's largest artery, which supplies blood to the rest of the body, including the heart muscle. The vessels which carry blood back to the heart are known as veins.

The atria are separated from the ventricles by the tricuspid valve on the right side and the mitral valve on the left, and the ventricles from the arteries by the pulmonary valve on the right side and the aortic valve on the left side. The valves work like canal lock gates. They open to allow blood to gush from the atria into the ventricles, and from the ventricles into the arteries and they slam shut to prevent the blood from flowing backwards.

Just as a mechanic can sometimes diagnose an automobile fault by listening to the engine, a doctor can nearly always pinpoint a faulty heart valve by listening in through a stethoscope. Blood returning from the body and the lungs enters the atria. The atrio-ventricular valves then open to allow the flow of blood to the ventricles. The ventricles then contract and the atrio-ventricular valves snap shut, producing the first heart sound. The blood then flows up the main arteries (the aorta and the pulmonary artery), the ventricles relax, and the aortic and pulmonary valves snap closed, resulting in the second heart sound.

Contrary to popular belief the heart does not produce a 'bom-bom-bom' sound. Rather it produces a rhythmical lup-dup-pause, lup-dup-pause sequence. The hissing or shushing sounds between the usually reassuring lup-dups indicate turbulent blood flow. These sounds are known as murmurs and are usually caused by diseased heart valves, either leaking or narrowed, and by turbulent blood flow through a congenital communication between the high and low pressure area, for example a defect in the septum or partition between the atria and ventricles. So-called hole-in-the-heart babies are born with an incomplete or perforated septum. Another cause of heart murmurs may be stenosis, or abnormal constriction of orifices within or associated with the heart, or the persistence of a channel (ductus arteriosus) between the pulmonary artery and the aorta after birth.

However, murmurs are heard in normal hearts as well. 'Innocent murmurs' as these are called are not associated with disease.

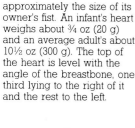
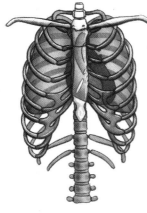

The ribcage protects the heart, which is approximately the size of its owner's fist. An infant's heart weighs about ¾ oz (20 g) and an average adult's about 10½ oz (300 g). The top of the heart is level with the angle of the breastbone, one third lying to the right of it and the rest to the left.

Louis Washkansky in the first few days after his transplant operation in South Africa's Groote Schuur Hospital in 1967. His death, after 18 days of hour by hour surveillance, was due to a massive pneumonia infection which inexorably decreased the respiratory surface of his lungs. The surgical techniques used to transplant his new heart were perfectly successful.

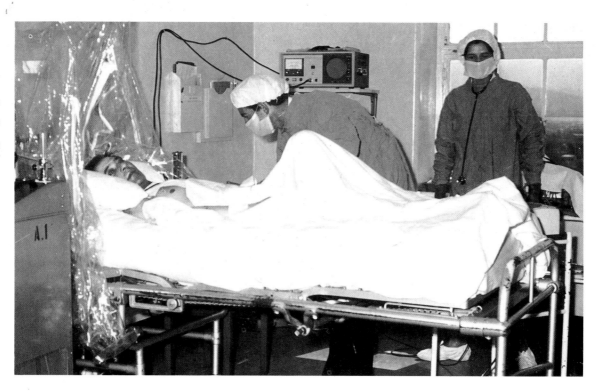

Cardiac muscle and rhythm

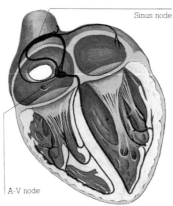

Sinus node

A-V node

Electrical pathways
of the heart. Starting at the
sinus node, the electrical
impulse spreads across the
right atrium to the
atrioventricular node, then
down the septum which
divides the ventricles and so
to the ventricular walls
themselves.

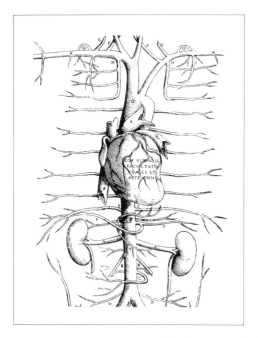

The medieval heart,
according to Andreas
Vesalius. Vesalius was born
in Brussels in 1514 and
taught anatomy at Padua
University in Italy. He
opposed Ancient Greek
theories of medicine,
insisting that anatomy can
only be learned through
careful dissection. His
researches revealed the
interrelation of the heart and
the great blood vessels and
paved the way for William
Harvey's description of the
circulation of the blood
in 1628.

The heart muscle is arranged concentrically
around the chambers of the atria and the ventricles
so that the volume of these chambers is diminished
and enlarged by the alternate contracting and
relaxing of the heart. This rhythmical squeezing
action of the muscle acts with the valves of the
heart to achieve the desired flow of blood in the
correct direction. Obviously, the effective action of
the heart depends on the competence of the pump
and the valves. If the muscle of the ventricles is
diseased or weak, the ability of the heart to do the
work required may be compromised, and the
activity of the pump will be impaired.
Alternatively, if the valves leak, the blood may
oscillate back and forth ineffectually instead of
flowing purposefully in the proper direction.

Special features of heart muscle Unlike other
muscle cells, heart cells have a remarkable capacity
for automatic, monotonous contractility. If, for
example, the 'cement' that binds together the cells
of the chick embryo heart is dissolved and the
suspension is examined under a microscope, each
liberated individual cell can be seen to contract and
relax rhythmically as an independent unit with its
own particular rhythm. Since the human heart
consists of many millions of muscle cells, it is clear
that chaos would result if every cell were to beat at
its own rate and rhythm. The effective action of the
heart depends entirely on the coordinated,
concerted action of the organ as a whole. The way
in which this coordination is achieved, and an
understanding of the mechanisms that exist to
ensure that the individual cells beat in unison at a

rate that best suits the needs of the body, requires a
closer look at the microscopic structure of the heart
muscle and at some of the physiological processes
that occur when the heart contracts and relaxes.

If a section of the human heart is examined
under a microscope, it can be seen that the muscle
cells are joined together in a sort of branching
network, so that each cell is in intimate contact
with at least two of its neighbours. At rest, the cells
exhibit a very interesting electrical phenomenon.
Due to the chemical processes that occur within it,
each cell builds up an electrical charge across the
membrane that surrounds it, so that the outside of
the cell is positively charged and the inside of the
cell is negatively charged. In this respect, the cells
may be compared to minute flashlight batteries that
build up a voltage between the positive and
negative poles due to chemical processes within the
battery. Immediately before contraction, the cell
membrane 'leaks', and the voltage difference
between the two sides is momentarily dissipated by
a transient 'short circuit'. This phenomenon is
known technically as depolarisation and is followed
by contraction of the cell.

These electrical phenomena serve a twofold
function. Depolarisation of the cell not only
initiates contraction in that cell, but also it initiates
depolarisation of the neighbouring cell. In other
words, cells use minute currents of electricity to
communicate with each other and, in this way,
depolarisation followed by contraction proceeds
through the heart as a wave of coordinated
electrical activity followed by a wave of contractile
or mechanical activity. After contraction, the leaky
cell membrane is repaired and the voltage across it
is restored by repolarisation. The entire cycle—
depolarisation, contraction, then repolarisation—
is repeated continuously.

Control of heartbeat The pacemaker or initiating
centre for this electrical impulse is known as the
sinus node. This is a specialised group of cells
which is situated in the right atrium close to the
point of entry of the great vein (vena cava) draining
the upper half of the body. The sinus node initiates
each wave of depolarisation, which then passes
through the muscle cells of the atria to a second
group of specialised cells, a sort of relay station,
which is situated at the junction of the atria and the
ventricles. This is known as the atrioventricular
node (usually abbreviated 'A-V node'). From here,
the impulse passes down two bundles of specialised
heart cells running along either side of the wall
separating the right ventricle from the left
ventricle. These bundles distribute the impulse to
the muscle cells of the right and left ventricles.

The progress of each impulse through the heart
can be followed by using an electrocardiograph to
record the electrical signals that are conducted to

The cardiac cycle

At the end of the rest period, diastole, blood passes from the vena cava into the right atrium through the tricuspid valve. At the start of the active contraction phase, systole, blood is pumped from the left ventricle through the aortic valve into the aorta. As systole proceeds, blood is also pushed from the left ventricle through the pulmonary valve to the lungs. At the end of systole and the beginning of diastole blood from the vena cava again enters the right atrium and oxygenated blood from the lungs enters the left atrium through the mitral valve.

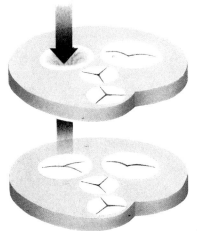

End of diastole

Systole

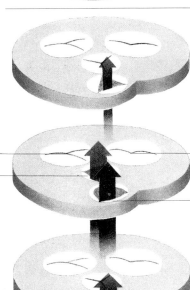

Tricuspid valve

Pulmonary valve

Mitral valve

Aortic valve

Start of diastole

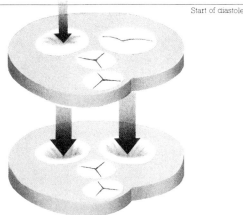

the outside of the chest. For every heart beat the normal electrocardiogram shows a number of distinct waves. The first small, flat wave, known as the P-wave, represents the wave of depolarisation passing through the atria. The second wave, a large sharp spike known as the R-wave, reflects the depolarisation of the muscle of the ventricles. The third, or T-wave, is a low, flat wave that represents repolarisation of the ventricles.

If the sinus node is damaged by disease, the A-V node assumes control and initiates each cardiac impulse. This disorder is known as A-V rhythm. If the A-V node is damaged so that impulses from the sinus node cannot get through to the ventricles, some other focus in the ventricles takes over as the pacemaker, and the condition known as heart block results. A surgically implanted pacemaker in the heart is the medical equivalent of a new ignition system in an automobile. Ideally the heart should be under the control of the sinus node, for this normal pacemaker not only initiates heartbeats at a good basal rate but also receives nervous impulses from the rest of the body that help to match heart rate to the need for blood supply. When we run or climb stairs, for example, the muscular exercise involved requires an augmented supply of blood and a correspondingly increased heart rate. This is achieved by sensitive detectors in the lungs and large arteries that sense the need for increased blood supply and consequently relay the information to the sinus node through the nerves that impinge upon it.

Nervous and hormonal controls Matching heart rate to body requirements does not solely depend on an intact nerve link to the sinus node. Through the process of evolution another control mechanism has been provided, in the form of hormones such as adrenaline and thyroxine that are able to transmit messages to the sinus node and the muscle cells by way of the bloodstream. These control mechanisms act like accelerators and brakes, speeding up and slowing down the cardiac cycle according to what the body is doing.

The sympathetic and parasympathetic nervous systems, operated from the brain, also play a major role in controlling the cardiac cycle. The parasympathetic system, reaching the heart through the vagus nerve, is a brake. The sympathetic nerve is an accelerator, strengthening the beat of the heart as well as quickening it. The two nervous systems are controlled and coordinated by the vasomotor centre which lies in the medulla at the base of the brain. The vasomotor centre responds to strong emotions like love and fear and ensures overall coordination. But heart rate is also influenced by the presence of hormones such as adrenaline and thyroxine in the bloodstream.

Power supply to the heart

An interesting sidelight on the heart's control mechanism is that in patients who have received heart transplants the heart is denervated—it has no connection with the brain. Nevertheless a transplanted heart recognises the body's call for increased cardiac output through nerve receptors in its upper chambers and in the roots of the large vessels. The heart muscle also reacts to hormones in the same way as a normal heart. Thus a transplant patient can increase his heart rate in response to stress or a rise in temperature, and decrease it when he is at rest.

Adrenaline is one of the factors which dictate physiological response to sexual intercourse. The speed of the heart rate during sexual intercourse varies with age and with the emotional and physical intensity of love-making. During the late teens and early twenties the super-charge of love-making can take heart rate up to near the maximum, about 200 beats per minute. This is accompanied by a sharp rise in blood pressure. In contrast love-making between a contented, relaxed middle-aged couple may only produce heart rates of up to 120, with little change in blood pressure. These two examples represent 'safe' extremes. For healthy young lovers top gear has few risks.

Heart attack survivors are sometimes nervous about continuing love-making because the heart and the circulation system are more than normally taxed in sexual intercourse. The effort of intercourse for most ex-coronary patients is comparable to that of a brisk stroll; so any patient who is symptom-free after a walk should be able to enjoy intercourse without fear. As a general rule, however, abstinence is usually recommended for the first three to four weeks after an attack, but this is an area where professional medical advice should always be sought.

Love-making is just one of many activities which can cause a dramatic increase in heart rate. Although on average the heart beats 70–80 times a minute, rates of 180 beats per minute have been recorded for motorists in normal traffic conditions, and even as high as 200 for racing drivers.

Energy supply The heart is fuelled by glucose and fat from the bloodstream. Once in the heart cells, glucose and fat are broken down into lactic acid, the same substance that is responsible for the sour taste of curdled milk. When the glucose and fat are broken down in this way, a certain amount of energy is released and can be used by the heart for contraction. But this is an inefficient process, and far more energy can be released for the heart's use by combining this lactic acid with oxygen to produce carbon dioxide and water by a further chemical process.

Energy for the heart's work is released from

Exercise in any form means that the heart has to pump harder to supply oxygen to the muscles doing the work. Exercise keeps the heart in trim. Frequent moderate exercise is better health insurance than exhausting bursts of activity at irregular intervals.

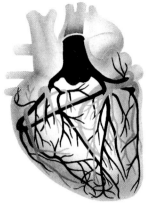

Fuel lines in the heart
The heart muscle requires its own supply of oxygenated blood. The arteries which serve the heart are the coronary arteries. These sprout from the aortic sinus and then double back into the heart where they subdivide many times, overlapping in the areas they supply. Should one artery become blocked the branches of another can to some extent make up the deficit. Deoxygenated blood from the heart muscle is collected and fed into the right atrium, where it mixes with the blood entering from the vena cava.

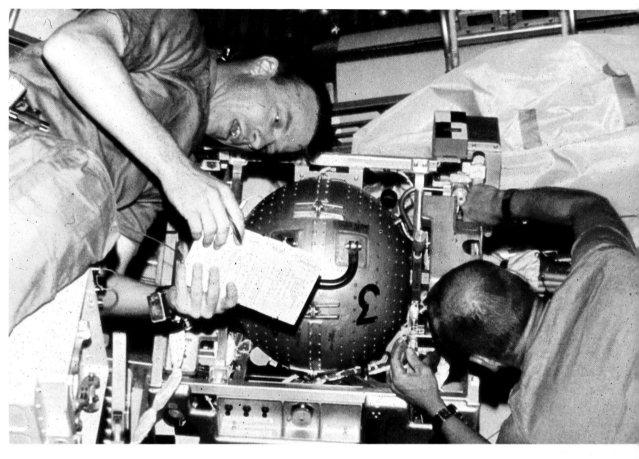

chemical fuels when they combine with oxygen in the muscle cells in much the same way that energy is released as heat from wood by burning it in the presence of oxygen. When oxygen supplies are limited, the breakdown of glucose and fat can proceed no further than lactic acid.

This has two effects: (1) the relative inefficiency of the lactic-acid mechanism for energy production results in insufficient energy for the heart to function properly; (2) the accumulation of lactic acid within the muscle cells irritates the sensitive nerve endings in the heart muscle and a cramping pain is experienced—the pain of what is known as angina pectoris.

Obviously then, the heart muscle, like all other tissues in the body, requires oxygen and chemical foodstuffs to function, but as these can reach the muscle only by the bloodstream, the heart itself requires a supply of blood.

Blood supply This is provided by two main arteries, known as the left and right coronary arteries. Both leave the aorta, the large artery receiving the blood from the left ventricle, almost immediately above the aortic valve situated at the outlet of the left ventricle. The left coronary artery divides into two large branches almost immediately so that there are, in effect, three large blood vessels supplying blood to the substance of the heart.

The coronary arteries do not remain isolated tubes, each responsible for supplying blood to only one area of the heart, but divide into a ramifying complex network of smaller blood vessels which eventually join up with each other. These act as communicating links between the coronary arteries, and they serve a very important function: if the blood supply to one area of the heart is impaired by occlusion, or obstruction, of its major artery, the other arteries can maintain the flow of blood through these linking channels. This is a fail-safe mechanism which is known as the collateral circulation.

By a process of repeated subdivision, the smaller arteries eventually become even smaller blood vessels. These are known as capillaries. The capillaries are distributed throughout the substance of the heart in close contact with the heart muscle cells. Their thin walls allow oxygen and nutrients to spread easily from the blood into the cells, and carbon dioxide, lactic acid, and other waste products to pass from the cells into the capillaries, to be carried away from the heart. The capillaries then unite into progressively larger vessels to become the coronary veins which drain back into the right atrium. In this way the heart pumps enough blood—about one-twentieth of its total output—through the coronary arteries to supply itself.

Space lab astronauts
Astronauts are chosen not only for their intelligence and nerve but also for their physical fitness. Like a well-tuned athlete's, their heart must have a low resting rate. This enables them to withstand greater stress and greater variation in oxygen concentration.

Heart defects of the newborn

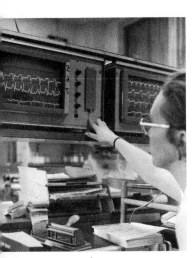

An electrocardiograph (ECG) is an instrument for monitoring electrical changes in the heart muscle. It can detect disturbances of rhythm, damage to the heart muscle, and even the presence of certain poisons which affect the heart muscle. It also signals the sudden absence of any pulse in the event of cardiac arrest.

Basically there are two main categories of heart disease, congenital and acquired. Congenital abnormalities one is born with; acquired abnormalities are those developed after birth. Today most congenital conditions can be corrected by open heart surgery. But by far the majority of heart defects are of the acquired kind, the result of progressive deterioration of the coronary arteries (as in most developed Western societies) or of damage to the heart valves caused by rheumatic fever (mainly in underdeveloped countries).

Congenital heart disease

In embryo the heart starts as a simple tube which grows and twists into an S shape. By the fourth week of pregnancy it is divided by constrictions into five segments; by about the sixth week the four chambers have been formed and further complex developments are taking shape; by about the eighth week the heart has assumed most of the features retained until birth. Thus the early part of pregnancy is of the utmost importance to the embryonic heart. The complex developmental process allows a great variety of possible errors in construction and underlines the importance of prenatal care, an issue we will return to shortly. Affecting one in every 100 newborn babies, congenital heart abnormalities may consist of either one, several, or multiple defects which can also involve the brain or other organs.

Through careful screening in the first few days of life most congenital heart abnormalities can be detected very early, though some may not show themselves for several years. Early diagnosis and treatment can prevent future complications.

Surgical advances Most congenital heart abnormalities, even complex ones, can now be treated successfully thanks to the advent of the cardiac catheter and advances in the techniques of cardiac surgery, both with and without the heart-lung machine.

Children with congenital heart disease fall mainly into one of two groups: cyanotic (blue) and non-cyanotic (with normal colour). The blueness of a cyanotic baby is due to the mixing of venous blood, which has not passed through the lungs, with oxygenated blood, which of course has.

Septal defects This term describes what are known popularly as 'hole-in-the-heart' complications. The chambers of the heart are partitioned by septa. If there is a hole in the septa a proportion of the oxygenated blood in the left side of the heart will pass into the right side and recirculate through the lungs. Consequently the heart has to do more work than necessary since part of its effort is devoted to pumping already oxygenated blood through the lungs for a second time. The strain becomes increasingly apparent if the defect is not repaired.

The leak or 'shunt' will be from right to left if a

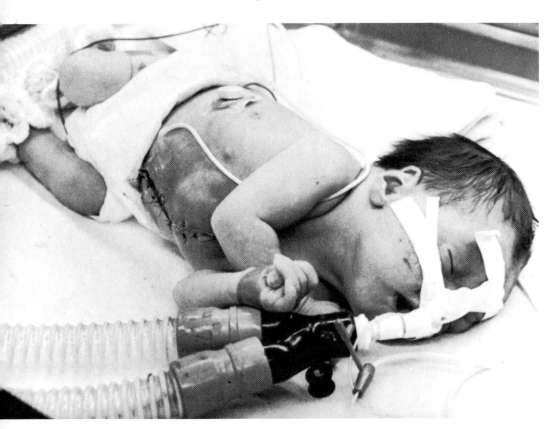

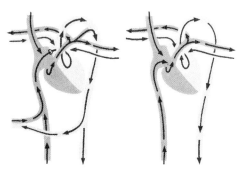

Foetal cardiac circulation In an unborn infant the ductus arteriosus joins the pulmonary artery to the aorta (left), enabling blood to bypass the lungs. Usually it closes within 10 to 15 hours of birth (right). If it fails to do so the unwanted connection can be corrected surgically.

Congenital heart defects are relatively common. This infant, recovering after surgery, was born with a very rare condition known as ectopia cordis, in which the heart lies outside the chest. Only 64 such cases have been recorded in the last 300 years.

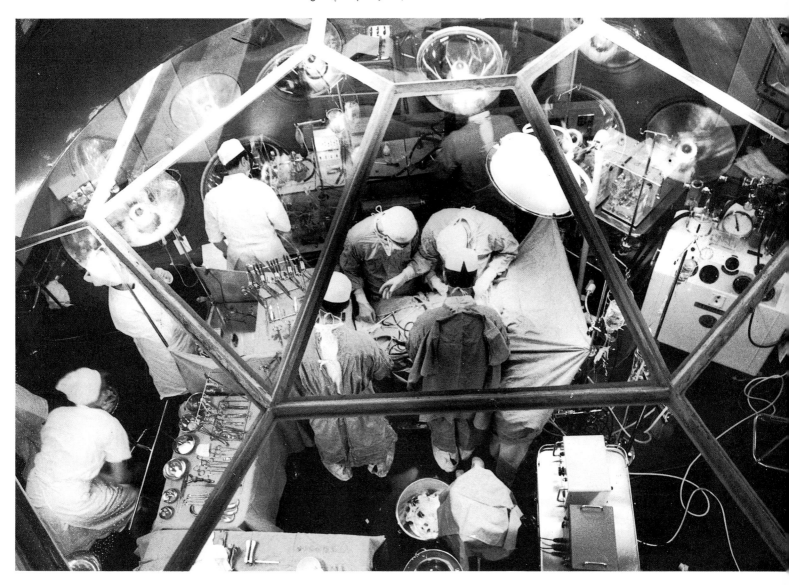

Open heart surgery
has advanced dramatically
in the last 20 years. Most
congenital defects can be
corrected soon after birth;
coronary bypass operations
are now quite
commonplace; pacemakers
can be implanted to correct
faulty rhythms; artificial
valves can be inserted to
replace diseased ones; and
new hearts can be swopped
for old. Coronary
angiography (injecting the
coronary arteries with
radio-opaque substances
and taking X-ray pictures) is
the most useful and sensitive
means of assessing the
coronary arteries.

septal defect occurs in combination with outflow
obstruction (narrowing of the channel carrying
venous blood to the lungs). In this case venous
blood is recirculated before it has been replenished
with oxygen and the patient turns blue.

There are several different surgical answers to
septal defects. Large defects are covered with
plastic grafts; small ones are closed by suturing.
The technique employed depends on the location
and size of the hole and the septum concerned.

Tetralogy of Fallot A common cause of 'blue'
congenital heart disease, this involves four related
defects; these are pulmonary stenosis (narrowing of
the pulmonary arteries), overriding of the aorta,
hypertrophy (excessive growth) of the right
ventricle and a ventricular septal defect.

Patent ductus arteriosus In the womb the baby
gets oxygen not from its own lungs, but from its
mother's blood supply. Until birth the ductus

arteriosus, a vessel about ¼ in (5 mm) in length and
diameter, bypasses blood away from the infant's
lungs. At birth the ductus normally closes and
shrinks as the baby's own lungs start working. If it
fails to close, some of the oxygenated blood passes
through it and back into the lungs. Correction is by
cutting the ductus and suturing the ends.

Prevention of congenital heart disease German
measles (rubella) in the first three months of
pregnancy can produce heart abnormalities in some
babies and underlines the importance of
immunisation. In Western countries immunisation
is recommended between the ages of 11 and 14.
Some specialists believe that the foetus may also be
endangered by low oxygen pressure and therefore
advise pregnant women against high altitude travel.
Drugs should be avoided wherever possible, as
should smoking. Smoking, in the early weeks
especially, can harm the baby. Similarly, alcohol
consumption can have adverse effects.

Acquired heart disease

Heart conditions which develop after birth fall into two main categories: valvular disease and coronary heart disease. The latter is also referred to as ischaemic heart disease since its root cause is insufficient blood supply to the heart.

Valvular disease The main culprit in valvular disease is rheumatic fever, the most common cause of heart disease in children and young adults. The prevalence of rheumatic fever has declined in the industrialised countries over the last 40 years, but it is still seen in epidemic proportions in underdeveloped countries and accounts for severe valvular defects in young children.

Children with chronic rheumatic heart disease may die within weeks or months if their hearts suffer permanent damage. However, many cases of valvular abnormalities arising from rheumatic infection are detected among adults in their thirties to fifties. Many such patients cannot recall episodes of acute rheumatism early in life and may have only a vague memories of pains or frequent sore throats.

The mitral and aortic valves are the ones most commonly affected by rheumatic heart disease. In either one there may be leaks or narrowing resulting from thickening and scarring, but the aortic valve is especially prone to leaking and the mitral valve to thickening and scarring.

Treatment of valvular complaints due to rheumatic fever represents one of the major successes of cardiac surgery. After surgery patients can expect to lead moderately active lives under medical care. About 10 to 15 per cent experience fresh scarring and have to undergo second operations. The artificial valves are made from human tissue and plastic materials.

Ischaemic heart disease

Ischaemia literally means 'keeping back blood'. Starved of blood, and the oxygen and nutrients it contains, the heart muscle dies. The insidious culprit here is atheroma, a fatty deposit which gradually causes atherosclerotic changes—narrowing, blocking, hardening—of the arteries. Pumping against increased resistance in the arteries the heart has to work harder. To do so it needs more oxygen. But the arteries which supply the heart muscle, the right and left coronary arteries, are themselves narrowed and clogged. And so a vicious circle is established.

Replacing an aortic valve
This sequence of pictures shows the delicate surgery involved in replacing a defective aortic valve, in this case a Bjork valve. For all open heart operations the breastbone must be cut and held open with an instrument called a spreader, and for the duration of surgery on the heart the patient must be connected to a heart-lung machine. Having opened the heart at the level of the aortic valve the surgeon threads the new artificial valve down into position in the aortic ring of the heart.

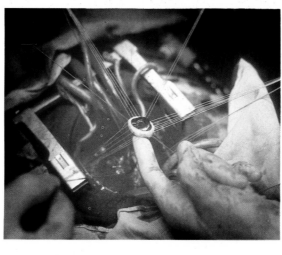
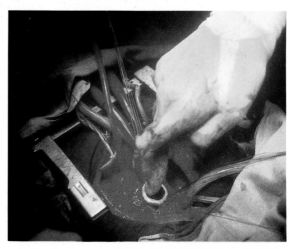

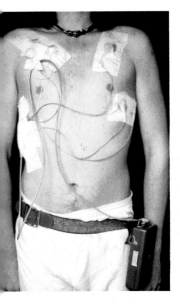

ECG electrodes
placed on the body measure the variations in electric current produced by depolarisation and repolarisation of the heart muscle. Electrodes on the chest wall as well as on the limbs allow greater accuracy of diagnosis in certain conditions.

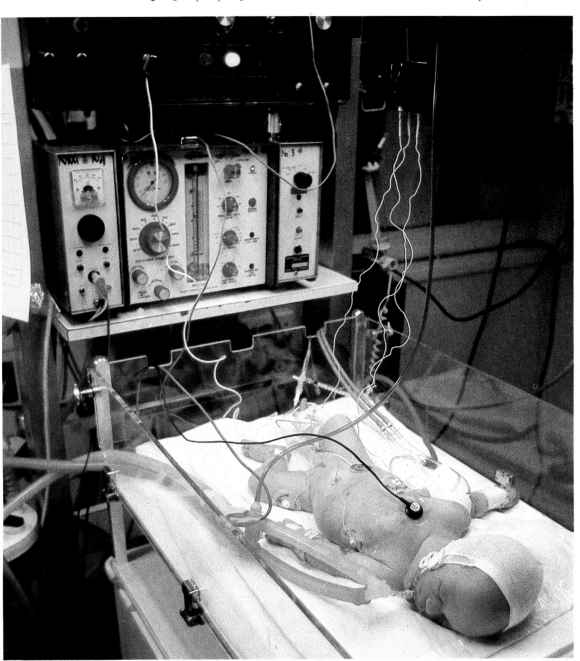

A plastic mitral valve,
a lifesaver in the form of an inexpensive 1½ in (35 mm) ring of plastic. This type of valve was first developed in the sixties. The mitral valve prevents oxygen-rich blood flowing back from the left ventricle into the left atrium.

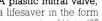

Electronic monitoring
devices in the intensive care unit (above) closely parallel those used to diagnose faults in car engines (left). In the past ten years there has been much cross-fertilisation of ideas between medical and automotive engineers, especially in the field of non-destructive testing.

Atheroma: the enemy of arteries

Emergency admission
Sudden chest pain brought on by clogged coronary arteries is a very common cause of emergency admission to hospital. In the United States nearly a quarter of fatal heart attacks occur in the under-65s. On the other hand deaths from heart attacks have dropped by 25 per cent in the last ten years. This has been attributed to better emergency services and coronary care, but also to better understanding by the public of the dangers of smoking and overeating.

Atheroma Atheroma is a degenerative disease of the arteries that is suffered by humans and by some other primate species as well. The word atheroma itself is derived from two Greek words: *atheros*, meaning 'gruel', and *oma*, meaning 'tumour', and it aptly describes the mushy swellings that distort the linings of the blood vessels of all adult men and women. It is a strange condition and one that is so common among adults that it could almost be regarded as a normal concomitant of ageing were it not for two facts: first, it is more pronounced in some people than in others and, second, it may affect the supply of blood to critical organs such as the heart, the brain and the kidneys.

Atheroma of the coronary arteries must be looked at against the background of detailed information about the arteries themselves. The left ventricle of the heart pumps its blood into a single large artery known as the aorta. This vessel, which is approximately 1 in (2.5 cm) in diameter when healthy, curves slightly upwards and to the left into a graceful arch before passing down the back of the chest and abdominal cavity to divide into the two great arteries that supply the legs and pelvic organs with blood.

Basically, an artery wall consists of three distinct layers. The innermost layer, lining the inside of the blood vessel or lumen, is a thin membrane known as the intima. Glistening and

The unseen enemy
With the passage of time the inner walls of major arteries become coated with atheromatous plaques. These increase the risk of rapid and total blockage of vital arteries (thrombosis). Alternatively atheromatous deposits weaken artery walls causing them to bulge (aneurysm) and eventually rupture.

smooth, this layer presents an ideal streamlined surface to the blood flowing by. The second layer, the media, lies immediately adjacent. It is a much thicker layer and is made up of muscle fibres and elastic filaments. By maintaining a steady state of contraction, the muscle fibres exert a constant pressure on the column of blood in the artery, thus controlling the diameter of the artery and the blood pressure of the column of blood within. The elastic filaments in the media lend resilience to the arteries, so that each time blood is ejected into the arterial network, the vessels expand and recoil. In this way, the spurt of pressure that results from the delivery of blood into the arterial system is transformed into a smooth curve of pressure that forces the blood along the arteries during that part of the heart's cycle when the ventricles are not contracting. The third layer which envelops the outside of the arteries is tough and fibrous. Known as the adventitia, it helps to support the arteries and to maintain their cylindrical shape.

If the aorta is removed from a person of any age and slit down its length, various patchy whitish-yellow streaks can be seen in the intima that show considerable variation in size and shape. They are either flat or protrude very slightly into the lumen of the aorta, and they do not interfere with the smoothness of the innermost lining. These streaks are caused by minute fat droplets contained within cells in that lining. Those areas of the media and the adventitia in the neighbourhood of these fatty streaks are completely normal, and, as far as is known, these streaks are harmless and probably bear no relation to the second type of deposit found on the innermost lining of arteries.

Deposits of the second variety, known as atheromatous plaques, are present to a varying degree in all adults in the developed world. Like the fatty streaks described above, they vary considerably in size and shape, but they are much larger and protrude into the passageway of the arteries. At a relatively early stage of their development, these plaques consist of little lumps or nodules of scar tissue in the intima and in the centre of each nodule is a small cavity containing a yellowish, mushy material known as cholesterol. Under the microscope, these plaques show three additional significant features: they can be seen to contain numerous white blood corpuscles—the cells that congregate in any area of inflammatory irritation in the body; the muscle fibres and elastic filaments in the lining underneath the atheromatous plaque are destroyed, leaving the media thin and weakened; and flecks of calcium salts are found in the substance of the scar tissue of which the plaque is composed.

Whether or not the plaques are harmful is determined by subsequent developments. Any of the following may happen.

☐ The nodules may enlarge to such an extent that they obstruct the flow of blood through the artery, in much the same way that water pipes become choked with calcium salts. The choking of an artery is a slow process that takes many years to reach the stage where blood flow is significantly endangered; when it does, narrowing or partial blocking results and is known as stenosis.
☐ The nodule may ulcerate into the artery so that the mushy contents of the cavity within are discharged into the bloodstream. These particles of cholesterol and calcium are then carried in the blood until they lodge in, and block, a blood vessel whose diameter is too small to allow them free passage. If this small blood vessel happens to be the only one supplying blood to a critical part of the body, such as the brain, the consequences may prove severely disabling.
☐ When the nodule ulcerates, it disrupts the smooth surface of the intima, creating ideal circumstances for the formation of a blood clot. Such a blood clot, if firmly attached to the ragged surface of the small ulcer, may grow and block the artery—a phenomenon known as thrombosis. If, however, it is loosely attached, it may be broken off and may block a more remote artery, like the cholesterol and calcium particles mentioned earlier. Since blood clots tend to form rapidly, blockage of an artery by thrombosis is usually a sudden event.
☐ The nodules may ulcerate into a tiny blood vessel within the substance of the arterial wall, leading to haemorrhage into the middle lining, under the intima. This is a rare complication that is seldom the cause of arterial obstruction.
☐ Several adjacent nodules may join together, resulting in a fairly wide area of thinning and destruction of the muscular and elastic middle lining. When this happens, the weakened arterial wall bulges outward due to the pressure of the blood within. These bulges—known as aneurysms—may burst with catastrophic results.

Although coronary heart disease and other related conditions are predominantly disorders of middle and old age in Western countries, the atherosclerotic process begins in childhood. Post-mortem investigations of United States airmen killed in Korea showed that nearly half had a significant degree of atherosclerosis. Interestingly the average age of the airmen was only 22. As yet no one knows why only half of these men should have been affected; similarly, we do not know why some heavy smokers survive to a healthy old age, unaffected by either coronary heart disease or any of the cancers associated with smoking. But it is just as important to find out why so many people survive for so long without contracting heart disease as it is to clarify why so many people die prematurely because of it.

Early warning of heart trouble

Angina Sometimes the first sign of heart trouble is an attack of angina, a word derived from the Latin for chest pain. This occurs when the supply of blood to the heart does not match the vigorous activities which make the heart beat faster. The acute distress and discomfort of angina can serve as an early warning sign of a potentially far more serious complication.

Angina usually causes pain in the middle of the chest. It is also frequently felt in the neck or under the jaw and down the left or both arms. Usually starting with exertion and disappearing with rest, angina can be caused by any sort of excitement, including sport, sexual intercourse, or anger. A heavy meal, particularly one rich in fat, can also precipitate an attack. Exhaust fumes and smoking too much can cause an attack because the carbon dioxide from the smoke replaces some of the oxygen from the blood. Carbon monoxide combines with blood in the same way as oxygen, except that it does so about 250 times more readily. It is estimated that a person who smokes 13–20 cigarettes a day destroys some 10 per cent of the blood's oxygen-carrying capacity.

In the treatment of angina the most important aim is to eliminate the risk factors. By stopping smoking, reducing weight, exercising regularly and leading a normal active life, a person can often improve or eliminate painful symptoms. Measures such as these have to be maintained. Only too frequently patients resolve to follow the doctor's instructions but return to their old bad habits within a few months, establishing new coronary problems. Drugs used in the treatment of angina can help to bring risk factors such as hypertension under control and to relieve pain.

Surgical treatment is also possible in some cases. In particular the vein bypass operation has proved extremely successful. A typical operation involves two separate stages. In the first part the vein graft is prepared, and in the second the graft is inserted between the aorta and the diseased coronary artery.

Once the patient is anaesthetised, a surgeon with an assistant removes a portion of a superficial vein in the leg. At the same time a second surgeon with a second assistant opens the chest and prepares the patient to be connected to the heart-lung machine.

The vein removed is called the saphenous vein and it runs from the dorsum of the foot to the groin. Surgeons these days prefer to use the portion of the vein below the knee, as this is better adapted to stand high pressures. Under normal circumstances a vein contains numerous valves along its length, the function of which is to break the column of blood up in sections in the standing position, thus reducing the pressure on the lower extremities. Care must therefore be taken that when the vein is connected to form the bypass, it is done in such a way that the valves will not obstruct

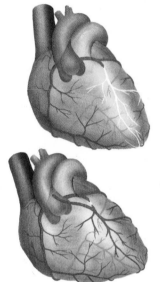

Bypassing a blockage in a coronary artery by grafting a section of vein between the aorta and a part of the artery distal to the block. This procedure has enabled many angina sufferers to lead a moderately busy life rather than live in constant fear of the slightest exertion.

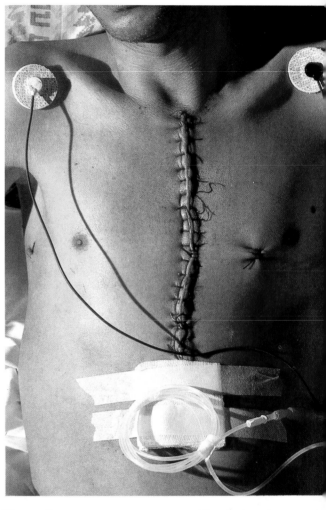

After cardiac surgery The long midline incision made for open heart operations may appear horrific but it is absolutely necessary. The chest must be opened wide enough to allow room for manipulation. The split breastbone is wired together after surgery

the blood flow to the heart muscle. This is achieved by turning the vein upside down.

A section of vein of the required length is removed through a skin incision along its course. It is then flushed with heparinised saline to distend it and see if there any leaks; if there are, these are stitched up.

Meanwhile the second surgeon has opened the chest, exposed the patient's heart and connected the patient to the heart-lung machine which will take over the function of the heart and lungs while the surgeon is operating on the coronary arteries. Once total cardiopulmonary bypass has been effected, a clamp is placed across the aorta above the openings of the coronary arteries. This stops the blood supply to the heart muscle. A cold cardioplegic solution is then flushed into the heart muscle through a small catheter inserted into the lumen of the isolated piece of aorta. This causes complete relaxation of the heart muscle and a lowering of its temperature. This ensures that the

Keeping fit
Old age and exercise are not mutually exclusive. In the 1981 London Marathon a man of 78 ran the full distance with energy to spare. Exercise keeps all vital systems—heart, circulation, respiration, digestion—working efficiently and working longer. The old adage *mens sana in corpore sano* still stands.

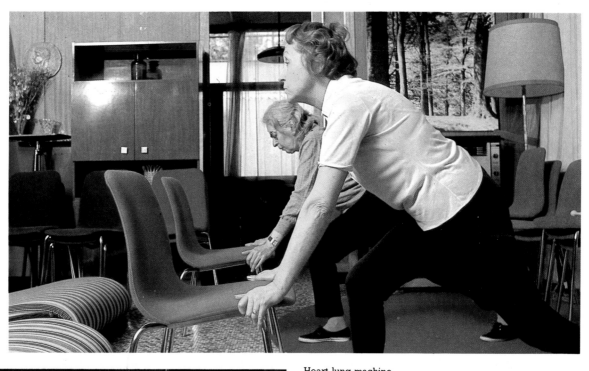

Heart-lung machine
This highly complex machine keeps patients alive during open heart and other types of major surgery. It collects deoxygenated blood before it enters the heart, reoxygeneates it, and then pumps it back into the aorta.

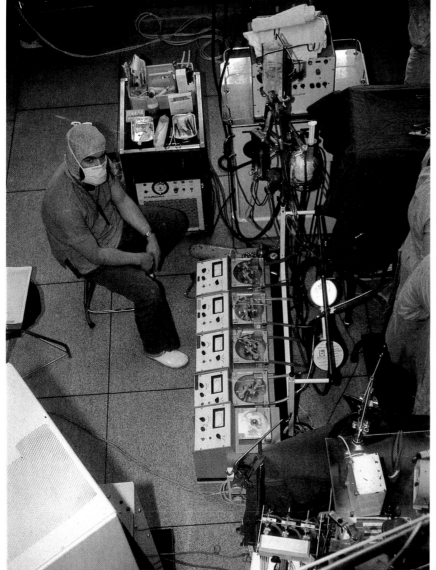

myocardium (the middle and thickest layer of the heart) is protected during absence of blood flow to the heart muscle.

A portion of the affected coronary artery distal to the block (on the side away from the heart) is now exposed and opened longitudinally for about ¼ in (5 mm) and the end of the vein is stitched to the opening (a procedure known as anastomosis). The vein is then measured for length—it must reach to the root of the aorta—and the remaining piece used if necessary to bypass other blocked arteries. The free ends of the anastomosed sections of vein are then stitched into the root of the ascending aorta.

In the final stage of the operation the main branches of the right and left coronary artery (the right coronary or the posterior descending branches of the right coronary, the anterior descending branch of the left coronary artery, the diagonal branch and the lateral branches of the circumflex coronary artery) are resupplied with blood.

Heart attacks

Myocardial infarction Infarction is the term used when death of a portion or the whole of an internal organ occurs as a result of interference with its blood supply. When this happens to the heart muscle we call it myocardial infarction. This interference with the blood supply is either due to atherosclerotic changes in the wall of the vessels, narrowing the lumen to such an extent that the blood which does flow through is not enough to keep the more distant part of the organ alive, or to secondary thrombosis (blood clot) or some other blockage of a diseased vessel.

When a myocardial infarction results in destruction of a large portion of heart muscle, heart output is seriously affected. This reduction in output is known as cardiogenic shock and usually the patient will die unless cardiac output is augmented with some form of mechanical device. This mechanical support is continued until such time as the patient's own heart recovers or a cardiac transplant can be performed.

Another form of heart attack can arise because of what is known as acute coronary insufficiency. A temporary obstruction or cramp in the artery results in a sudden fall in blood supply to the muscle, producing a painful cramp. Blood supply improves after some minutes or hours, the heart muscle starts to function again, and the symptoms disappear completely.

Shocks save lives
The machine shown here is a defibrillator. By placing its two contacts on either side of the chest and discharging a shock of up to 200 volts across them, a heart that has stopped beating can be shocked back to life.

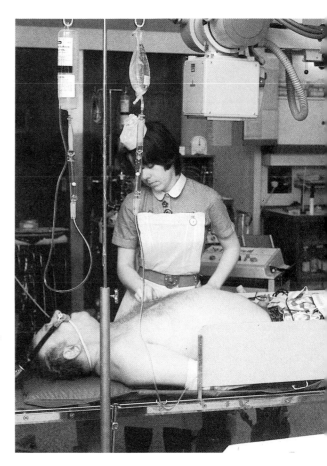

Heart failure The life-threatening myocardial infarct can create other problems involving power or heart failure. This arises when one or both of the ventricles fail to maintain an adequate circulation because of a reduction in the force with which they normally contract.

Heart failure occurs under two fairly distinct sets of circumstances. In the first instance the heart may fail while the infarct is still fresh and the patient is in the acute stages of the illness. In the second instance, the heart may fail at a later stage when the infarct itself has healed but the scarred ventricle remaining is unable to pump sufficient blood to support the needs of the body under circumstances of increased demand.

Electrical disturbances Ischaemic heart disease can also affect the heart's electrical system, described earlier, in one of two ways: either the heart muscle will develop focal areas of irritability, or the transit of the impulse from the sinus node to the muscle will be interrupted by interference with the conducting pathways.

The first of these abnormalities can cause what are called arrythmias or variations from the normal heartbeat rhythm, and the second can lead to a variety of disturbances.

These electrical disturbances constitute the major causes of preventable death from ischaemic heart disease. An American surgeon, Dr Claude Beck, from Cleveland, Ohio, highlighted this fact many years ago by advancing the concept of 'hearts too good to die'. Beck recognised that a very small infarct—far too small to cause a significant loss of ventricular muscle mass—could, by acting as what he called a 'trigger area', throw the heart into electrical chaos, completely arresting its pumping action. It is as if an automobile were brought to a halt, not by mechanical failure or by lack of gasoline, but by a defect in the distributor.

The importance of this realisation lies in the fact that just as it takes a skilled mechanic only a few seconds to repair the distributor, so it requires no time at all to restore the electrical system of the heart to a stage where a potentially lethal problem is averted. Advances in the understanding of the nature of electrical disturbances of the heart is one of the great achievements of heart disease research.

There are various types of arrythmias classified according to two criteria: the site of the abnormal impulse and the frequency of impulse generated. For example, atrial, nodal or ventricular arrhythmias signify that the origin of the arrhythmias is the atrium, the A-V node or the ventricle respectively.

Some arrhythmias, such as atrial ones, are common and give little cause for concern. However, ventricular arrhythmias—known as

Coronary emergency unit
On arrival at the hospital the heart attack victim is attached to a heart monitor, his pulse and breathing carefully checked, and an intravenous line set up in case drugs need to be given quickly. When his condition has stabilised he is moved to a coronary care unit (right).

Coronary care unit
Even if there are no complications, most heart attack patients are scrutinised very carefully for at least 24 hours after admission. This patient's ECG is being recorded continuously. He is also receiving oxygen, and has an intravenous connection should quick-acting drugs need to be administered.

Pacemaker on X-ray
Some funny things turn up on X-rays! Occasionally patients who have had a pacemaker for a long time forget to mention it when being X-rayed. Fortunately a pacemaker is easy to diagnose.

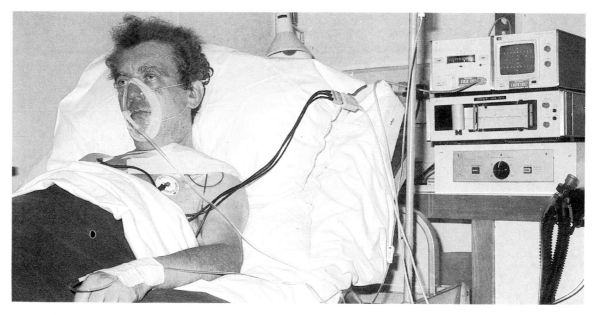

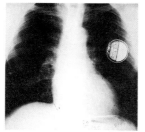

Cardiac pacemaker
This artificial 'stimulant' is usually placed under the skin on the side of the chest. The simplest type of pacemaker acts at a fixed frequency of 70 beats per minute. Other types are designed to pick up the natural impulses from the sinus node and deliver them to the ventricles. The batteries which power such implants have a life of about five years.

ventricular fibrillation (VF)—are invariably fatal unless normal rhythm is restored within a few minutes. Instead of contracting normally, the VF heart flutters uselessly and quickly. In the first instance, VF is usually treated with electric shock (defibrillation) or by thumping the chest.

Drugs are also used to treat arrhythmias. The intensive and constant care required by patients with irregular heartbeats after the death of some heart muscle cells has given rise to the growth of intensive care or coronary care units, in which all requirements for emergency care treatment are immediately at hand. These units are responsible for a substantial reduction in deaths from arrhythmias and it is rare today to hear of a patient who, having received competent care in an intensive care unit, succumbs with a 'heart too good to die'.

Heart block, a different kind of arrhythmia known as a bradyarrhythmia, occurs when ischaemia affects the pathways that carry the impulse from the sinus node to the ventricles. As a result, the atria and ventricles contract independently of each other—the atria under the control of the sinus node and the ventricles under the control either of the A-V node or, more commonly, of a ventricular pacemaker that develops spontaneously when impulses fail to reach the heart muscle from the atria. However, the ventricular pacemaker beats only 40 times per minute—far too slowly to meet the body's needs. It also tires easily and may stop altogether, resulting in death.

Artificial pacemakers have helped to overcome many problems arising from heart block. These are small battery-operated electrical devices that administer repeated electric shocks through wires connected to electrodes in direct contact with the heart. Each small, carefully timed and regularly repeated shock initiates a wave leading to ventricular contraction. The rate at which these shocks are administered can be regulated and hence the ventricular rate controlled.

In most instances heart block is a transient phenomenon that disappears as the heart recovers. Occasionally the blocked heart can be speeded up sufficiently with drugs. When, as occasionally happens, the conducting pathways between the atria and the ventricles are permanently damaged, permanent heart block results and a permanent pacemaker becomes necessary. Installation involves a simple operation in which the electrodes are attached to a battery-operated pacemaker implanted in a convenient site under the skin. With modern miniature electronics and long-life batteries, this can be done easily and quickly and it causes very little inconvenience to the patient.

Risk factors in heart disease: diet

Coronary league table
In countries with a Western lifestyle mortality from coronary heart disease has now reached epidemic proportions. This table, based on figures from WHO, shows deaths per 100,000 among men aged 45 to 54 in the period 1971–4.

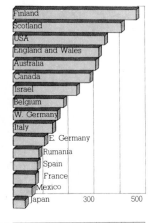

Stress and heart rate
The effects of travelling in three normal, healthy 35-year-old men, one a train passenger, one a car driver, one a bus driver. The train really does allow you to sit back and relax. Driving a car causes greatest stress when overtaking, braking suddenly or running into fog or rain. The bus driver's heart rate peaks at the start of duty, then settles down to the many minor hassles of driving through a busy city.

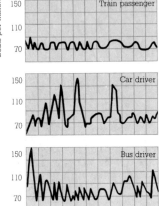

Coronary heart disease Evidence is available today to indicate that there are some people who for genetic reasons are liable to develop more severe atheroma than others. But it is now widely agreed that diet is a major risk factor over which we can exercise control. Other factors may combine with diet or have a knock-on effect, but no single one is solely responsible and it is impossible to say categorically that one particular risk factor is more important than another. The risk factors include:
☐ Maleness, middle age and a Western-type lifestyle
☐ Diet
☐ High blood pressure (hypertension)
☐ Smoking
☐ Obesity
☐ Lack of exercise
☐ Stress
☐ Personality

Risk factors The presence of one risk factor, such as obesity, might lead to the appearance of another, such as hypertension. By the same token, the risk for any individual with both these risk factors will increase still further if, for example, he or she smokes or has a sedentary occupation.

The problems are aggravated further by the lack of consensus in many scientific studies as to the significance of the various risk factors. There are those who say that it is not worthwhile taking any preventive measures in the absence of final scientific proof about, for example, the alleged benefits of a low fat/low cholesterol diet. If this view was accepted by doctors at large they would not advise against smoking for there is no *conclusive* proof that smoking causes lung cancer; however, there is a mass of unassailable circumstantial evidence that it does so. Likewise there is no *conclusive* scientific evidence that physical exercise is beneficial, although common sense and experience tells us that it is so.

At the other extreme of the medical spectrum there are those who say that doctors should strive to eliminate all known risk factors from all individuals. True primary prevention would have to start before birth with correct maternal feeding during pregnancy as a preparation for breast feeding, and continue with healthy eating in childhood. Between these two extremes—the negative and the over-zealous—is the midway course: action based on the balance of probability. The advocates of this pragmatic approach recognise that in medicine, as in all other fields of science, absolute truth is usually unattainable.

Diet In the Third World poverty almost inevitably means malnutrition; paradoxically in Western industrialised countries malnutrition is the result of wealth and over-nutrition. Coronary heart disease is restricted largely to Western countries where diets rich in saturated animal fat and cholesterol contribute towards high cholesterol levels in the blood. Various studies have concluded that the risk of ischaemic heart disease increases directly with cholesterol concentration.

In coronary heart disease blood fats have been the source of major concern. The most important of these are cholesterol, which is consumed in small amounts, but is an important component of all cells, and triglyceride, which is the main food fat. Raised levels of both these fats are associated with coronary heart disease, although to date far more scientific work has been done into the significance of cholesterol levels because, until recently, these have been easier to measure than the triglycerides.

It is tempting to label cholesterol as the villain of the piece. Today Scotland has the world's highest mortality rate from coronary heart disease, with the disease accounting for about a third of all deaths under the age of 50. Nevertheless the Scots do not have higher cholesterol levels than elsewhere in the UK; rather they show an increase in triglyceride levels and differences in the composition of body fats, which probably accounts for their greater tendency to thrombosis.

Epidemiological studies which relate mortality from coronary heart disease to diet and the other risk factors have shown almost without exception, that societies with a low fat/low cholesterol diet have little or no coronary heart disease. Reading such studies the public at large tend to assume that cholesterol in itself is bad. This is not true; only *high* levels of cholesterol are bad. Cholesterol is essential to life and is an important constituent of every cell. It accounts for one-eighth of the dry weight of the brain; it helps to regulate metabolism, the building up and breaking down of cells; it is involved in energy supply; it is the basic building block for many hormones; and in the skin it is turned into Vitamin D by sunlight.

Cholesterol can be produced by most cells, but is principally formed in the liver (which accounts for more than three-quarters of supplies), the bowel walls and the skin. Obese people may produce more cholesterol than thin, healthy people. For example, a person who is 30 per cent overweight may produce a 75 per cent excess of cholesterol. However, this may not be because they take in more dietary cholesterol than others, but because their livers respond to a fattening diet by producing more cholesterol. Research suggests that the liver of a healthy person responds to a high dietary intake of cholesterol by producing less. In other words, in some people the real problem might not be a high cholesterol level itself, but an inability to cope with what is present. Researchers are now studying the particles which carry cholesterol and other fats in the blood. These particles include:
Low density lipoprotein (LDL) This carries supplies

of cholesterol from the liver to the other parts of the body. Some LDL cholesterol is deposited on the blood vessel walls and can contribute to the build up of atherosclerosis.

High density lipoprotein (HDL) This removes cholesterol from the bloodstream for excretion in the liver; as a result blood vessels are kept clear, ensuring a free flow of blood.

Very low density lipoprotein (VLDL) This carries energy-rich triglyceride fat to the muscles. VLDL which is not burnt up is transported to the liver where it is converted into LDL.

Patients with ischaemic heart disease tend to have high LDL and VLDL levels and low HDL levels. The risks of disease tend to rise as LDL and VLDL levels increase and HDL levels decrease.

More than 20 years ago scientific investigators in Framingham, Massachusetts, USA, conducted cholesterol checks on 5,000 healthy people. Follow-up checks have been made ever since and the subjects are now examined routinely every two years. The highest rates of coronary heart disease have been found among the subjects who had initially high cholesterol levels. This classic Framingham study confirmed earlier research by Dr Ancel Keys of Minnesota, USA, one of the most outstanding nutritionists and epidemiologists of modern times. He and his colleagues investigated the significance of cholesterol levels in seven different countries and their work has weathered some three decades of scientific criticism without any serious modification

The introduction to this section stressed the importance of viewing the risk factors collectively. According to various studies exercise can lower triglyceride levels and possibly, to a slight extent, cholesterol levels. Conversely, it has been found that stress can increase cholesterol levels. For example, in one North American study, the cholesterol levels of accountants were found to increase during the peak period of their working year, two months before tax returns were due in. After the returns their levels fell again.

Between 1963 and 1975 coronary heart disease among Americans aged between 37 and 75 fell by a quarter. This same period was marked by the following significant changes in food consumption in the USA:

Milk and cream	−19%
Butter	−31%
Eggs	−12%
Animal fats	−56%
Vegetable fats	+44%

(polyunsaturated margarines and oils)

During the same period tobacco use dropped by 22 per cent.

A healthy breakfast
Rice and beans may not suit every palate, but many Westerners would be healthier if they ate more bulk and fibre and less sugar, concentrated protein and animal fat. Ideally, good dietary practice should start in the womb.

Battle of the bulge
Obesity is a health hazard, but contrary to popular belief glandular causes are uncommon. Overeating and underexercising are far more frequent culprits. However, it is true that fatness tends to run in families and that fat children tend to become fat adults.

Arteries in danger
This resin cast of the coronary arteries shows the dangerous bulges which appear in artery walls weakened by destruction of the muscle layer.

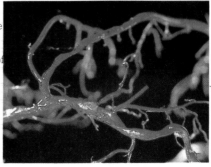

Other risk factors in heart disease

High blood pressure (hypertension) This major risk factor is often referred to as 'the silent killer' because it tends to be unaccompanied by any warning symptoms. Diagnosing hypertension is not always easy because blood pressure—the force within the arteries which maintains the circulation—is prone to constant fluctuation. The cardiovascular system deals with fluctuations either by increasing or decreasing the resistance of the muscular arteries by dilation or contraction. Detection of hypertension is becoming increasingly common with the growing emphasis within medicine on preventive treatment. Nevertheless, it is estimated that one in every five people has hypertension and that a third of these are not even aware of the fact.

Severe hypertension may cause strokes, heart failure or kidney failure; mild or moderate hypertension may speed up atherosclerosis or cause congestion of blood vessels supplying part of the brain or heart. The incidence of strokes in industrialised countries is now falling as a result of more frequent diagnosis and treatment of high blood pressure but it has yet to be seen if treating hypertension will also produce a fall in coronary heart disease.

The effects of hypertension can be aggravated by smoking. In a North American study of longshoremen in San Francisco, it was found that the number of heart attacks among smokers was ten times higher than among non-smokers with normal blood pressure. The perils of smoking are examined in Body Maintenance on page 200.

Lack of exercise

Better to hunt in Fields for Health unbought,
Than fee the doctor for a nauseous Draught.
The Wise, for Cure, on exercise depend;
God never made His Work, for Man to mend.
Fables Ancient and Modern, John Dryden

Exercise can benefit the heart by strengthening cardiac muscle and thereby increasing the heart's pumping capacity. As a result the heart does not have to work so hard to pump blood around the body. A desk-bound editor's weak flabby heart, for example, may have to work twice as hard as a long-distance athlete's to run the same distance in the same time. In such a case, the editor's heart may be half to two-thirds the size of the athlete's and probably beats at twice the rate.

In a study of drivers and conductors on English public transport vehicles, it was found that deaths from coronary heart disease were twice as common among the sedentary drivers. It was concluded that going up and down the stairs to collect fares kept the hearts of the conductors in better shape, and furthermore they did not have to contend with the stresses of driving through heavy trafic. However, on closer scrutiny it emerged that the drivers, on

The jogging craze
Overeating and lack of exercise have a lot in common. Both establish a vicious circle—the more you eat the more your body wants to eat, and the less you exercise the less capable you are of exercising—and both are damaging to one's self-esteem. If you are healthy but unfit, jogging is a very efficient way of burning up excess calories and regaining muscle tone. Combine jogging with walking to get used to it.

average, required larger uniforms than the conductors, which suggests there were more basic differences, apart from the amount of exercise taken, that determined the higher incidence of coronary heart disease in the drivers.

The benefits of exercise have been recognised for hundreds of years and today an ever increasing number of people are seeking to counterbalance the potentially adverse effects of the sedentary life by taking up activities such as jogging, squash and tennis. There is no doubt that sensible exercise can improve our sense of well-being and that healthy hearts benefit from exercise. Given this awareness it is tempting to conclude that exercise also protects us from heart disease. But in fact the evidence is still not conclusive; there are studies which both support and contradict this generally held belief.

For example, in their Seven Countries study, Dr Ancel Keys and colleagues in the USA reported an incidence of coronary heart disease in Finland of 198 men per 10,000 per year. Finland is a country where a rugged outdoor life is the rule—only ten per cent of middle-aged men are classified as sedentary—yet the coronary heart disease rate reported by Dr Keys was the highest in Europe, higher even than in the USA, where 60 per cent of middle-aged men are classified as sedentary. In other words, no amount of exercise can counteract an unhealthy diet, although it may be responsible for mortality being lower than might otherwise be the case.

This is yet another illustration of the complexity of the heart disease story. It may be that a rich diet or heavy smoking undermine the beneficial effects of exercise. Alternatively, the benefits of exercise may be more pronounced after some forms of activity than after others. According to one theory short, rigorous bursts of exercise may be better than the sustained activity demanded by most manual work.

In one five-year study 1,700 British male executives were asked to record their activities on Fridays and Saturdays, and to categorise them as either 'vigorous' or 'sedentary'. Only 11 per cent of those who developed coronary heart disease undertook 'vigorous' activities. Of those who did not develop coronary heart disease, 25 per cent were vigorous. The coronary heart disease risk among the vigorous group was found to be only one-third that of the other group.

However, this does not mean that a sedentary man or woman should suddenly launch into vigorous exercise; physical activity is only beneficial as long as it remains within an individual's personal capacity. Excessive exercise is as potentially dangerous as no exercise at all. Medical advice should be sought for specific needs.

Obesity Obesity can put strain on the heart. Various studies have shown that the number of risk factors associated with atherosclerosis rise as body weight increases. One of the most important of these is high blood pressure. Another risk factor linked to obesity is a raised level of cholesterol in the blood; fat people also tend to have higher levels of triglyceride fats in the blood than thinner people. It is estimated that blood vessel and heart disease might fall by more than a quarter if obesity was eliminated from Western countries.

Stress Tension, anxiety, fear or anger can result in an increase in pulse rate and blood pressure as adrenaline and noradrenaline production is stepped up to prepare the cardiovascular motor for fight or flight. In people with healthy hearts the production of adrenaline and noradrenaline is a normal and indeed desirable response. The body must be alerted to emergencies and these two hormones do the job very well. But in patients with coronary heart disease emotional outbursts may precipitate a heart attack, a response to increased heart rate and blood pressure rather than to the stress itself.

The Stock Exchange where fortunes and reputations are won and lost—a highly stressful environment for both winners and losers.

Face to face with the law Confrontation and mutual suspicion are fuelled by hormones which automatically increase heart rate and blood pressure. Of little consequence when we are young, violent feelings place considerable strain on the heart when we are old.

Composition of blood

Blood is possibly one of the most emotive and feared of all body substances. From cuts and grazes to fearful road accidents, blood is associated with emergencies and we fear it as children fear the dark. Blood is also surrounded by myth and misconception. In everyday speech, blood can be 'blue', synonymous with aristocratic breeding; 'hot', showing anger or passion; or even 'pure'.

Our horror of blood was highlighted in World War II when Britain's scientific advisers recommended using donated human blood in black pudding, a type of blood sausage. Animal blood is acceptable human fodder, but human blood is not, it seems. Yet it is acceptable to consume it intravenously unless you belong to a religious sect which forbids blood transfusion.

Human blood is no more nutritious than animal blood, except in Transylvanian fiction. But centuries of superstition and blood magic still have a hold over the public imagination, as the Dracula industry proves. Nor does anger really make the blood boil, though it does increase heart rate, increasing the speed at which blood is pumped around the body.

Some blood myths died along with the people who found comfort in them. Robin Hood, the English folk hero who robbed from the rich to give to the poor, died from blood-letting. Hundreds of years before the pharmacological tranquilliser doctors treated stress and other disorders by letting blood. Frederick the Great submitted himself to this treatment to calm his nerves before battles.

The composition of blood

Blood is the body's internal transport system, the means by which raw materials are carried to the factories, power stations and smallest consumers of the body—from major organs to every individual living cell.

Blood is composed of cells and fluid. The fluid, called plasma, is faintly straw-coloured and consists of at least 90 per cent water. Plasma accounts for 55 per cent of blood volume and cells for 45 per cent.

The vast majority of blood cells are oxygen-carrying red cells, as many as five million of them in each pinprick of blood. They are called red cells because they contain the pigment haemoglobin, which gives the blood its distinctive colour. Haemoglobin picks up oxygen from the lungs and releases it to every living cell in the body. The blood's most important function is to carry oxygen. Cells deprived of oxygen quickly die.

Red cells are manufactured by the bone marrow and the red cell industry is a prolific one; each day some 200,000,000,000 red cells are produced. Views differ as to how long red cells remain in active service but according to one view they remain in circulation for 110 to 120 days. If this is so, an individual red cell can make more than 40,000 journeys around the body in a month.

The rate of red cell formation is regulated by the hormone erythropoietin which is produced in the kidneys. Production can vary for a number of reasons; a reduction of oxygen intake into the lungs can affect production, for example. Some rare kidney tumours can produce an excess of erythropoietin whereas some kidney diseases can result in a decrease.

Normal red cell production depends upon the body having an adequate supply of iron and two main vitamins: B12 and folic acid. Deficiencies in these can arise either as a result of poor diet, or from failure to absorb these vitamins from the small intestine.

Anaemia (which means literally 'loss of blood') due to faulty absorption of Vitamin B12 is known as pernicious anaemia. Before this vitamin was synthesised and injected, sufferers were treated with a diet of vitamin-rich raw liver.

Iron deficiency can also result from chronic bleeding or repeated pregnancy unless the mother is given enough extra iron to replace that lost during the formation of the baby's blood.

White blood cells or leucocytes provide the body with a line of defence against injury and infection that is second only to the skin. There are several sorts of white cells, each programmed to perform a specific task but granulocytes and lymphocytes make up the majority.

Granulocytes are formed in the bone marrow like the red blood cells but they are one and a half times larger. They live for about nine days and have freedom of movement, unlike red cells which are simply carried along in the blood. Speedily activated by infected or injured tissue, granulocytes squeeze their way through the blood vessel walls and engulf bacteria. This intimate cellular embrace is often death to the bacteria and to the granulocytes themselves. Pus is really millions of dead white cells. Because their numbers increase three- or four-fold during infection, granulocytes are of major diagnostic importance.

Lymphocytes are slightly larger than red cells and are concerned with immunity and combating infection. There are two main groups, the B and T lymphocytes. The B cells are ordinarily concerned with making antibodies, while the T cells have a dual role: they control immune mechanisms and kill alien cells and organisms. Some viruses, such as the glandular fever virus, can be neutralised by T lymphocytes but not by granulocytes.

Lymphocytes cannot distinguish desirable from undesirable foreign bodies so they attack transplanted tissue as they would any other invader, aggressively, unless induced by drugs to do otherwise. New anti-rejection drugs have made a major contribution to spare-part surgery.

Certain aspects of white cell behaviour are

Voodoo ritual killing
Blood-letting, real or symbolic, plays a part in many religious ceremonies, but its significance varies. In some rituals blood is a thank offering, in others an appeasement.

Fainting on parade,
one of the few reliable signs that summer has arrived in London! Prolonged standing in hot sun reduces blood pressure in the arteries of the brain. Fainting is a reflex effect, part of the body's very efficient early warning system. As soon as the head comes down to the level of the heart the flow of blood to the brain is restored.

Blood transfusion
Millions of pints of blood are donated and used every year, and need usually exceeds supply. The body simply cannot make new blood fast enough to maintain blood pressure after a serious accident or a major haemorrhage. Blood can be stored for about three weeks at a temperature of 39°F (4°C), but it cannot actually be frozen without damaging the red cells.

enigmatic; their diverse role is not fully understood. A deeper understanding of their function would probably elucidate the factors which trigger leukaemia. Literally meaning 'white blood', leukaemia is a condition brought about by vast over-production of white cells, often 50 to 60 times normal production.

Among other things leukaemia disrupts production in the bone marrow of both red cells and blood platelets, also known as thrombocytes. Platelets are cells which stick together in response to a cut or a wound. As such they are part of a highly complex process, involving a dozen or more factors, which results in clotting of the blood. Clotting staunches bleeding and creates a scaffold on which to build new tissue. As the platelets stick together they release a hormone, serotonin, which causes the neighbouring blood vessels to constrict.

Blood clots when a soluble substance in it called fibrinogen is converted into insoluble strands of fibrin through the action of an enzyme, thrombin. This enzyme does not usually exist in detectable amounts but is formed when bleeding occurs.

There are many chemicals involved in clotting and they have been given names and numbers. The most famous is Factor VIII, the anti-haemophilic factor. Haemophilia itself is characterised by uncontrollable bleeding; it is an inherited disorder which is only manifest in boys.

Blood groups: compatibility and paternity

There are various blood group systems in current use. The best-known, the ABO system, classifies blood by detecting the presence or absence of certain antigens, which are chemical substances present in most human blood. Some blood contains A antigens, or B antigens, or both; some contains neither. So there are four possible ABO classifications: A, B, AB, and O (blood containing neither A nor B).

Blood used for transfusions must be compatible with the blood group of the recipient. Group O blood contains anti-A and anti-B antibodies. Group A blood contains anti-B antibodies and group B blood anti-A antibodies. AB blood has neither anti-A nor anti-B antibodies.

The other well-known blood classification system is the Rhesus system, discovered in 1940 by the Austrian scientist and Nobel Prize winner, Karl Landsteiner, who also pioneered the ABO system. Approximately 85 per cent of humans possess a particular set of antigens known as the 'Rhesus factor'; they are said to be Rhesus positive (Rh+). The remaining 15 per cent are known as Rhesus negative (Rh−).

Parents of 'Rhesus babies' have incompatible blood. Problems arise if the blood of the baby of an Rh negative mother is Rh positive and the mother has Rh positive antibodies. These can reach the baby's circulation via the placenta and destroy its blood cells.

Rh negative women develop the positive antibodies only if Rh positive cells enter their circulation. This is likely to occur only if they are given an incompatible blood transfusion with Rh positive cells or if, in pregnancy, Rh positive cells 'spill over' from the baby. In fact this is most likely to occur at childbirth when cells from mother and baby intermingle. It is possible, however, to eliminate the risks to subsequent babies by giving the mother large quantities of Rh positive antibodies. This has to be repeated with each pregnancy or abortion where there is an Rh positive baby. The treatment can ensure normal, healthy infants in future pregnancies.

Paternity blood tests Blood tests are frequently used in paternity suits and sometimes disclose more than the parties bargain for. In one extraordinary study designed to investigate antibody formation, it was found that some 30 per cent of the married couples in the study had one or more illegitimate children, probably without the husbands or the wives being aware of it. This unsuspected finding, quite irrelevant to the central purpose of the investigation, so embarrassed the doctors involved that the study was abandoned.

The results of this study were not widely publicised, though they were discussed at an international symposium several years ago by three

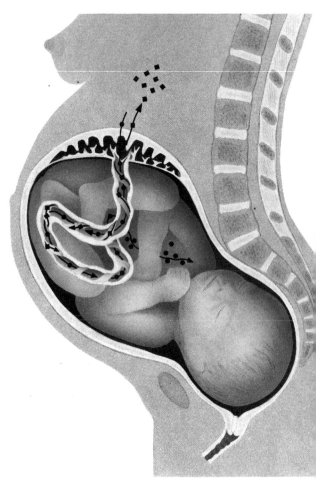

Haemolytic disease occurs when there is sufficient mixing of the mother's and the baby's blood to cause the mother (Rh negative) to produce antibodies in response to the baby's Rh positive red blood cells. If enough of the baby's red cells are destroyed it may be 'blue' at birth. Most mothers do not actually form antibodies with their first pregnancy, though later pregnancies are increasingly at risk. Roughly 1 baby in 200 is affected by Rhesus incompatibility.

O group blood can be given to people with A, B, AB and O group blood. If you have O group blood you are a 'universal donor'. Transfusions were extremely hazardous until the work of Karl Landsteiner early this century. Though the idea of transfusion is ancient and fairly obvious, no one really knew how to put new blood into an ailing body until William Harvey discovered the circulation. Harvey showed that it must be put into a vein.

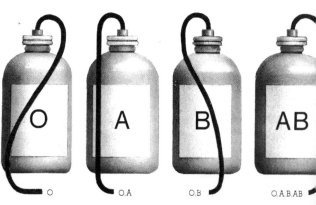

O   O.A   O.B   O.A.B.AB

Cross references
Antibody response 110
Transplant rejection 111
Heredity 14

Fathers and children
Proof of paternity is necessary in hundreds of court cases every year, and blood tests are used to provide the evidence. Unfortunately tests can only confirm that a man is *not* the father of a child, and even then not with 100 per cent certainty.

Karl Landsteiner
is mainly remembered today for his pioneering work on blood groups, but he also discovered the polio virus and developed a test for syphilis.

eminent men: Dr E. Philipp, the consultant obstetrician and gynaecologist at the Royal Northern Hospital, London; Lord Kilbrandon, then Lord of Appeal in Ordinary; and Sir John Stallworth, then Nuffield Professor of Obstetrics and Gynaecology at Oxford University. This is what was said:

Dr Philipp "We blood-tested some patients in a town in southeast England and found that 30 per cent of the husbands could not have been the fathers of their children."
Sir John Stallworthy "What was the extent of that group?"
Dr Philipp "Not large—between 200 and 300—but large enough to give us a large shock."
Lord Kilbrandon "Mr Philipp, surely the figure of 30 per cent is a minimum? What you established was that 30 per cent could not be the children of their mothers' husbands, not that 70 per cent of them were."
Dr Philipp "Yes, it is a minimum."

The point Lord Kilbrandon was making is that blood tests cannot prove that a man is the father of a child, only that he is not. In paternity disputes the forensic scientist or serologist sets out to make an 'exclusion'. He compares the blood of the child with that of the mother and the alleged father and if the alleged father's blood does not correspond with that of the child, paternity is ruled out. For example, a man who has O group blood and a woman who has B group blood cannot produce an A group child. In practice the ABO system is not a very effective way of disproving paternity since it gives the serologist only a 17 per cent chance of making an exclusion. There are 15 other types of test, based on different blood group systems. These are routinely used in paternity disputes. Combining all these tests, the serologist has an 80 per cent chance of making an exclusion. Further tests, not used routinely, increase the chance of making an exclusion to nearly 100 per cent.

Circulation of the blood

The circulatory system is yet another body system amazing in its compactness and efficiency. The blood vessels of the average adult would stretch 60,000 miles (96,500 km) if they were unravelled, and they transport blood to some 60 billion cells. Every cell in the body depends on oxygen and their only access to it is through the blood.

Heart and arteries The life-sustaining circulatory process begins and ends in the heart. The right side of the heart pumps blood through the lungs where waste carbon dioxide is exchanged for oxygen. The re-oxygenated blood is then sent to the left side of the heart. From there it gets pumped into the body's largest artery, the aorta, which is nearly 1 in (2.5 cm) in diameter.

Emerging from the left ventricle, the aorta rises for 2–3 in (5–7 cm) and then arches, like a walking-stick handle, backwards towards the spine before descending. The aorta can be thought of as the trunk of the circulatory tree with the arteries being the branches. Those that branch off first carry the blood to the neck, brain and arms. Branches farther down supply blood to the intestines, liver, kidneys and legs.

Circulation and distribution Impulses from the sympathetic nerves regulate the rate of blood flow through the arteries and also the distribution of the blood to the various tissues of the body. The arteries, with their strong muscular and elastic walls, respond to these impulses either by contracting, which reduces blood flow, or by relaxing, which increases blood flow.

When we eat, blood flow to the digestive system is increased, reducing blood flow to the limbs. When we take exercise the reverse happens. Blood flow to the digestive tract and the kidneys can be cut by as much as three-quarters, or even more, during very strenuous exertion.

Under normal conditions the muscles receive about 20 per cent of the blood pumped from the heart. But the brain receives 25 per cent, a disproportionate amount considering that the muscles account for two-fifths of body weight. Blood supply to the brain, about 250 ml every minute, is constant; it has to be or we would cease to function properly.

The twigs of the circulatory tree are the arterioles, small arteries which branch off the main arteries. These in turn divide into capillaries.

Capillaries These are the smallest blood vessels in the body, only 1/25 in (0.06 cm) long and a hundred times smaller than that in diameter. These tiny vessels are the last link in the chain of delivery from the lungs to the cells. The blood stays in the capillaries while oxygen, glucose, hormones and other essential substances are swapped for carbon

One-way traffic
Veins have two-flap valves inside them which ensure that blood flows in one direction only, and if necessary against the pull of gravity—oxygen-depleted blood must be taken away even from the tip of the big toe. Weak valves, leading to varicose veins, are sometimes hereditary but the most important direct cause of damage to them is prolonged standing, and in women added pressure on the veins of the pelvis during pregnancy.

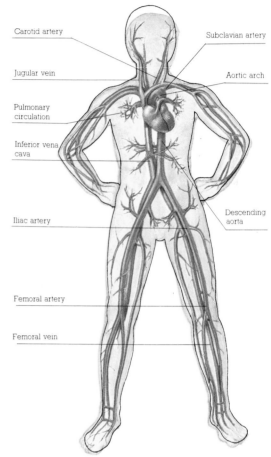

Carotid artery
Jugular vein
Pulmonary circulation
Inferior vena cava
Iliac artery
Femoral artery
Femoral vein
Subclavian artery
Aortic arch
Descending aorta

The double system
The point that eluded all physicians and philosophers up until the time of William Harvey was that the body has a double, not a single, circulation system. The basic system is from heart to arteries (red), to veins (black), and back to the heart. But at some point blood must pick up oxygen from the lungs. This means that blood returning from the body must be pumped to the lungs through the pulmonary arteries and back into the heart through the pulmonary veins. This is why the heart has four chambers and not two.

dioxide and other waste products. The swap is made through the capillary walls which are only one cell thick. How this exchange occurs, and in particular how large molecules such as proteins and hormones pass through capillary walls and cell membranes, is one of the miracles of biochemistry.

Veins Cell waste is discharged into the veins for excretion through the kidneys or through the lungs. The veins take blood back to the heart and the heart pumps it to the lungs where it receives fresh oxygen.

Since the veins do not have to withstand the same pressure as the arteries they are not as strong. They are also larger in diameter. Blood pumped into the aorta travels at about 15 in (37.5 cm) a second; by the time it reaches the capillaries it has slowed down to about 1/50 in (0.05 cm) a second. This directly reflects the fall in pressure from

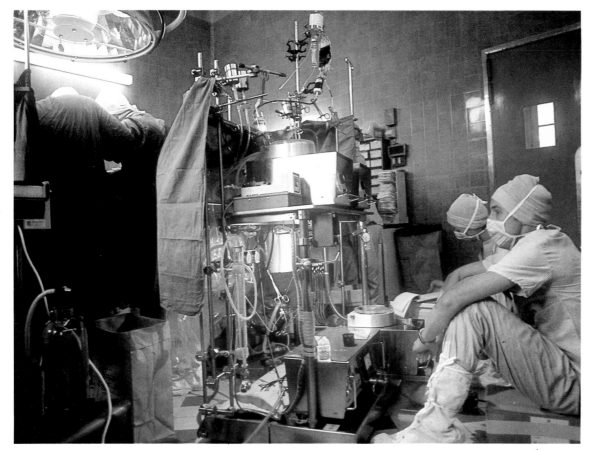

The flow must go on
During major surgery the cumbersome intricacy of the heart-lung machine performs the pumping and oxygenating functions far more elegantly performed by the heart and lungs. A roller pump and heat exchanger control flow and temperature.

Well-jacketed arteries
are able to withstand the high pressure of the blood flowing through them and also maintain pressure throughout the arterial system. The muscular and elastic tissue in artery walls ensures that surges of blood from the heart are converted into a less jerky flow. Nevertheless a severed artery bleeds in spurts.

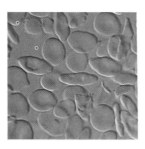

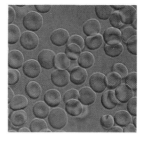

A pinprick of blood
contains about five million red blood cells. Healthy cells (right) live about four months, but if they are destroyed faster than the bone marrow can replace them anaemia develops. In sickle cell anaemia the red cells are deformed (left) and extra fragile because the haemoglobin they contain has been faultily synthesised. Clumped red cells (middle) cannot function properly and eventually form a clot.

100 mm mercury in the arteries to 0 mm, atmospheric pressure, in the capillaries.

Blood is able to flow uphill through veins because they have valves inside them—two-flap valves which operate rather like river lock gates—which prevent the blood from flowing backwards. Such valves are of particular importance because of our transition from four-legged to self-balancing two-legged creatures. As a result of the changeover the distance covered by blood returning from the feet to the heart increased by half, which means that blood has to travel at least $4\frac{1}{2}$ ft (1.4 m) uphill.

Varicose veins develop when these valves stop working properly. Instead of running smoothly through the veins from valve to valve, the blood is stockpiled and stagnates. In severe cases this creates back pressure resulting in swollen feet. Varicose veins which resemble either worm-like tubes or 'spider' varicosities behind the knees and around the ankles, can cause extreme pain and discomfort to the sufferer.

Varicose veins are associated with occupations which demand prolonged standing. Housewives and policemen are especially vulnerable. Any condition which results in swelling of the abdomen, such as chronic constipation, pregnancy and obesity also increases the risk of varicose veins. One in two women over the age of 40 is estimated to suffer from varicose veins, as opposed to one in four men of the same age.

Treatment varies according to severity. Support stockings or resting as often as possible with the legs in an elevated position are two commonly used forms of treatment but surgery may be needed in severe cases. A varicose vein can be surgically tied or removed, in which case the blood has to use alternative veins.

Blood pressure and hypertension

Fainting Fainting is a sign of temporary decrease in blood flow to the brain; the blood pools in the legs, reducing the flow to the heart which in turn reduces the flow from the heart to the brain.

Blood flow can be inhibited if one stands still for any length of time. Usually it can be restored to normal by very small movements, even toe wriggling or shifting to the other foot. But prolonged immobility, for example when soldiers stand on parade, can cause a faint.

Blood pressure Each time the heart beats the arteries momentarily expand in proportion to the force of the blood being pumped through them. This expansion can be felt when the pulse is taken, by pressing the fingers onto the radial artery in the wrist. The flutter that is felt is the change of pressure transmitted from aorta to wrist at a velocity approaching 20 ft (6 m) a second, a very high velocity indeed. This change in pressure takes only a tenth of a second to reach the wrist. The blood does not flow at that speed however; it flows much more slowly, taking several minutes to get from the aorta to the wrist.

Blood pressure in the arteries is high but in the veins it is much lower. Pressure throughout an artery is constant and so can be measured at any point along its length. The most convenient place is the arm, using a sphygmomanometer and a stethoscope. To measure blood pressure a doctor applies pressure to the upper arm with an inflatable cuff attached to the sphygmomanometer and then listens in to the beat of the brachial artery with the

stethoscope. The sphygmomanometer, which has a mercury gauge, registers the pressure transmitted by each heartbeat (systolic pressure) and the pressure between the beats (diastolic pressure).

At birth systolic pressure tends to be about 40 mm Hg (millimetres of mercury), rising in the first month of life to about 70. In an average young man doing nothing in particular systolic pressure is about 120 and diastolic about 80. This pattern remains reasonably constant until we reach our mid-twenties and then tends to increase gradually. The average 60-year-old man has a systolic pressure of about 140; in the average 80-year-old man blood pressure is nearer 160. Unfortunately ageing arteries lose their elasticity.

'Normal' blood pressure is estimated to be around 120/80, the values for the average young man. In fact what is normal for one person is not necessarily normal for a similar person of the same age. The arbitrary dividing line between 'normal' and 'abnormal' blood pressure which requires treatment is often taken as 140/90, assuming that this level is maintained or exceeded over a period of time. Readings have to be repeated to establish the true norm in any one individual. During one examination, for example, blood pressure may be shown as 170/100. A week later the level may be 150/90. In fact, a second reading taken only half an hour after the first may differ by as much as 40 mm for the systolic value and 10 mm for the diastolic. Casual readings may therefore give an entirely erroneous idea of an individual's blood pressure. A reading may be high simply because the patient

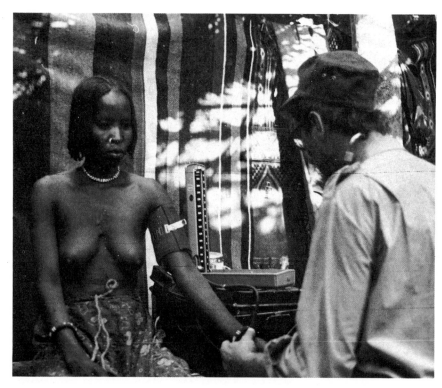

Measuring blood pressure
The sphygmomanometer is an elementary diagnostic tool for doctors worldwide. Here a woman of the Saharan Tabu tribe receives medical attention. The doctor inflates the cuff of the sphygmomanometer to momentarily stop the blood flow, then allows it to slowly deflate. As he hears the blood flow beginning through his stethoscope he reads off the systolic pressure. Diastolic pressure is read when the cuff is sufficiently deflated for normal blood flow to return.

Cross references
How the heart functions **81**
Ageing **156**
Lifestyle **182**
Coronary heart disease **96**

feels anxious or worried about the idea of his blood pressure being measured or, perhaps, because he has been subjected to stress at home or work.

Hypertension High blood pressure or hypertension is one of the three major risk factors of coronary heart disease, with obesity and smoking. It has been called 'the silent killer' because it tends to be unaccompanied by any warning symptoms. The effects of hypertension can be aggravated by smoking. In a North American study of longshoremen in San Francisco, it was found that the number of heart attacks among smokers was ten times higher than among non-smokers with normal blood pressure.

Complications of hypertension include kidney failure, stroke and coronary heart disease. The incidence of strokes in industrialised countries is now falling as a result of the increased diagnosis and treatment of high blood pressure. It has yet to be seen, however, if treating hypertension will also produce a fall in coronary heart disease. It is estimated that one in every five people is hypertensive and that a third of these are not even aware of it.

A study some ten years ago by the Irish Heart Foundation showed that five per cent of all men between 25 and 65 years of age had diastolic blood pressure readings of 110 or more and another 14 per cent had diastolic levels of between 95 and 109. It was found that nearly 20 per cent of the sample, who were representative of all Irish men, had mild or more severe hypertension. Only 30 per cent of

these had had their levels noted and of these only 30 per cent were considered to be receiving adequate treatment. In other words, as Professor Risteard Mulcahy has pointed out in his book *Beat Heart Disease*, only about one in eight of those men with problems was being treated satisfactorily. The same frequency of hypertension has been reported in other European countries and also in the USA.

Extreme cases of hypertension are usually easy to diagnose but the marginal cases are more difficult to detect. The problems of diagnosis can be compounded by the fact that the hypertensive may feel well and energetic and therefore feels no need to visit a doctor to have his or her blood pressure checked.

Drugs can reduce blood pressure and therefore relieve the strain on the heart and arteries. Proper treatment can bring pressure down to within normal bounds or at least within acceptable ones. Unfortunately many patients fail to take their drugs as prescribed, believing that since they feel well they have no need of medication. A point to remember, however, is that drugs do not cure high blood pressure—they only control it.

Uncomplicated hypertension does not demand elaborate investigations before treatment starts. In severe cases, however, the doctor may call for specialist investigation which may involve a few days in hospital. Tests are conducted to find out the cause of the problem, the state of the arteries and the key organs, and the significance of risk factors such as diet and smoking.

The vulnerable age
A busy executive reverts to the innocent pleasures of boyhood. Relaxation does not come easily to most people suffering from hypertension, a condition aggravated by worry, overwork and endlessly striving for status or perfection.

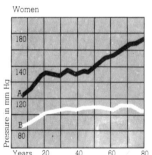

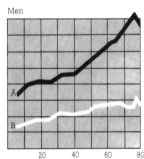

Age and blood pressure
Blood pressure levels rise with age, and with them the risk of heart and kidney ailments and strokes. Middle aged men tend to be most at risk, hence the lower average of the values shown for men over the age of 60.

A Systolic
B Diastolic

Lymph and lymph nodes

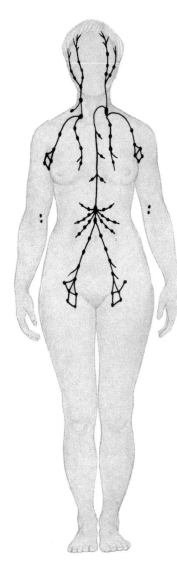

The blood carries oxygen and nutrients to the cells and waste products like carbon dioxide from them. However, not all the plasma (blood fluid) involved in these exchanges is reabsorbed into the circulation. That which is left behind in the spaces between the cells is removed by the lymphatic system, along with substances which are too big to squeeze through the capillary walls into the bloodstream. These include cell debris, fat globules and tiny protein particles; once in the lymphatic system and mixed with plasma, these are known as lymph. Thus the lymphatic system is the secondary transport system and the means of draining the intercellular spaces. The lymphatic system is also part of the body's defence system.

Excess fluid and other cargo is absorbed into lymph vessels, which are similar to blood vessels and lined with one-way valves, like veins, to prevent back flow. Small lymph vessels join adjacent ones to form larger channels which lead to the neck where they empty into large veins.

Most of the lymph is eventually channelled into the 16-inch-long (40 cm) thoracic duct on the left hand side of the body from where it drains into the left subclavian vein. The right thoracic duct, a mere ½ in (1 cm) long, drains only the upper half of the right hand side of the body. The imbalance in this division of labour is not understood.

Every minute the thoracic duct alone empties between 4 and 10 ml of lymph into the blood; if the lymph fails to reach the blood, plasma protein levels start to fall and blood volume drops. Every day the lymphatic system restores to the blood some 60 per cent of its plasma volume and approximately 50 per cent of the total amount of proteins lost from the capillaries.

Lymph nodes Lymph nodes are found at certain strategic points along the medium-sized lymph vessels at the knee, elbow, armpit, groin, neck, abdomen and chest. Acting as filters to trap bacteria and other debris, lymph nodes vary greatly in size. Normal lymph nodes may be felt in the groin. Swollen lymph nodes may be felt in the armpit of a person with an infected hand or in the neck of somebody with infected tonsils.

Lymph vessels serve as carriers for cancer cells. For example, cells emanating from a malignant breast growth will travel along lymphatic vessels and multiply in the armpit lymph node. The node will enlarge and cease to function normally, enabling successive cancer cells to bypass it and affect other nodes in the lymphatic chain. This is why lymph nodes receiving lymph vessels issuing from a tumour are often removed along with the tumour. Unfortunately, it is not always possible to remove all the affected nodes.

Lymphocytes, a type of white blood cell, are packed in the lymph nodes. Lymphocytes produce antibodies, proteins which rise up against invading proteins known as antigens.

The spleen and the thymus gland are also part of the lymphatic system. The spleen is involved in the removal of the blood cells and bacteria from the blood. Except for this, all its other functions can be carried on by other organs, though children who have no spleens may have less immunity to bacterial infection than other children.

Overlying the heart, the thymus consists largely of developing lymphocytes. After puberty it begins to shrink in size. Its role in the early years of life is not fully understood, but it appears necessary for the normal development of immunity.

The major lymph nodes shown here filter the lymph collected from tissue spaces all over the body. Nodes which drain infected areas are liable to become inflamed and tender to the touch. Elephantiasis (page 208) is a condition brought on by blockage of lymph vessels in the legs; the culprit is a minute parasite worm!

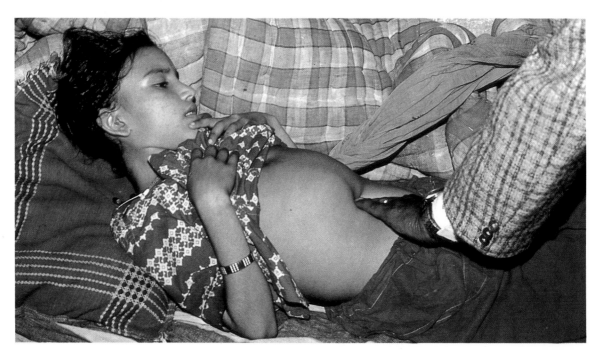

Cross references
Composition of blood **100**
Circulation and
distribution **104**
Cancer **228**
Thymus fire fighter **70**

Inside a lymph node

In real life even the largest lymph nodes are only 1 in (2.5 cm) across. Each node has several incoming lymph vessels but usually only one outgoing vessel, and its inner structure is vaguely lobular. As in the kidney, the core of the node is known as the medulla and the outer part as the cortex. The analogy is apt because a lymph node, like a kidney, provides an intricate network of spaces through which fluid is slowly filtered, its noxious contents being destroyed and its valuable contents recycled.
The follicles in which lymphocytes multiply in times of infection are located in the cortex.

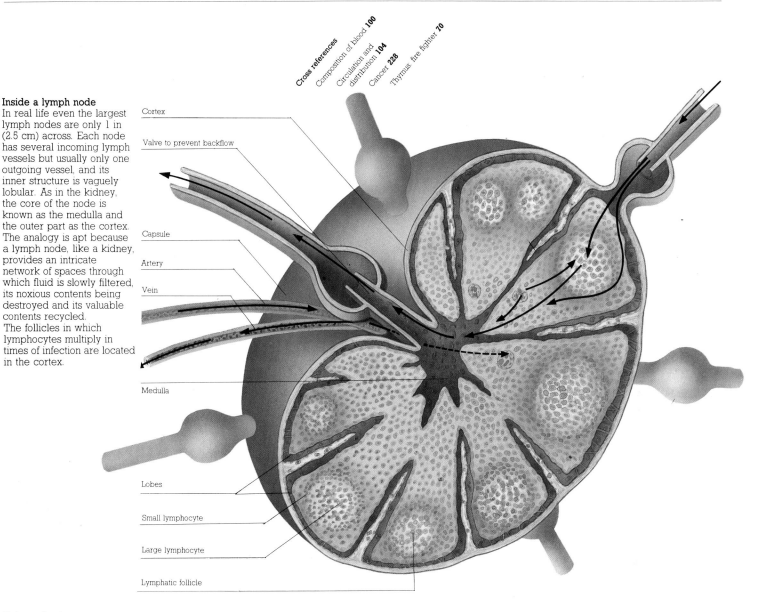

Cortex

Valve to prevent backflow

Capsule

Artery

Vein

Medulla

Lobes

Small lymphocyte

Large lymphocyte

Lymphatic follicle

Enlarged spleen

The spleen lies between the bottom of the stomach and the diaphragm, and in a healthy child should be about 3 in (8 cm) long and weigh no more than 3½ oz (100 g). But in children or adults who have suffered repeated episodes of blood-borne infection, malaria for example, it enlarges to huge proportions (splenomegaly). Left: a doctor palpates the abdomen of a young woman to find out to what extent her spleen has enlarged. Right: a suitable case for splenectomy; the border of this little boy's enlarged spleen is outlined in grease crayon.

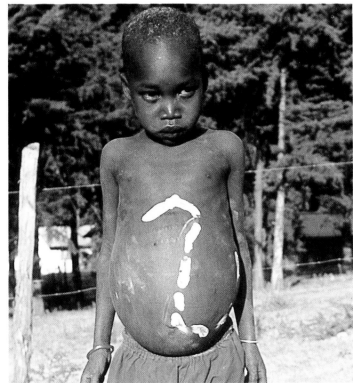

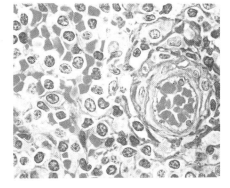

Section through spleen

A photograph of a stained microscope slide showing densely packed lymphocytes and phagocytes in the spleen. In the foetus the spleen produces red and white blood cells as well but in a healthy adult the bone marrow assumes this role. The phagocytes of the spleen dispose of ageing or damaged red blood cells and other debris in the blood. The lymphocytes secrete antibodies.

Immunity: defence against invasion

Most of us suffer only once in our lives from diseases like chickenpox. For this we have our remarkable immunological memory to thank. It builds up a profile of invading bacteria, viruses and other foreign materials, and combats any new invasion with an army of specifically primed proteins called antibodies. These are produced by some of the lymphocytes (white blood cells). Other lymphocytes are capable of killing invading microbes and transplanted foreign cells. Invading organisms act as antigens; it is in their presence that antibodies are generated.

It sounds simple enough, but the immune system is anything but simple. To begin with, immunologists calculate that any one man or mouse can produce 100,000,000 different kinds of antibodies. Secondly, each antibody has to be 'custom built'. An antibody against chickenpox virus will have no effect against measles virus and vice versa. The antibody attaches itself to the molecules on the virus surface rather like a key fitting a lock. The 'door' will not open if the wrong 'key' is used. This calls for extraordinary precision since small bacteria measure about $1/1000$ mm each way and viruses are even smaller. As many as 20,000 viruses can fit into a small bacterial cell.

There are various theories as to how antibodies are formed, one being that long lines of them are formed using the antigens as moulds, rather like the dies in a machine tool workshop, in accordance with instructions from the immunological memory. This attractive-sounding theory could be said to expand one of the underlying themes of this book. If it were true, we could argue that not only are the machines we build designed in our own image, but also the means by which we make them.

A second theory concerns what is known as clonal selection. This supposes that for each of the different potential kinds of antibodies, there must be a different kind of lymphocyte, each capable of forming one and only one antibody. The proponents of this theory suggest that each particular antigen stimulates a specific lymphocyte to reproduce. The offspring, all identical and known collectively as a clone, then produce the antibodies.

Antibody response It may take a week or ten days for antibodies to form against a new antigen. It is as if the production line is ready to gear up to a new threat at the flick of a switch. But while the antibody machinery is gearing up the disease or infection becomes established.

The immune response to the common cold or to influenza is precisely the same as to chickenpox or measles, yet few of us get through the year without a cold or a bout of flu. This is because cold and flu viruses change and evolve from year to year, unlike those responsible for German measles or chicken-

Busy amongst the pollen
A high pollen count on a summer's day spells misery for hay fever sufferers—throat, eyes and lips itch unbearably, exposed skin feels hot and prickly, and breathing becomes almost asthmatic. The direct cause of such symptoms is inflammation due to production of histamine in areas of skin or mucous membrane in contact with pollen.

Harvesting flu vaccine
Influenza is a disease of unpredictably fluctuating virulence because flu viruses have the ability to change their antigenic structure. This means that vaccines effective against known strains are ineffective against new ones. The Hong Kong flu epidemic of 1968 was caused by a hitherto unknown strain. Here flu vaccine, grown in eggs, is harvested with a small vacuum pump. Before it can be injected it has to be concentrated, purified and tested.

pox. Thus antibodies formed in response to previous colds provide only limited immunity, if any. There are so many different strains of colds and flu that immunity against one does not guarantee protection against another.

Transplant rejection Foreign tissues like organ transplants are normally rejected by the immune system. This has been overcome partly by matching recipient organs to the donor by a process called tissue typing. This technique enables the identification of specific antigens which can be matched between the recipient and donor. In addition, certain drugs, immuno-suppressive agents, are given to suppress the normal immune response. The current emphasis in overcoming rejection has been in better selection of donor and finding more powerful immuno-suppressive drugs.

Cancer The immune system in every normal person is constantly battling against cancer. Some immunologists believe that malignancies are always

rising in the body and that nearly always these are recognised by the immune system as foreign and knocked out. Once in a while a malignancy defies the surveillance system and cancer develops.

Hence the increasing emphasis on immune therapy in cancer research, although the present position is one of potential hope rather than clear-cut success.

Group immunity Just as individual people are more resistant to some diseases than others, so are some populations whose contact with disease gives them an immunity denied to other more geographically isolated groups. For example, tuberculosis only became widespread among Australian aborigines when they came into contact with the first European colonists. The white man was largely immune, the aborigine was not. Similarly, a quarter of the people of Fiji died last century when measles was imported from Europe. The white man was immune, but the Fijians unfortunately were not.

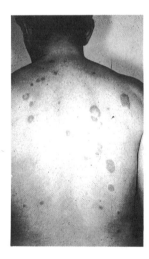

Allergy to penicillin
Adverse reactions to penicillins and other antibiotics are not uncommon, but far more worrying to researchers is the ease with which bacteria, among them the staphylococci and gonococci responsible for wound infections and gonorrhea, develop resistance to them.

Patch testing
to identify contact allergens. Allergies due to inhaled allergens are investigated using the Modified Prick Test. This involves placing a single drop of allergen extract on the skin and gently lifting the skin with a needle. If an angry weal develops after 10 or 20 minutes there is an allergy.

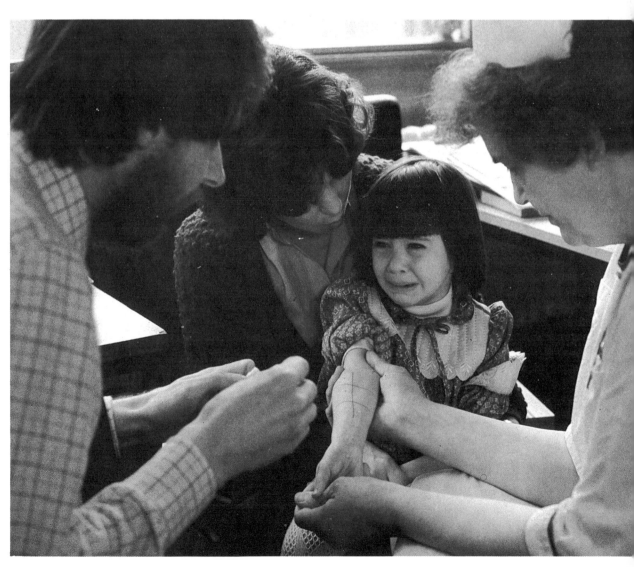

Allergies, auto-immunity and vaccines

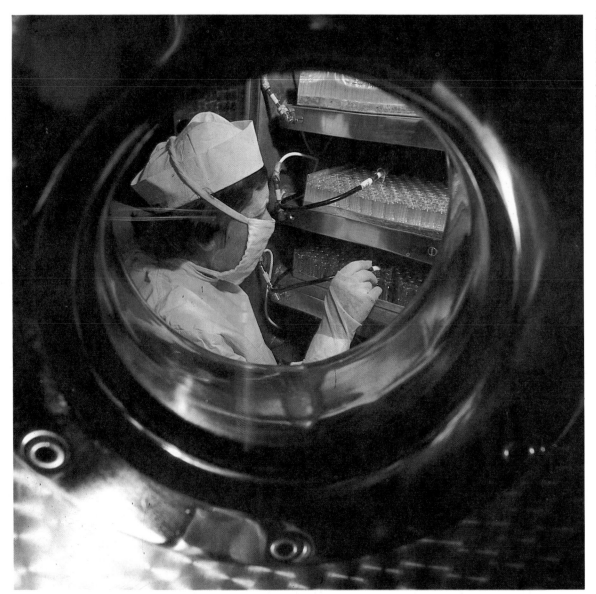

Immunology laboratory
An important part of an immunologist's work is to identify infectious antibodies associated with various infections in human serum samples. If a laboratory animal is immunised with a given antigen, serum from its blood will contain antibodies which destroy microbes of that antigen. It can therefore be used to identify the same microbe in human serum.

Allergy Writing in the first century B.C., the Latin poet Lucretius coined the saying: 'One man's meat is another man's poison'. He might have been writing about allergies. Arising from an inability to tolerate certain substances, mainly dusts, pollen, medicines or other chemicals, allergies are a symptom of a defect in the immune system.

The Austrian doctor, Clemens von Pirquet, one of the pioneers of immunisation, suggested that immunity and allergy were opposite sides of the same coin. In allergic people the system is unable to discriminate between a threatening substance and one which is harmless or even potentially nutritious. It wages full-scale warfare on innocent chemical invaders, producing hay fever when this occurs in the eyes and nose and asthma when the lungs are the site of this hyper-reactivity.

Auto-immunity This is an abnormal immune response by the body to one of its own tissues.

Antibodies treat the tissue as if it were foreign. Such tissues are known as auto-antigens and the antibodies formed against them as auto-antibodies.

Auto-antibodies are associated with many different diseases, including rheumatoid arthritis, ulcerative colitis, pernicious anaemia and certain goitres which arise through damage to the thyroid gland.

One of the most remarkable traits of the normal immune system is its ability to recognise 'self' and refrain from attacking body tissues as if they were antigens. This tolerance mechanism is not fully understood, but unravelling it would probably shed new light on the problems of auto-immunity. According to one theory, during foetal and early life, before the immune system is fully mature, the body suppresses production of lymphocytes which would otherwise attack crucial tissues.

Artificial immunity It has been recognised for

thousands of years that some diseases confer a lifelong immunity on those who survive them. Smallpox is one such disease and the earliest attempts to produce artificial immunity were directed against this ancient scourge, probably in the 11th century in China.

In Europe immunisation started with Edward Jenner's discovery in 1798 that an injection of cowpox virus could provide protection against smallpox. The virus provoked in the body the same immune response as smallpox. Today immunisation is available against a wide range of viral and bacterial diseases. It may involve injections of live, modified microbes which provoke an immune response without causing the disease—this is the method employed against tuberculosis, yellow fever, rabies and poliomyelitis—or alternatively injections of dead microbes killed in ways that preserve their capacity to confer immunity, such as cholera, influenza, typhoid and whooping cough vaccines.

Only one child in ten in the developing countries is immunised properly. Under the World Health Organization's 'Expanded Programme on Immunization' the aim is to provide vaccination for all children against tuberculosis, polio, measles, tetanus, whooping cough and diphtheria by 1990. One reason why so few children are being immunised now is simply that vaccines do not travel well. They must be kept cold or they quickly become useless. But in developing countries hygiene must go hand in hand with vaccine.

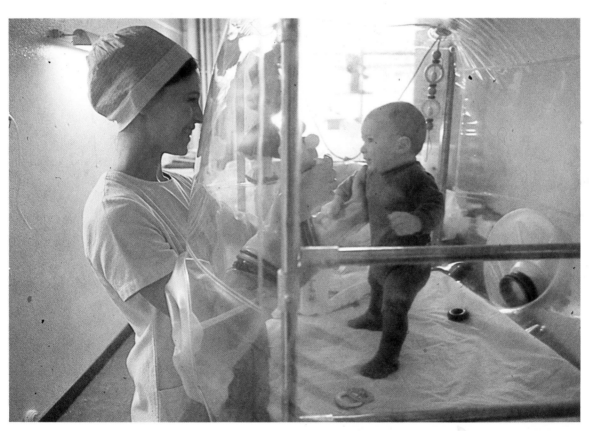

A sterile environment is essential for babies born prematurely and with hardly any resistance to infection. In the United States immunisation against diptheria, tetanus, whooping cough and polio is routinely given in the first six months of life, with vaccines for measles, German measles, and mumps at one year.

Immune to tooth decay? The bacterium *Streptococcus mutans* thrives on the sugar we eat, and secretes acid and a sticky substance called dextran which bore through tooth enamel. Researchers at Guy's Hospital in London are working on a vaccine which will protect teeth against *S. mutans*, and so far their experiments look promising. This could greatly reduce national budgets for dental care— dentists in the United States fill over half a million cavities a year.

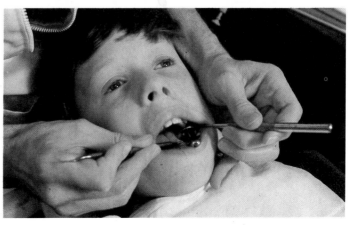

Breathing: exchanging carbon dioxide for oxygen

The heart pumps blood around the body. In turn, the blood carries oxygen to and carbon dioxide from every cell in the body. The lungs remove the carbon dioxide from the blood and exchange it for oxygen. To achieve this, the lungs of the average adult take in nearly a quarter of a million tons (tonnes) of oxygen a year.

The energy for this cycle of life comes originally from the sun. Plants absorb sunlight and, by the process of photosynthesis, use it to convert water and carbon dioxide into oxygen and sugar. If there were no green vegetation on earth, life would be limited to a few bacteria and viruses. It is a sobering thought that all animal life forms ultimately depend on plants, and for this reason the campaigners who strive to conserve grassland and forests and who fight against the pollution of the air, land and sea must be listened to. Man has a frightening potential to devastate the plant life which keeps the atmosphere of the earth oxygenated, cool and breathable.

When we breathe in we absorb the oxygen produced by photosynthesis and use it to create energy for the body. When we breathe out we expel carbon dioxide, a waste product as far as we are concerned, but absolutely crucial to plants for the process of photosynthesis.

Each molecule of food we consume contains a little bit of solar energy; the main energy sources are glucose and fat which are carried around the body in the bloodstream. Just as in an automobile, the fuel pipe delivers gasoline to the engine so, in the human body, the blood delivers energy-rich substances to billions of engines, the body cells.

In an automobile the engine fires when gasoline combines with oxygen—a process called internal combustion. In the body machine the engines fire when oxygen combines with fuel in the cells. Carbon dioxide is the by-product of this combustion in the cells. The blood picks up the carbon dioxide and transports it to the lungs from where it is expelled through the nose or mouth. So in the human machine the nose and mouth are both fuel inlets and waste outlets.

Oxygen in the body helps generate energy from food in precisely the same way as energy is liberated from a piece of fat when it is thrown into the fire. In fact, equal amounts of fat in the body and fat in the fire would produce the same amount of energy. In the body, however, the process is not explosive and not all the generated energy is burnt up immediately as heat. Some of it is stored to provide warmth, promote growth, activate muscles and trigger chemical changes.

Lung capacity The lungs have an extraordinary surface area to cater for our vast and continuous need for oxygen. They have an area of somewhere between 800 and 1,000 sq ft (74–93m²) which is

Breath control
is every bit as important to a weightlifter as to an opera singer. All movements must be coordinated with those of the diaphragm and intercostal muscles so that the muscular effort of breathing does not interfere with the effort of lifting and maintaining balance.

Atmospheric pollution
During the great London Smog of 1952 there were 2,000 more deaths than expected for the time of year. The main irritant in polluted city air is sulphur dioxide, a major cause of chronic bronchitis.

Wait for it . . .!
A really explosive sneeze can propel mucus droplets a full 20 ft (6 m). The narrow nasal passages concentrate the force of air.

some 40 times the external surface area of the body, or approximately the size of a tennis court! Lung capacity explains why we have greater stamina than many other animals. Humans, as opposed to other animals, can do heavy muscular work for hours without stopping. Other animals such as frogs may be frisky for short periods but they cannot sustain rapid movement. A frog's 'respiratory exchange' area is not much bigger than the skin's surface area.

But we have to breathe in a large volume of air to get the oxygen we want. The earth's atmosphere contains 5,000 million million tons of gas but only 20.95 per cent is oxygen; almost all the rest is nitrogen, mixed with very small quantities of other gases such as argon, carbon dioxide, helium, nitrous oxide, ozone and xenon.

An all-oxygen atmosphere is not at all desirable.

Cross references
Blood **100**
How the heart functions **81**
Releasing energy with and without oxygen **39**
Control of breathing **116**
How we breathe **117**

Olympic runners
like Steve Ovett and Sebastian Coe only indirectly depend on the ability of their lungs to swop carbon dioxide for oxygen. It is their circulation, the system that delivers oxygen to and removes waste from working muscles, and the ability of their muscles to burn glucose efficiently, which decide whether they win or lose.

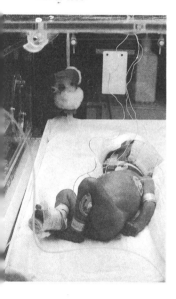

Oxygen—use with care
Oxygen may be necessary to sustain a pre-term baby with immature lungs, but the rate of delivery must be kept under strict surveillance. Too much oxygen can damage a baby's eyes.

Judging by experiments on animals, whose lungs were damaged after a few days' exposure to pure oxygen, we cannot live by oxygen alone, at least not at ordinary atmospheric pressure! It is possible in outer space but as the American space programme tragically showed, oxygen is a fire hazard.

Sneeze speed The amount of oxygen in the blood at any given moment is enough to keep a resting person alive for four minutes and an active person alive for one minute. Breathing rate varies with age, sex and muscular activity. It is faster in children and women than in men and is rapidly increased by exercise. One of the most astonishing features of the respiratory system is its ability to change pace in order to accommodate every sneeze, cough, hiccup, sigh or laugh. In fact the breathing rate accompanying a sneeze is four times faster than the world sprint speed record; the highest recorded 'sneeze speed' is a remarkable 103.6 miles (165.76 km) per hour.

Air intake When a world champion runner such as Sebastian Coe moves from a standing start into top gear there is a dramatic increase in air intake, heart rate and blood flow. The sort of changes which take place are these.
□ A 6-fold rise in the speed at which the blood circulates; the faster the blood flows, the greater the amount of carbon dioxide exchanged for oxygen in the lungs in a given time, and the faster fresh oxygen reaches the cells. Working at maximum capacity the heart pumps 40 pints (23 l) or more of blood a minute around the circulation. This supplies the body with about 1 gallon (5 l) of oxygen a minute.
□ A 3-fold rise in the volume of blood distributed to the active muscles; during exercise blood is diverted from inactive areas such as the digestive tract to the muscles doing the work.
□ An 18-fold rise in total blood flow to the muscles; for those interested in statistics, this is the first factor multiplied by the second, or 6 multiplied by 3.
□ A 15-fold rise in air intake; the number of breaths a minute increases by a factor of 2, and the volume of air taken in with each breath also rises.
□ A 54-fold rise in the volume of oxygen taken up by the muscles; more oxygen is extracted from the air we breathe in a given time during quick, deep panting than quiet, relaxed breathing. At rest every 0.18 pints (100 ml) of blood passing through the muscles arrives with some 0.03 pints (19 ml) of oxygen and departs with only 0.007 pints (4 ml), a 3-fold rise in oxygen uptake by the muscles. This 3-fold rise, multiplied by the 18-fold rise in total blood flow, gives the phenomenal 54-fold rise referred to above.

Lung structure

An indictment of industry?
Health conscious Japanese in many of Japan's biggest industrial conurbations have resorted to wearing smog masks in the street. Traffic police, especially at risk from the poisonous effects of carbon monoxide from car exhaust, are issued with oxygen masks.

Panting during strenuous exercise does more than increase oxygen supply; it also helps to cool the system, just as sweating does. We lose heat all the time through breathing and the faster we breathe the more heat we lose. Panting is a very efficient means of adjusting body temperature. In the case of dogs, who have no sweat glands, panting is the only way of adjusting body temperature.

Heat loss through breathing occurs for two reasons: first, because incoming air is heated up from atmospheric temperature to body temperature; and second, because outgoing air becomes saturated with water vapour in the moist warmth of the lungs. It is this water vapour that we see when we breathe onto a mirror; in fact we lose nearly 1 pint (0.56l) of water every day just through breathing.

Control of breathing

Breathing is regulated by nerve cells in the medulla oblongata at the base of the brain. These cells constitute a respiratory centre which responds to oxygen and carbon dioxide levels in the blood and controls the muscles involved in breathing. A high level of oxygen decreases the breathing rate; a high level of carbon dioxide increases it. This mechanism is so sensitive that the volume of air breathed in and out doubles in response to a rise of only 0.3 per cent in the carbon dioxide level.

The rate and depth of our breathing is normally adjusted automatically but we can override the respiratory centre and hold our breath or pant at will, but only for short periods, and never long enough to commit suicide. Normal respiratory rhythm can be inhibited by impulses from the cerebral cortex, a higher part of the brain. The ability to hold one's breath for long periods depends on many factors, not least mental state and determination. In 1959 Robert Foster, aged 32, stayed underwater for 13 minutes 42.5 seconds in a Californian swimming pool. But for 30 minutes before his descent he hyperventilated or breathed rapidly in order to breathe in extra oxygen. At the other extreme, oxygen deprivation at high altitudes can cause unconsciousness without any warning at all. This is something many pilots have learnt in the safety of a pressure chamber. If the oxygen supply in a pressure chamber is turned off, the 'pilot' loses consciousness; when it is turned on he recovers without any awareness of having blacked out.

Inside the lungs The trachea (windpipe) descends vertically for about 5 in (12.5 cm) and then divides into airways called the bronchi. These then sub-divide into much smaller airways, the bronchioles, which carry the air into the alveolar ducts of the lungs. The bronchioles open into the alveoli or air sacs, where oxygen is absorbed as carbon dioxide is released.

No one knows for certain how many alveoli there are in the average pair of human lungs, but there are many theories. Estimates include 300 million, 350 million, and even twice these figures. It is strange to think that humans have reached the moon before having charted the minutiae of the human body. The dimensions and capacity of the alveoli are awesome. Each alveolus is surrounded by blood capillaries so tiny that only one red blood corpuscle can pass through them at a time. There are some four to five million red corpuscles in a pinprick of blood. The space between blood and air during the exchange of gases in the alveoli is $1/25{,}000$ in (0.0001 cm). Design as intricate as this makes the marvels of microchip technology look a little ungainly.

During gaseous exchange in the lungs the carbon dioxide-rich, oxygen-depleted blood changes from dark red to bright red, a direct indication that the oxygen-carrying pigment, haemoglobin, has picked up fresh oxygen. Blood enters the lungs via the pulmonary artery and is taken to the alveoli in the pulmonary arterioles. The blood, now coloured a bright red, leaves by way of the pulmonary veins which take it to the heart and then into the general circulation.

High altitude Research suggests that a pilot's capacity for coping with novel or abnormal experiences in the air will be impaired if he

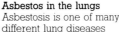
Cross references
Lung capacity **114**
Brain **50**
Composition of blood **100**
Circulation and distribution **104**
Muscles **36**

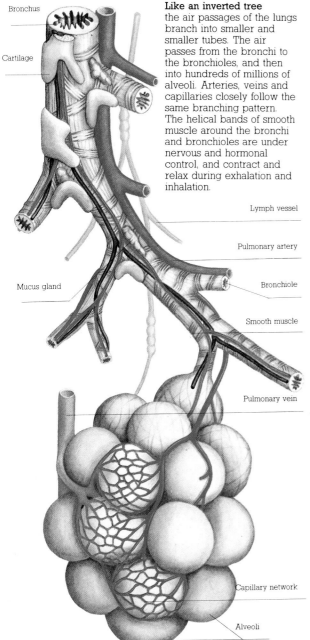

Like an inverted tree
the air passages of the lungs branch into smaller and smaller tubes. The air passes from the bronchi to the bronchioles, and then into hundreds of millions of alveoli. Arteries, veins and capillaries closely follow the same branching pattern. The helical bands of smooth muscle around the bronchi and bronchioles are under nervous and hormonal control, and contract and relax during exhalation and inhalation.

Bronchus
Cartilage
Mucus gland
Lymph vessel
Pulmonary artery
Bronchiole
Smooth muscle
Pulmonary vein
Capillary network
Alveoli

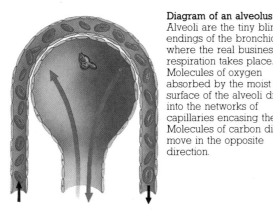

Diagram of an alveolus
Alveoli are the tiny blind endings of the bronchioles where the real business of respiration takes place. Molecules of oxygen absorbed by the moist surface of the alveoli diffuse into the networks of capillaries encasing them. Molecules of carbon dioxide move in the opposite direction.

Asbestos in the lungs
Asbestosis is one of many different lung diseases which come under the general heading of pneumoconiosis. Asbestos is a complex silicate of magnesium, calcium and iron and is inhaled as microscopic fibres. Once lodged in the lung these cannot be disposed of by the body's usual defences. However the effects of asbestos dust may take from 20 to 40 years to develop. The first signs are breathlessness accompanied by a dry cough and weight loss.

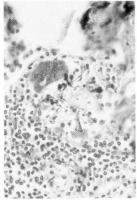

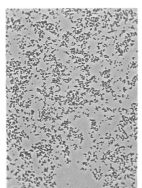

Rod-shaped bacteria,
Haemophilus influenzae,
attack the mucous membranes of the nose and throat for preference. *H. influenzae* can also cause pneumonia and meningitis.

Extra oxygen
is given when the lungs are unable to take up enough oxygen from the air, as in bronchitis or pneumonia when part of the absorptive surface of the lung is infected and out of action. High concentration oxygen is also used in resuscitation.

breathes ordinary air above 5,000 ft (1,524 m). Flying apart, many people actually live at much higher altitudes than this. Nairobi and Johannesburg, for example, are 6,000 ft (1,830 m) above sea level while Bogota is some 2,000 ft (600 m) higher. In cities such as these, the visitor may initially get out of breath climbing stairs but the body soon adjusts to the rarified atmosphere. Within a few days, the bone marrow manufactures extra oxygen-carrying red blood cells to absorb the available oxygen. The limit for permanent acclimatisation is believed to be about 3 miles (4.8 km) above sea level. Mountaineers have survived for short periods at higher altitudes without using oxygen cylinders. Mount Everest (28,798 ft or 8,777 m) was recently climbed for the first time without oxygen cylinders. Records are made to be broken, but this one will stand for all time and for two reasons: first, Everest is the world's highest mountain, and second, the summit of Everest represents the limits of endurance of the human respiratory system.

How we breathe

The rhythmic impulses of breathing, activated by the brain, are registered in the diaphragm, the sheet of muscle which divides the chest from the abdomen, and in the rib or intercostal muscles. As a result the diaphragm contracts and flattens and the intercostal muscles pull the ribs outwards and upwards. An increase in chest volume follows, pressure within the lungs decreases, and a vacuum is created.

Air rushes in to equalise the pressure. The diaphragm and the intercostals then relax, decreasing the chest volume, and air escapes back into the atmosphere. This process draws in more than 3,000 gallons (13,638 l) of air a day, 21,000 gallons (95,466 l) a week and 1.15 million gallons (5.3 million l) a year. If the diaphragm breaks down, the intercostal muscles are sufficient to sustain breathing. If *they* fail, then the diaphragm alone is sufficient—another of the many fail-safe relays in the body.

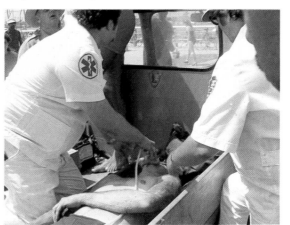

Lungs and respiratory complaints

For several reasons it is better to breathe through the nose than through the mouth. First, the nose can smell the air it breathes in, the smell-perceiving cells being high up in the nasal cavity. Second, the nose has a built-in air filter in the form of coarse nostril hairs which trap large dust particles that might otherwise irritate the delicate lining of the lungs. Third, the blood which supplies the mucous membrane inside the nose warms incoming air. Even on a frosty day inhaled air, by the time it reaches the back of the throat, has been warmed to near body temperature.

The air is sucked down to the epiglottis, a little flap of skin behind the tongue which shields the airway from food and saliva. From here it gets sucked through the larynx or voice box into the trachea or windpipe.

The trachea is composed of a series of incomplete hoops of cartilage. These keep the airway open regardless of the position of the head or neck. If you try pressing your jaw down onto your chest, inclining your head onto your shoulder or even pushing your head back as far as it will go, you will still be able to breathe—the trachea is completely elastic. The first of these positions, in which the jaw is pressed onto the chest, is the most difficult in which to breathe. In fact there is a theory that Jesus Christ may have died from suffocation as his head fell forward from exhaustion and as his rib muscles and diaphragm ceased to work efficiently: as he hung from his arms, enormous strain was placed on these organs. This theory was advanced by Dr Brehaut of Algiers, on the evidence of crucifixions carried out during World War II. If his hypothesis is correct, those artists who have shown Christ with his head tipped backwards or sideways are wrong.

The right lung is slightly bigger and heavier than the left one, which has to share that side of the chest with the heart. Together both lungs weigh about $2\frac{1}{2}$ lb (1.13 kg). The tops of the lungs reach to just above the collar bone.

The lungs are most frequently described as 'delicate' and, nearly as frequently, as 'elastic'. Although the lung linings are delicate, it would appear that they stand up to the onslaught of city life surprisingly well. Professor Julius Comroe of the University of California has estimated that city dwellers ingest a daily 20,000 million particles of foreign matter. Fortunately the respiratory tract is lined with defensive mechanisms against trespassers. In the lungs themselves are cells called macrophages which engulf and destroy the bacteria and foreign matter that escape the coarse nostril hair and the fine hairs or cilia which line the entire respiratory tract. The cilia are intermingled with cells which exude mucus. Invaders trapped by the mucus are propelled up to the mouth by cilia to be either spat out or swallowed. Under the microscope the constantly moving cilia resemble a field of corn

Oxygen as First Aid
This man is receiving emergency oxygen for a severe myocardial infarction. Cases of haemorrhagic shock and carbon monoxide poisoning are similarly treated. The kind of oxygen mask used in hospitals can deliver oxygen in any concentration up to a rate of 10 litres a minute.

blowing in the wind. Elaborate as the lung defences are, there are still some foreign particles which elude them and settle permanently, in the lungs.

Complaints of the respiratory system

The common cold This is caused by a virus which infects the mucous membrane of the nose and throat, and not by exposure to wet or cold. Colds rarely last for more than a week.

There is no such thing as a cold cure, which may be depressing, but at least explains why there are so many different 'remedies' for sale. Many of these are useless, even as symptom relievers. The lucrative myth about the curative powers of cold remedies is perpetuated simply because a cold is actually self-resolving. Sufferers attribute their recovery to commercial remedies when the real credit should go to the immune system which fights to overcome the invading viruses.

Losing heat by panting
Rapid shallow breathing is a
very effective way of
vaporising water from the
lungs and cooling down. For
animals with furry coats, and
without the sweat glands we
humans have all over our
body, panting is the only
means of controlling body
temperature.

Low oxygen pressure
at high altitudes stimulates
production of extra red
blood cells. The inhabitants
of all the major mountain
ranges of the world have
extra red cells. Altitude
sickness—nausea,
dizziness—seldom occurs
below 10,000 ft (3,000 m)
and then only in the
unacclimatised.

Aspirin and paracetamol (acetaminophen) are
the only drugs worth taking orally for a cold; they
will not cure the infection but they might provide
relief. Analysis of the ingredients of many cold cure
mixtures shows that they will not reduce the
duration of a cold. In addition some of the cures are
dangerous and can be taken in more pleasant
forms. Here are some of the ingredients of
commonly available cold cure mixtures:
Caffeine Some remedies contain about 50 mg; a
cup of tea usually contains between 50 and 100 mg,
and a cup of coffee between 100 and 150 mg.
Caffeine stimulates the central nervous system,
increases muscular power and lessens fatigue.
Doses under 100 mg are unlikely to have any
significant stimulating effect.
Ascorbic acid (Vitamin C) An orange contains as
much as most cold remedies.
Promethazine hydrochloride and doxylamine succinate
These are anti-histamine drugs used mainly for
allergies. They can dry up a runny nose or clear a
blocked one. They should be taken only before
going to bed as they induce drowsiness and may
affect driving ability.
Pholcodine and dextromethorphan These are cough
suppressants and have no effect on anything other
than a cough.
Ephedrine sulphate This is a vasoconstrictor—that
is, it constricts blood vessels and can help a blocked

A Scuba diver
is unencumbered by airlines
or a heavy diving suit. His
breathing apparatus is self
contained and carried on his
back. Nevertheless the
pressure of the air he
breathes must be as great
as the pressure of the water
against his chest or his lungs
will not work. At a depth of
33 ft (10 m) the pressure is
double that at the surface.

Bronchitis, tuberculosis, lung cancer

Irritant dusts
inhaled over many years cause local inflammation of the lungs and the formation of scar tissue. Each patch of scar tissue represents a permanent loss of respiratory surface. At one time pneumoconiosis caused by coal dust was inevitable in miners. Preventive measures today include regular examination and a change of job at the first sign of trouble, improved ventilation, and reduction of dust by damping it down.

A lung examination
by the bronchography method. The right bronchial tree is outlined first and viewed from the front and side, and then the left lung is outlined and viewed obliquely.

up nose, but it should not be taken in conjunction with other drugs, in particular those prescribed for depression or heart trouble.

Alcohol Some cold remedies contain an amount of alcohol equivalent to a small glass of sherry. Alcohol and antihistamines enhance one another's sedative effects. Scientific evidence shows that alcohol has no beneficial effect on the cold, but it may help you to relax and forget about it.

Bronchitis and emphysema Bronchitis can be chronic or acute. Acute bronchitis normally lasts for only a few days and is followed by complete recovery. It usually arises from the spread of a viral infection such as a sore throat or common cold, with subsequent infection by bacteria. Chronic bronchitis is a disabling, killing disease that arises from persistent irritation of the bronchi. Approximately 20,000 people a year die from chronic bronchitis. Cigarette smoke is the most common bronchial irritant and the major cause of this disease. Other air pollutants such as dust and fumes also play a role. The effects of exposure to one risk can be intensified by exposure to others.

The characteristic symptom of chronic bronchitis is a persistent cough with sputum. The smoker may think that the phlegm he or she coughs up in the morning is normal. But it is not. Instead it is evidence of inflammation in the bronchi. The body responds to this inflammation by increasing the number of mucus-exuding cells in the bronchi. The mucus coughed up by a smoker is slime that normally lubricates and coats the air passages. In healthy bronchi, the mucus is removed by the cilia which sweep it up to the throat where it is swallowed in saliva. In chronic bronchitis the mucus is not removed because the cilia have been damaged or destroyed. So the mucus is coughed up instead. The combination of excess mucus and

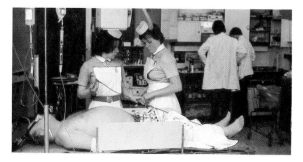

damaged cilia impairs drainage and promotes bacterial growth. Breathing becomes progressively harder as the bronchi become narrower and lung tissue is destroyed.

Just as an automobile will not fire on all cylinders unless the petrol combines freely with oxygen, so too the body cannot function without enough oxygen. Severe bronchitics may be unable to walk very far without suffering extreme discomfort. They may, in fact, be unable to walk at all and be restricted to crawling on their hands and knees.

Emphysema (derived from the Greek word meaning 'to puff up') is usually associated with a long history of bronchitis. It strikes at the air sacs causing them to over-inflate and eventually rupture. Consequently lung efficiency diminishes.

Pneumonia This involves inflammation of the lung substance, usually beginning with a resistance-lowering viral infection such as a cold or influenza. Bacteria, especially pneumococci which are found in all healthy mouths and throats, then invade the lungs. The inflammation causes fluid to exude into the alveoli which become waterlogged.

Pneumonia is classified further according to the target area. Lobar pneumonia, for example, affects the whole of one or more lobes or divisions of the lungs. Bronchopneumonia strikes at the alveoli

Cross references
Smoking **200**
Inside the lungs **116**
Cancer **228**
Immune system **110**

close to the large air passages, usually in both lungs simultaneously.

The three main bacterial causes of pneumonia are streptococci, including pneumococci; staphylococci; and the inappropriately named influenza bacillus (*Haemophilus influenzae*).

Tuberculosis The World Health Organization (WHO) estimates that tuberculosis kills as many as three million people a year, mostly in the Third World. The 'primary focus' of infection is usually situated in the lungs but can affect any organ.

Tuberculosis is caused by the bacterium *Mycobacterium tuberculosis*. This thrives on the debilitating effects of malnutrition and poverty. It can survive in dust for weeks and can contaminate still air for several hours, but cannot tolerate sunlight and fresh air.

The bacteria enter the body through the throat, the lungs or the intestines. In pulmonary tuberculosis, the primary focus produces an abscess. The body usually builds up fibrous scar tissue around the affected site; if not, the bacteria spread throughout the lungs and perhaps the whole body. The victim may spit blood, develop a chronic cough and find inhaling painful, sweat profusely, lose weight and appetite. Antibiotic drugs like streptomycin have greatly reduced the threat of tuberculosis, at least in Western countries.

Lung cancer Some 95 per cent of the victims of lung cancer, one of the most devastating of the cancers, are smokers. Sometimes cases are discovered from routine X-rays but usually the disease is diagnosed after it has become well established; in many cases it has already metastasised or spread to another site—usually the liver, the spine or the lymph nodes.

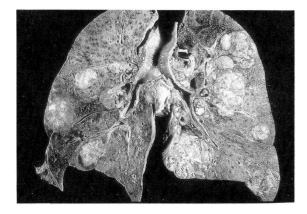

Cigarette smoke,
which contains several highly poisonous ingredients, has replaced other air pollutants as the main cause of lung disability. In restricted spaces non-smokers breathe in up to 50 per cent of the contaminants broadcast by those doing the smoking. For too many youngsters smoking still symbolises maturity and 'cool'.

Cancerous lung
Lung cancer is one of the commonest, nastiest and least curable forms of cancer, and probably the easiest to prevent. A post-mortem examination of a lung cancer victim, revealing the general devastation shown here, would probably cure most smokers. The black areas are deposits of tar. Cancer begins with degenerative changes in the mucous membranes of the airways which tobacco tars cause.

Bronchography
An ordinary X-ray often fails to show chronic bronchitis until it has reached an advanced stage, so a technique called bronchography is used instead. Radio-opaque iodised oil is introduced into the trachea and as the person breathes it migrates into the bronchi and bronchioles, making them opaque to X-rays. Here one can see the airways cut off by mucus and other obstructions.

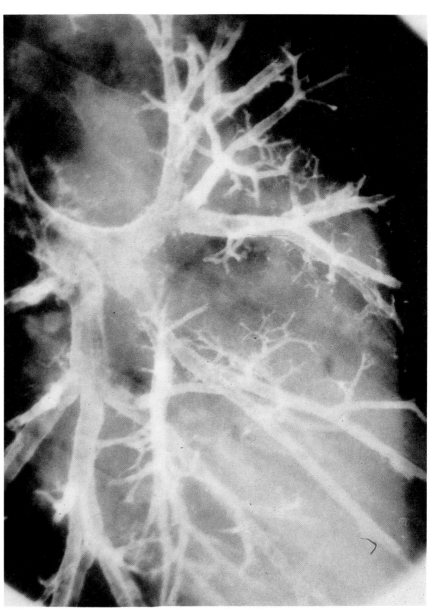

Digestion: journey to the stomach

The dis-assembly line
we call the digestive system employs both mechanical and chemical operatives. Compared with that of a grazing animal like the cow the human alimentary canal is non-specialised—it deals reasonably well with wide variations in diet. But it was designed to deal with more bulk and more fibre, and less concentrated forms of protein, fat and sugar, than the average 20th century Westerner presents it with.

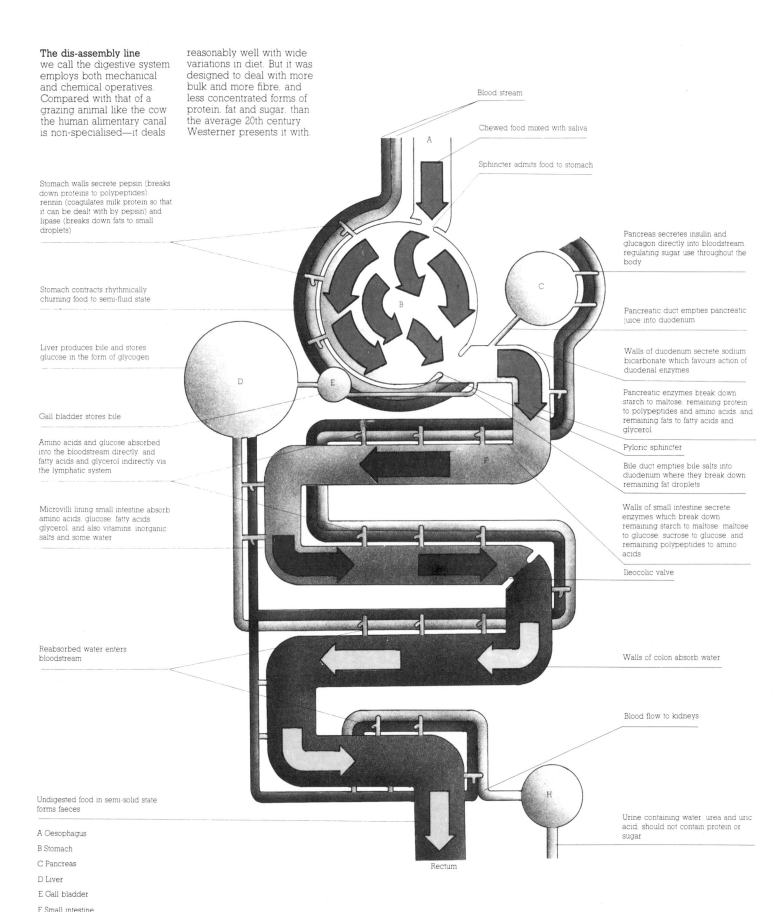

Blood stream

Chewed food mixed with saliva

Sphincter admits food to stomach

Stomach walls secrete pepsin (breaks down proteins to polypeptides), rennin (coagulates milk protein so that it can be dealt with by pepsin) and lipase (breaks down fats to small droplets)

Pancreas secretes insulin and glucagon directly into bloodstream, regulating sugar use throughout the body

Stomach contracts rhythmically churning food to semi-fluid state

Pancreatic duct empties pancreatic juice into duodenum

Walls of duodenum secrete sodium bicarbonate which favours action of duodenal enzymes

Liver produces bile and stores glucose in the form of glycogen

Pancreatic enzymes break down starch to maltose, remaining protein to polypeptides and amino acids, and remaining fats to fatty acids and glycerol

Gall bladder stores bile

Pyloric sphincter

Amino acids and glucose absorbed into the bloodstream directly, and fatty acids and glycerol indirectly via the lymphatic system

Bile duct empties bile salts into duodenum where they break down remaining fat droplets

Walls of small intestine secrete enzymes which break down remaining starch to maltose, maltose to glucose, sucrose to glucose, and remaining polypeptides to amino acids

Microvilli lining small intestine absorb amino acids, glucose, fatty acids, glycerol, and also vitamins, inorganic salts and some water

Ileocolic valve

Reabsorbed water enters bloodstream

Walls of colon absorb water

Blood flow to kidneys

Undigested food in semi-solid state forms faeces

Urine containing water, urea and uric acid; should not contain protein or sugar

Rectum

A Oesophagus

B Stomach

C Pancreas

D Liver

E Gall bladder

F Small intestine

G Large intestine

H Kidney

Cross references
Taste **65**
Endocrine system **66**
The reflex response **50**

The body machine is built from and fuelled by food, about half a ton (500 kg) per person per year. The fuel inlet is the mouth, the beginning of the 25-ft-long (7.6 m) digestive tract, which ends with the anus, the waste outlet. During the process of digestion food is first battered to a creamy paste by a chemical Armageddon, and then either burnt up to provide energy, built up into other substances that the body needs, or excreted.

Mouth and oesophagus

In the mouth food is either cooled or warmed to the optimum temperature for digestion, and chewed by the teeth. It is also moistened with saliva, a sticky lubricating fluid containing an enzyme, ptyalin, which begins to split starch into simple sugars. About 3 pints (1.7 l) of saliva are produced daily from three pairs of salivary glands, the parotid, submandibular and sublingual glands. The parotid glands, situated just in front of and just below the ears, are the ones that swell up painfully during mumps; the submandibular glands are a little below and behind the tongue; and the sublingual glands are underneath the tongue.

Food then passes down the throat to the gullet or oesophagus. The opening to the wind-pipe or trachea is closed during swallowing. Strong waves of muscular contraction, known as peristalsis, squeeze the food downwards. The process begins when 2 or 3 in (5–7.5 cm) of the oesophagus contract, setting off a wave which descends to the stomach at a rate of 1–2 in (2.5–5 cm) every second. The contractions are so strong that food would be forced down even if the eater were standing on his or her head.

Hiatus hernia The oesophagus passes through an opening in the diaphragm, the sheet of muscle that divides the thorax, the part of the body enclosed by the ribs, from the abdomen and belly. At its lower end the oesophagus is normally closed by a ring of muscle known as the cardiac sphincter. This muscle acts as a one-way valve, preventing the acid contents of the stomach from flowing backwards and irritating the oesophagus. If the opening in the diaphragm is enlarged a hiatus hernia occurs. In the case of 'sliding' hiatus hernias, which are the most common type, some of the upper part of the stomach slides into the chest when the person bends, stoops or lies down. In middle and late age hiatus hernia is extremely common, especially among obese people. The classic symptom is heartburn, especially when in bed at night; this is felt as a burning pain which may extend into the chest. The cause of it is regurgitation of acid from the stomach into the oesophagus. Only very severe cases require surgery. In most cases the treatment is to eat less at a time, take antacids and generally reduce weight.

Stomach: the acid bath

From the oesophagus, the food passes into the stomach, a J-shaped storage tank, positioned not behind the navel, as is widely believed, but much higher in the abdomen. In fact the stomach is actually situated under the diaphragm and is protected by the rib cage.

Most people think of their stomachs with warm affection, which is perhaps a strange way to regard an acid bath, which is precisely what the stomach is. For many hundreds of years it was believed that food merely putrefied in the stomach. However during the 1700s the French scientist René de Réaumur performed a remarkable set of experiments with a kite, a bird that regurgitates anything it cannot digest. Réaumur lowered small pieces of sponge into the bird's stomach and when these came up again he discovered that they had absorbed a liquid strong enough to reduce pieces of meat into liquid form. He had isolated gastric juice, a mixture of hydrochloric acid (strong enough to burn the skin) and powerful enzymes.

Very few bacteria can withstand hydrochloric acid and so the stomach is rarely infected by invading microbes, unlike other parts of the body. The acid is secreted by cells lining the inner wall of the stomach, which has a coating of mucus to protect it from corrosion. The stomach represents one of nature's finest self-protective achievements even though it is not widely recognised as such. It 'sterilises' the food we eat and stops the rest of the gut from being infected by bacteria.

The most important digestive enzyme secreted by the stomach is pepsin. Formed when a substance called pepsinogen combines with hydrochloric acid, pepsin breaks down protein foods such as meat.

The Russian physiologist Ivan Pavlov was the first to investigate the digestive secretion of the stomach and salivary glands in any detail, and his researches won him the Nobel Prize in 1904. Experimenting with dogs, he showed that the secretion of gastric juice is under nervous control from the brain. In man as well as dogs the smell or anticipation of food is sufficient to stimulate secretion. Nerve impulses from the brain act directly on the juice-producing cells in the stomach wall, but they also act on certain cells in the upper part of the stomach, stimulating them to produce the hormone gastrin, which in turn stimulates the juice-producing cells into production. Gastrin secretion can also be initiated simply by the presence of food in the stomach; the hormone spreads through the local blood supply coaxing all the juice-producing cells to start secreting.

Gastrin is just one of a growing list of gut hormones. Normally gastrin secretion ceases as the acid level in the stomach rises.

Absorption in the small intestine

Normal gastric juice secretions are controlled partly by nervous impulses triggered by the smell, sight or even thought of food, and partly by the sort of food entering the stomach. People with low acid secretion may be more prone than normal to intestinal problems such as 'travel diarrhoea'.

The flow of food from the stomach to the duodenum varies according to its chemical composition. Carbohydrate-rich foods pass through within a few hours; protein-rich foods take longer; and fatty foods may take several hours.

The remarkable adaptability of the body is demonstrated by the fact that people can still digest their food reasonably well even if the entire stomach has been removed.

Peptic ulcers These can arise from over-secretion of acid and they cause erosions or holes in the lining of the oesophagus, the stomach, or the duodenum (the first part of the small intestine).

Ulcers occur probably through bad eating habits, including eating irregularly and eating over-refined 'junk' foods. They are uncommon in countries where traditional foodstuffs are still eaten in their natural state. Peptic ulcers can be acute or chronic. Acute peptic ulcers can develop within a few days and heal within two or three weeks, while chronic peptic ulcers may last for months. Nearly 10 per cent of men suffer from a peptic ulcer at some time before the age of 50, but women are less vulnerable. Peptic ulcers are associated with stress and can be aggravated by smoking.

Peristalsis continues even if you stand on your head. Muscular contraction in the various parts of the alimentary canal is not dependent on gravity. In fact the occasional inversion may even be beneficial, producing a slight shift in the abdominal contents.

Small intestine

The small intestine or small bowel is a long convoluted winding tube leading to the colon or large intestine. The first part, the duodenum, is a C-shaped tube 8–10 in (20–25 cm) long. It encircles the pancreas, passes behind the liver, in front of the right kidney and across the aorta, the body's largest artery. The second part of the small intestine is called the jejenum. It is about 8 ft (2.4 m) long and lies in the region underneath the navel. The third part of the small intestine, the ileum, is 12 ft (3.6 m) long, and winds down to the caecum, the first part of the colon or large bowel.

The small intestine is therefore about 21 ft (6.4 m) long and is a good example of compact biological design. But the inner surface area of the small intestine is an even better example; it has an inner surface about 200 sq ft (18.6 m²) in the average adult and is therefore some ten times bigger than the total surface area of the skin. The area is enlarged by millions of tiny finger-like projections called villi (from the Latin word *villus* meaning 'tuft of hair'), which protrude from the intestinal lining. Resembling a fine velvet-like carpet, these countless microscopic structures separate valuable particles such as protein, fat and sugar from waste material such as cellulose, an indigestible

ingredient found in all fruits and vegetables.

Before this happens, however, the partly digested food, or chyme, runs the gauntlet of the duodenum where it is bombarded by bile from the liver and digestive juices from the pancreas. Chyme entering the duodenum from the stomach contains a large proportion of hydrochloric acid, which is neutralised by the bicarbonate, an alkaline substance, in pancreatic juice. This juice also contains three enzymes—lipase, trypsin and amylase—which break down fats, proteins and starch respectively into small molecules ready for absorption by the villi.

People with coeliac disease do not have this carpet of villi. Their intestine is smooth, with a small surface area. Because food cannot be efficiently absorbed they show all the signs of malnutrition. Some 26,000 people are thought to have the disease in the United Kingdom alone. Once regarded as a disease of early childhood, it is increasingly diagnosed in adults. Many sufferers cannot tolerate gluten, a protein found in wheat flour; gluten actually stunts the growth of villi in

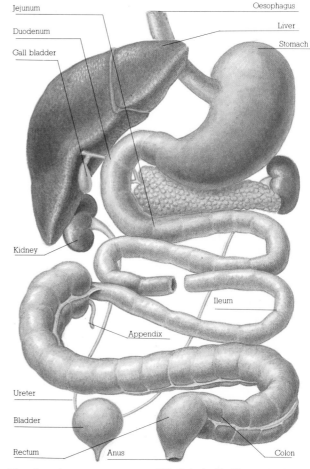

The digestive organs fill almost the entire abdominal cavity from the diaphragm to the floor of the pelvis. By far the largest amount of space is taken up by the small intestine, all

21 ft (6.4 m) of it. The contents of the abdomen are largely protected by the greater omentum, a four-layered apron of fatty tissue hanging down from the greater curvature of the stomach.

Cross references
Diet **187**
Stress **162**
Taste **65**
Sense of smell **62**

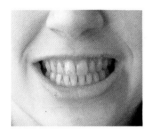

Cutters and grinders
The incisor and canine teeth at the front of the mouth do the cutting and the premolars and molars the grinding. Unfortunately foods containing acids and sugars are potentially damaging to the enamel of the teeth. Plaque, a mixture of saliva, bacteria and food debris, often starts the decay process, leading to caries and hard tartar. Disclosure tablets can be used to reveal deposits of plaque; in this picture plaque areas show up as pink.

the small intestine, but on a gluten-free diet the villi recover and absorb normally.

As fats descend into the duodenum the gall bladder contracts, expelling bile formed in the liver. Bile salts break down or emulsify fats in much the same way as detergents break down grease. Once they are in droplet form fats can be dealt with by various enzymes.

The digestive processes in the small intestine are regulated by hormones, chemical messengers secreted into the blood. The appearance of food and hydrochloric acid in the duodenum, for example, stimulates the release of the intestinal hormones secretin and pancreozymin. These in their turn stimulate the release of pancreatic juice. Bile flow from the gall bladder follows the release of cholecystokinin, another intestinal hormone.

Absorption Digestion is completed in the small intestine and virtually all absorption occurs there. Every day some 2½ gals (11.5 l) of digested food, liquids and gastrointestinal secretions flow through the digestive tract, but only ⅕ pint (about 100 ml)

is lost in the faeces. Before it is absorbed by the villi the chyme is broken down into constituent parts: proteins into amino acids, the body's building blocks; fats into fatty acids and glycerol; and carbohydrates into glucose.

The tiny amino acid and glucose molecules pass into the cells lining the villi and then into the small blood vessels which drain them. These vessels run into larger ones which eventually lead to the liver, where the products of digestion are broken down further and either stored or built up again for use by the body's cells.

Absorption in the small intestine is often an active, energy-consuming process. Most active absorption occurs rapidly in the central section of the small intestine, the jejunum. Here chemical pumps transport molecules of protein and sugar into the cells of the villus lining. Sometimes sodium ions act as carriers, and are then pumped back into the intestine to repeat the process.

Inorganic nutrients in particular tend to diffuse into the villi without active help. This is because more of these molecules are found in the intestine

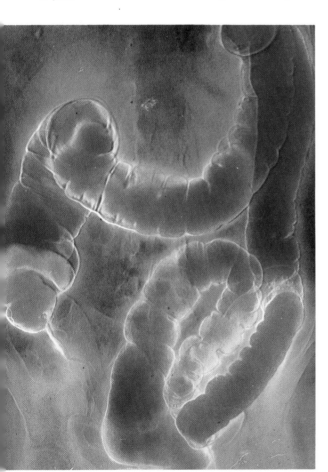

Up, around and down,
the colon forms the last lap of the digestive tract. The appendix can be seen at bottom left, close to the point of entry of the small

intestine. The haustra or pouches all along the length of the colon contain the faeces, eventually expelled through the rectum and anus.

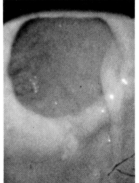

A stomach ulcer
develops when hydrochloric acid corrodes the mucous lining of the stomach. In such a situation the protein-destroying enzyme pepsin—not activated until it mixes with acid in the stomach cavity—starts eating away the wall of the stomach. However the mucous lining repairs itself very quickly, so small breaches seldom lead to ulcers. Stress, which can cause acid secretion even when the stomach is empty, is an important factor in the development of ulcers, of which stomach ache, heartburn and nausea are common symptoms.

The digestive tract
has the same basic structure throughout, with refinements. Steady throughput is maintained by the action of longitudinal and circular layers of muscle; the mucous lining of the whole system protects it from corrosion by acids and alkalis; glands in every part of the system except the colon pour fluid or enzymes into the gut cavity. The villi in the small intestine are a special adaptation: they secrete as well as absorb. The highly folded walls of the colon are another adaptation: they absorb only.

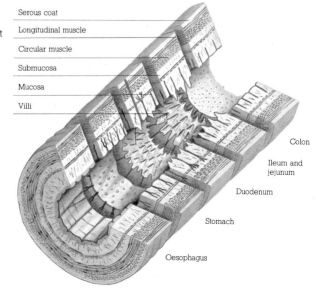

Serous coat
Longitudinal muscle
Circular muscle
Submucosa
Mucosa
Villi

Colon
Ileum and jejunum
Duodenum
Stomach
Oesophagus

Digestion: the final stages

than in the cells lining the villi, a difference in osmotic pressure always causes molecules in the more concentrated environment to move into the less concentrated. Blood flow in the villi keeps the concentration of nutrients in them low at all times to aid absorption, but not so low that molecules flood the bloodstream in quantities the body cannot cope with.

Fats are taken care of in a different way. Though the smaller fat molecules are absorbed straight into the bloodstream, the larger ones move into special channels inside the villi, the lacteals. These communicate with the lymphatic system, and as the villi contract and relax fat molecules in the lacteals are pumped into it. This is why lymph has a somewhat milky appearance.

Fats do not normally mix with water, but after reaction with lipase fat droplets in the intestine form tiny parcels known as micelles; these have a fatty inside but a water soluble outside, and are either dissolved in the membranes of the cells lining the villi or engulfed by them. Once inside the villi the micelles are rewrapped in a protein coat and released into the lacteals, and eventually into the lymphatic system and bloodstream.

All in all, the villi of the small intestine are extremely efficient absorption machines: only five per cent of fats and ten per cent of proteins escape.

Unlike the stomach the small intestine is a fairly comfortable environment for bacteria. These colonise the intestine within two or three days of birth. Some fungi are also present. In fact the fluid in the ileum contains between 1,000 and 1,000,000 micro-organisms per millilitre, but the nature of the bacteria population changes towards the large intestine. Except when the walls of the intestine or colon are damaged, these microscopic residents are quite benign.

Large intestine

It could be argued that the large intestine is inappropriately named since it is only 5 ft (1.5 m) long, 15 ft (4.6 m) shorter than the small intestine; but with a diameter of 2½ in (6.5 cm) it is three times wider. And if the universal use of laxatives is any guide, it is also of enormous concern to millions of people.

The large intestine is divided into the caecum, the colon and the rectum. Although associated with defaecation, the large intestine is not only concerned with excreting solid waste. Bacteria within the faeces synthesise several vitamins, including Vitamin K, which is used by the liver to produce substances to promote blood clotting.

The boundary between the small and large intestines is marked by the ileocolic valve which controls the flow of the chyme into the caecum and prevents it from flowing backwards. The downward flow is restricted to about 2 ml at a time.

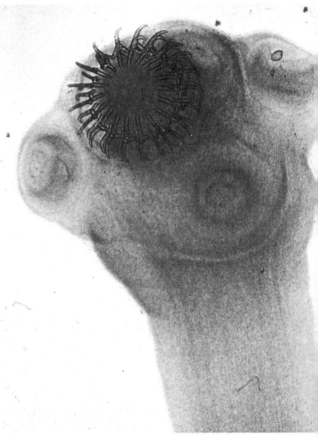

Head of a pork tapeworm *Taenia solium*, one of many parasites which find the human digestive tract an inviting habitat for part of their life cycle. Rich in dissolved nutrients, the gut is an ideal environment for parasites, provided they do not get swept away in the faeces. The head of this tapeworm, with its four large suckers equipped with twin row of hooks, makes an excellent anchor.

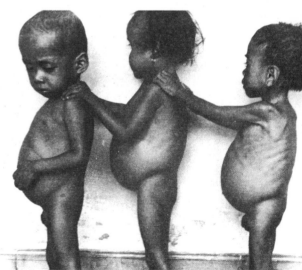

Inadequate nutrition leads to many different clinical conditions but a combination of protein and energy malnutrition (PEM), especially in the post-weaning period, leads to the condition seen in these Indonesian children: marasmus. Prominent bones and a swollen belly are typical of marasmus; only first-born children can stand upright unaided.

Cross references
Liver **128**
Pancreas **131**
Diet **187**
Putting bacteria to work **238**

Chyme, a mixture of water, intestinal secretions, undigested and indigestible substances, is gradually turned into faecal matter in the colon. The colon reabsorbs, and so saves, a lot of water which goes back into the bloodstream; as a result the faeces gradually become semi-solid. In fact all land-dwelling life forms are extraordinarily good at conserving water by reabsorption.

The appendix is a narrow blind tube issuing from the caecum about 1¼ in (3 cm) below the ileocolic valve. It is normally about 3 in (8 cm) long but tends to get smaller in adult life. Its correct name is the vermiform appendix, a reference to its worm-like shape. Generally thought of as useless in man, it is extremely well developed in herbivores, harbouring colonies of bacteria which help them to digest the cellulose in plant material. It could be that the human digestive system no longer needs this component, but its excellent links with the bloodstream and lymphatic system suggest that it might not be completely redundant; it could be involved in the immune system.

It is when the appendix becomes infected that its significance becomes least enigmatic. Every year thousands of people, most of them between the ages of 5 and 30, have their appendix removed. Acute infection and inflammation only occur if the entrance to the appendix becomes blocked. Since a burst appendix is fatal, surgery must be done immediately. Only 1 in 100,000 people die from appendicitis nowadays, but many more lose their appendix on the 'better safe than sorry' principle.

The journey through the large intestine is eased by mucus-secreting glands lining the walls; the lubricant they release also protects the walls from attack by any remaining digestive enzymes. The muscular walls of the colon contract, bunching it up into a large number of bulbous pouches known as haustra. As they fill up with faecal matter the haustra are relaxed and stretched; subsequently they contract, forcing their increasingly solid cargo towards the rectum.

Peristaltic movement in the large intestine is different from that which occurs higher up in the digestive tract because it occurs only three or four times a day, usually during or soon after a meal. Thus, what is known as 'mass movement' tends to be precipitated by the entry of food into the stomach. This process forces the faecal matter towards the terminal part of the colon. It may then move into the rectum, so stimulating the nerve endings in the rectal walls. This will initiate muscular action which culminates in defaecation.

Although absorption of water takes place in the large intestine, water still accounts for about 60 per cent of the weight of the faeces. Bacteria represent about 30 per cent of dry weight. The remainder consists of indigestible cellular material, dead cells from the intestinal lining and mucus secreted by the lining of the large intestine.

In the Western world the average weight of the daily stool is about 3½ oz (100 g), though weight increases if the diet has more vegetables, fruit and bran. The rural African or Asian, on a high natural fibre diet, may pass up to 16 oz (500 g) of faeces a day. It takes between 12 and 24 hours for matter to pass from one end of the large intestine to the other. In contrast, it takes between 2 and 6 hours for matter to pass through the stomach and a further 5 to 6 hours for it to pass through the small intestine.

'Passing wind' is the euphemism for voiding the gases—mainly hydrogen sulphide, methane and carbon dioxide—which are the natural by-products of digestive processes in the stomach and intestine. A normal bowel always contains a certain amount of gas. Flatulence, or excessive gassiness, causes distension and discomfort, and may be the result of dietary indiscretions, a digestive tract disorder, or the habit of gulping air with one's food.

Finally, it is worth saying something about the benefits of 'roughage', or perhaps 'softage' would be a better word. The colon is at its most efficient when it is relatively full. Roughage (cellulose, vegetable fibre, bran) is all food material which is not absorbed, and it makes the motions soft, moist and bulky so that they pass easily and swiftly through the bowel. This results in easy and regular defaecation.

Too little roughage in the diet can cause constipation, which in turn can cause unnatural contractions of the large intestine, which in turn can cause sections of the lining of the colon to bulge into small pockets, a condition known as diverticulosis. This is common in most older people in the Western world, but unheard of in African nations. It is especially serious if the bowel lining becomes infected (diverticulitis).

Solitary residence
is the general rule with human tapeworms, for the simple reason that there is not enough room in the human intestines for more than one at a time. The pork tapeworm shown here can grow to 25 ft (8 m) in length. Its somewhat commoner cousin, the beef tapeworm, grows even longer, though the maximum recorded length is 80 ft (25 m). Both species are acquired by eating undercooked meat.

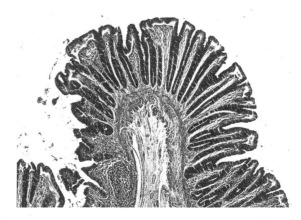

A microscopic section through the wall of the small intestine reveals millions of villi protruding into the cavity of the gut. These vastly increase the surface area available for absorbing digested food. Each villus has a central core of blood and lymph vessels, and a special surface membrane adapted for absorption.

Liver: structure and functions

'To you the lieur, heart and braine,' wrote William Shakespeare in his play *Cymbeline*. It is interesting but not surprising that the liver should take pride of place for it used to be known as the seat of love, passion and courage, hence being a coward was being 'lily livered'. However, the liver would be described better as the butler to the brain. It weighs some 4 lb (1.4 kg) in the average adult, is the largest and most versatile organ in the body, and has more than 500 different metabolic roles.

Anatomically simple but functionally complex, the liver is loosely attached to the diaphragm. It lies on the right side of the upper abdomen, largely protected by the ribs, and is composed of hundreds of thousands of polygonal structures called lobules. Each one of these lobules is packed with hundreds of roughly cube-shaped cells.

About 2½ pints (1.4 l) of blood flow through the liver of an adult at rest every minute. Unlike other organs the liver receives blood from two different sources: oxygen-rich blood comes from the hepatic artery and deoxygenated blood from the portal vein. This vein, which drains the digestive tract, the spleen, the pancreas and the gall bladder, is rich in newly digested nutrients. Having been broken down in the digestive process, these are then built up again by the liver.

Functions

Among its many functions, the liver stores glucose, the body machine's main energy supply, in the form of a substance called glycogen and converts it back into glucose when energy is required. The liver is also a vitamin bank; it manufactures cholesterol and blood proteins and blood clotting agents; it produces bile salts, detergent-like agents which promote digestion; it uses certain of the products of old red blood cells broken down in the spleen to build new proteins; and it also detoxifies.

Energy storage Food may contain very little actual glucose, so it is left to the liver to convert other sugars into glucose. If the cells require instant energy, the liver releases some of the glucose into the blood. The remainder is stored in the form of glycogen, a more compact substance than glucose—glucose would take up too much room if it was stored in its original form. When the liver's glycogen storage depots are full, the remaining glucose is converted into fat and carried to other storage areas. These include the area between the dermis, the inner layer of skin, and muscles. This layer of fat cells also helps to insulate the body.

As glucose is burnt up in the body, the glycogen in the liver is converted back into glucose and released into the blood for distribution to the cells. One of the liver's most important tasks, if not the most important, is to maintain adequate glucose levels in the blood and tissues. Glucose is the only fuel used by brain cells, which die within a few minutes if deprived of glucose. The pancreas controls the rate at which glucose is released.

The vitamin bank The liver's vitamin bank is so well stocked that a previously well-nourished person can function without showing any signs of deficiency for two to four years without B_{12} and for several months without extra Vitamin A. Vitamins B, D, E and K are also stored in the liver. Cod liver oil and halibut liver oil are rich sources of Vitamin A and D.

Blood manufacture The liver manufactures most of the blood proteins and blood-clotting agents such as fibrinogen and prothrombin. During bleeding, fibrinogen is converted into threads of fibrin which bind blood cells into a semi-solid mass. Prothrombin is converted into thrombin, a clotting enzyme or catalyst.

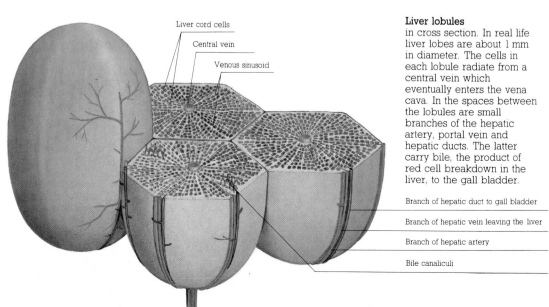

Liver cord cells
Central vein
Venous sinusoid

Liver lobules
in cross section. In real life liver lobes are about 1 mm in diameter. The cells in each lobule radiate from a central vein which eventually enters the vena cava. In the spaces between the lobules are small branches of the hepatic artery, portal vein and hepatic ducts. The latter carry bile, the product of red cell breakdown in the liver, to the gall bladder.

Branch of hepatic duct to gall bladder

Branch of hepatic vein leaving the liver

Branch of hepatic artery

Bile canaliculi

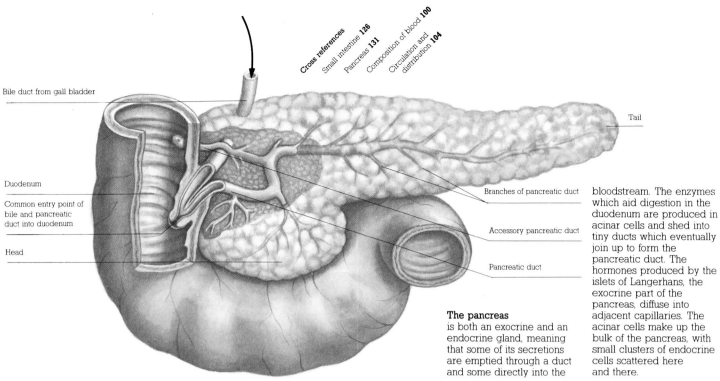

Bile duct from gall bladder

Duodenum

Common entry point of bile and pancreatic duct into duodenum

Head

Tail

Branches of pancreatic duct

Accessory pancreatic duct

Pancreatic duct

The pancreas
is both an exocrine and an endocrine gland, meaning that some of its secretions are emptied through a duct and some directly into the bloodstream. The enzymes which aid digestion in the duodenum are produced in acinar cells and shed into tiny ducts which eventually join up to form the pancreatic duct. The hormones produced by the islets of Langerhans, the exocrine part of the pancreas, diffuse into adjacent capillaries. The acinar cells make up the bulk of the pancreas, with small clusters of endocrine cells scattered here and there.

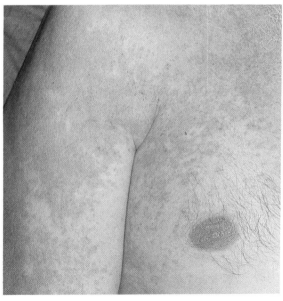

A chemical factory
is equipped to carry out many different fractionating, purifying and manufacturing processes. The liver is the body's central chemical factory, intimately involved in the manufacture of blood proteins and clotting factors, metabolising sugars and de-activating poisons.

Jaundice means yellow
staining of the skin, eyes and body secretions with the bile pigment bilirubin. There are at least a hundred different causes of jaundice. However, the three commonest types of jaundice are: haemolytic jaundice, in which excess bilirubin is due to excessive destruction of red blood cells, as in haemolytic anaemia; liver cell jaundice, in which the liver cells themselves become poisoned or infected; and obstructive jaundice, in which the bile ducts become blocked by gallstones or tumours.

Torture of Prometheus
As punishment for having stolen the secret of fire the gods condemned Prometheus to have his liver eternally pecked at by an eagle. Were the Greeks of 550 B.C. aware of the regenerative powers of the liver, or were they indulging in poetic fancy? Even if two-thirds of its cells are destroyed the liver is capable of completely regenerating them.

Gall bladder and pancreas

Hippocrates's views
on the subject of bile
persisted in some quarters
right up until the 18th
century. Bile was one of the
four 'humours' of the body,
together with blood, choler
and phlegm. Believed to be
one of the toxic products of
digestion, bile was also
regarded as the cause of
'melancholia' or depression.

About 2 pints (1.1 l) of bile a day are produced to excrete liver waste and to promote digestion by breaking down food in the intestine. The biochemical thrift involved in this process is quite marvellous—two tasks at opposite ends of the metabolic spectrum performed by the one agent.

It is not bile itself which breaks down fat globules in the intestine to tiny droplets but the salts which bile contains. These are formed from that emotive substance cholesterol, which, just to complicate the issue, is also one of the constituents of bile. The pigments which give bile its distinctive brown-green hue are made in part from remnants of haemoglobin from broken down red blood cells. Iron is also extracted from haemoglobin ready for recycling in the body.

In the industrial world the concept of recycling waste is relatively new. In the internal world of the body it is an established hallmark of success and nowhere more so than in the liver. The bile is first formed in the liver cells and then secreted into bile ducts. From these it is either carried directly into the duodenum, the first part of the small intestine, or into a storage tank, the gall bladder, which lies beneath the liver. When food passes from the stomach into the intestine, the gall bladder contracts, ejecting bile into the digestive tract. The bile breaks down food fats into tiny fat droplets in much the same way as soap breaks down grease when you wash your hands. Having done their job, 99 per cent of bile salts are resorbed in the ileum of the small intestine.

Gallstones These occur most frequently in people who make extra cholesterol which then becomes over-concentrated in the bile. Most gallstones contain some cholesterol; some are composed entirely of cholesterol; and others contain a fair proportion of calcium salts.

Cholesterol is now perhaps the most maligned fat-like substance in the Western world. It is derived from food, principally saturated animal fats, meat, eggs and milk, and the liver accounts for three-quarters of the body's supply. Cholesterol makes up one-eighth of the dry weight of the brain and it helps among other things to regulate the building and breaking down of cells. Cholesterol therefore is not quite the villain it is frequently made out to be.

Gallstones are found only in human beings and domestic animals and they become increasingly common with advancing age. Often they cause no discomfort and therefore evade diagnosis—in one large post-mortem study it was found that a quarter of the men and more than half the women had undetected gallstones.

Some gallstones gradually dissolve by themselves in response to a bile acid, chenodeoxycholic acid, which reduces cholesterol concentrations in the gall

A resin cast
of the blood vessels of the liver and adjacent organs. The white organ at the lower apex of the liver is the gall bladder.

Position of the liver
relative to the lungs and the stomach. The liver lies immediately beneath the diaphragm and is held in place mainly by pressure from the abdominal muscles and its attachment to the vena cava via the hepatic veins.

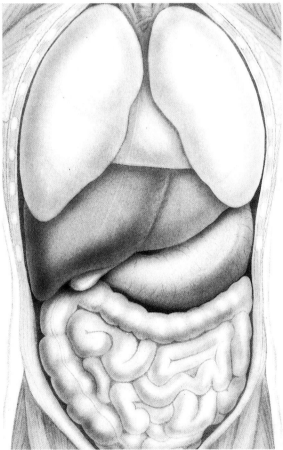

bladder. Painful gallstones can be removed surgically. They vary in size but a typical one is about the size of a pea.

Jaundice Jaundice, marked by a yellow discoloration of the skin, occurs if bile pigment accumulates in the blood. It is a sign either that too much pigment, known as bilirubin, has been formed, or that the liver cells are not disposing of bile in the usual way, or that the bile ducts are obstructed. If the cause is obstruction, no pigment reaches the intestine and the faeces are colourless; bile pigment derivatives are responsible for the colour of the normal stool. Obstruction will also

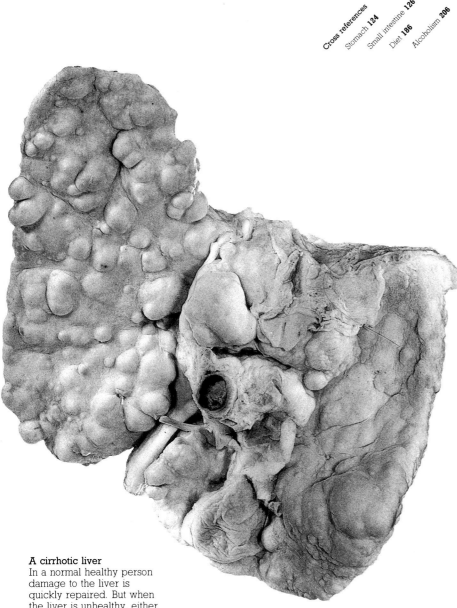

A cirrhotic liver
In a normal healthy person damage to the liver is quickly repaired. But when the liver is unhealthy, either because of chronic malnutrition or alcoholism, damaged tissue is replaced by hard yellowish lumps of scar tissue—cirrhosis comes from the Greek word *cirrhos* meaning 'tawny yellow'.

result in dark urine because the kidneys filter bilirubin out of the blood. Jaundice itself can also indicate damage to the liver, as in acute hepatitis, or the chronic illness cirrhosis. It is enormously important for the treatment of jaundice for the doctor to diagnose the cause of excess bilirubin correctly. If obstruction is the cause—usually with gallstones in the gall bladder doing the blocking or a tumour pressing on the bile duct—surgery is usually a satisfactory remedy. Haemolytic jaundice of the newborn is often treated by giving blood transfusions.

Cirrhosis Poisons, drugs and alcohol are neutralised by the liver before being passed to the kidneys for excretion. Although the liver is the body's detoxification plant it is easily damaged by alcohol. Damaged tissue is replaced by fibrous scar tissue resulting in a hard, knobbly liver. A person who indulges in a heavy drinking bout may put as much as two-thirds of the liver out of action, particularly if the liver is already damaged by too

high an alcohol intake. However, recovery is possible if existing damage is not too extensive. Similarly, if part of the liver is cut away, it will usually grow again. The regenerative powers of the liver cells are such that the liver can regain its original size within weeks or months depending on the amount lost. Neither the heart nor the brain have this extraordinary capacity to recover from surgical assault.

There are, of course, limits to the liver's tolerance; repeated exposure to excess alcohol in particular can cause permanent damage. In 1975 the costs to society in the USA alone, in health care, industrial losses, accidents and crime related to alcohol abuse, were estimated to be nearly $43,000 million. In USA deaths from cirrhosis, the fourth commonest cause of mortality among adult white males, now exceed 20,000 a year. France has the highest cirrhosis mortality rate, followed by Portugal, Italy, West Germany, Spain, USA, Canada, Sweden, Netherlands and UK.

Pancreas

The pancreas, a 6-in-long (15 cm) whale-backed gland situated behind and just below the stomach, is the major producer of digestive juices in the alimentary tract. Every day it produces as much as 2½ pints (1.5 l) of pancreatic juice, a clear colourless fluid. This fluid is directed to the intestine through the bile duct, the same duct that links the gall bladder to the intestine.

Pancreatic juice is alkaline and neutralises the acids entering the intestine from the stomach. It also contains many digestive enzymes, catalysts which control the breakdown of complex food substances into simple chemicals for absorption from the intestine into the blood. For example, one group of pancreatic enzymes activated in the duodenum splits proteins into smaller units called polypeptides. These are chains of amino acids, the building blocks from which cells manufacture new proteins.

The pancreas is alerted to incoming food by a message from the brain relayed via the vagus nerve. In its turn the brain is alerted by impulses from the taste buds. However, release of pancreatic juices is only partly under nervous control; it is also influenced by chemical substances produced in the duodenum in response to the arrival of acid from the stomach. This means that should one signalling system fail there is another to take its place.

Apart from its primary digestive function the pancreas is concerned with the chemical control of sugar in the body. This is done by secreting two hormones, insulin and glucagon, whose functions are complementary. Insulin causes cells to absorb sugar from the blood and glucagon does the opposite, acting mainly on the liver which is, as we have seen, a reservoir of sugars.

Kidneys and bladder

The hunger strike
was an important part of
Gandhi's civil disobedience
campaigns in
pre-independence India.
Today hunger strikes are
seldom off the front page.
Death from fasting, during
which the body may lose up
to half its weight, would not
be so protracted if water
were refused as well. With
prolonged fasting the
kidneys cease to perform
their usual job of regulating
blood volume by controlling
water loss. Water begins to
accumulate in starved
tissues, something which
does not normally happen
because protein
concentration in the blood is
high enough to ensure that
water is forced from the
tissues into the blood.

All life is aquatic and human life is no exception.
Although we do not live in water, the cells of our
bodies do. Water accounts for more than half our
body weight and ranks as our most important need
after oxygen. An adult man of average weight
contains about 79 pints (45 l) of water, two-thirds of
which is in the cells. Water maintains the size and
shape of cells and makes up some 90 per cent of
plasma, the fluid content of the blood. It is also the
medium in which all biochemical processes occur,
and it is vital that the composition of the body fluid
(Claude Bernard's 'milieu interieur') should remain
constant at all times.

The late Indian leader Gandhi and others who
have used fasting as a means of non-violent protest
have proved that we can live for several weeks
without solid food. Water is another matter—we
cannot survive without it for more than a few days.
We have to take in at least 3 pints (1.7 l) of water
each day to make good the water lost through
evaporation from the lungs, 0.5 pints (0.3 l); from
the skin, 0.9 pints (0.5 l); from the faeces, 0.2 pints
(0.1 l); and from the kidneys, 1 pint (0.6 l).

Kidneys

The kidneys are responsible for regulating the
amount of water, acid and salts in the body and for
ensuring that the body is not poisoned by an
accumulation of its own waste products.

The daily flow of blood through the kidneys is
about 425 gallons (1,930 l), but only about a
thousandth of this is converted into urine. The
remainder goes back into the circulation, a
remarkable instance of biological thrift. The
man-made combustion engine lacks components
for recycling fuel that is not completely oxidised;
unburnt fuel passes out of the exhaust pipe as
carbon monoxide and smoke. In the human body,
however, the kidneys ensure that potentially useful
substances are reabsorbed into the circulation.

The two bean-shaped kidneys weigh about 5 oz
(140 g) and are buried in fat. They lie close to the
spine at the back of the abdomen in front of the
twelfth ribs. Dark red in colour, they are about
1½ in (3.8 cm) thick, 2½ in (6.4 cm) wide and 4 in
(10 cm) long. However, these dimensions belie
their extraordinarily intricate design. Each kidney
is composed of a million or so nephrons or filters
which, if unwound and placed end to end, would
stretch for more than 50 miles (80 km).

Each nephron is fed with blood from the renal
artery by way of a tuft of tiny blood vessels called a
glomerulus (Latin for 'little ball') which acts as a
pressure filter. Relatively large particles such as the
red and white blood cells, the blood platelets and
blood proteins, are retained by the filter and
returned to the renal vein, while the filtrate enters a
bag of membrane called Bowman's capsule, named
after a 19th-century English surgeon. Access to this

capsule is restricted to substances and particles
which are small enough to filter through the walls
of the glomeruli. These include water, salts,
minerals, glucose, urea (waste from the chemical
breakdown of protein) and creatinine (waste from
muscle metabolism).

The filtrate, the basis of urine, passes into the
tubules of the nephrons where most of its water and
salt content is reabsorbed into the circulation.
During this process the tubules regulate the salt
and acid content of the bloodstream by an exchange
of electrolytes and hydrogen ions, a process
known as selective reabsorption. The concentrated
waste and fluid retained from this process passes
out of the nephrons as urine, travelling first
through a series of collecting ducts into a reservoir
known as the renal pelvis, and then draining into
the bladder through tubes called ureters.

Of the 300 or so pints (170 l) of water which filter
through the kidneys each day, only about 2½ pints
(1.5 l) on average are excreted in the urine. This
means that the tubules reabsorb more than 99 per
cent of water before it reaches the ureters.

If there is too much fluid in the body, the
kidneys excrete more; if there is too little fluid,
they do the opposite. During hot weather we
excrete less urine because we are losing more fluid
through the skin in the form of sweat. In cold
weather, the kidneys excrete more.

Selective reabsorption is controlled by
hormones, the most important being anti-diuretic
hormone (ADH) from the pituitary gland at the
base of the brain. In turn the pituitary is controlled
by the hypothalamus, sometimes called the 'brain
within the brain'.

The excretion of salt, an essential component of
all living tissue, is controlled by another hormone,
aldosterone, from the outer layer (cortex) of the
adrenal glands, which sit on the top of the kidneys.
If the salt level in the body is low because of excess
sweating or acute or prolonged diarrhoea, the
amount of aldosterone increases and the amount of
salt reabsorbed from the filtrate rises.

Under normal conditions glucose is completely
reabsorbed. In diabetes, however, the high level of
glucose in the blood means that more glucose
appears in the filtrate than can be reabsorbed and
thus appears in the urine. The volume of urine
increases to accommodate this glucose, leading to
persistent thirst, often a first symptom of diabetes.

The kidneys play an active part in the production
of at least three different hormones. For many
years it has been known that renin, a hormone
involved in the control of blood pressure, is
produced in the kidneys; erythropoietin, another
hormone produced by the kidneys, stimulates the
bone marrow to produce red blood cells. More
recently it has been learned that Vitamin D is
'activated' within the kidneys.

Cross references
Composition of blood **100**
Hypothalamus **66**
Pituitary **66**
Urogenital problems **219**
Adrenal glands **70**

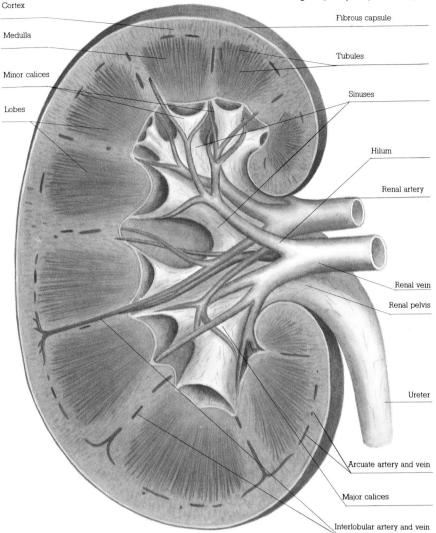

Cortex
Medulla
Minor calices
Lobes
Fibrous capsule
Tubules
Sinuses
Hilum
Renal artery
Renal vein
Renal pelvis
Ureter
Arcuate artery and vein
Major calices
Interlobular artery and vein

Bladder emptying
is usually a controllable reflex but the desire to urinate becomes pressing once the bladder is more than half full or if one is suffering from cystitis. Urgency may also be caused by the presence of stones in the bladder or by an enlarged prostate gland.

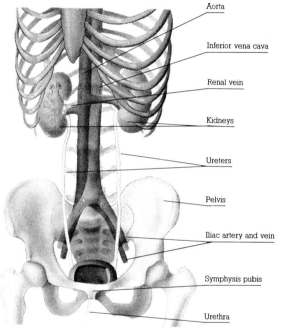

Aorta
Inferior vena cava
Renal vein
Kidneys
Ureters
Pelvis
Iliac artery and vein
Symphysis pubis
Urethra

Kidney: the filtering plant
Nitrogenous waste, the end product of protein breakdown in the body, is filtered out of the blood by the million or so nephrons packed inside each kidney. Because they regulate excretion of water the kidneys also help to regulate blood pressure, blood consisting of about 50 per cent water.

Bladder

The two ureters, which carry the urine from each of the kidneys to the bladder, are muscular tubes about 10 in (25 cm) long. When empty the bladder is shaped rather like a pear, but as continuous dribbles from the ureters fill it up, it becomes more oval in shape. A full bladder holds about 1 pint (0.6 l) of urine, although the desire to urinate, signalled by pressure receptors in the bladder walls, begins when it holds only half that amount. The bladder-emptying reflex is more likely to be activated during the day than at night, especially if we are physically busy or involved in a bumpy journey which shakes our insides about.

Bladder infection is common, especially in women, probably because the female urethra is shorter than the male one and therefore a quicker invasion pathway for infecting organisms. Cystitis, or inflammation of the bladder, is usually easy to diagnose. Symptoms include increased frequency of urination, a burning pain while passing urine and sometimes the actual appearance of blood in the urine. It can become a chronic complaint.

Urogenital system
The bladder rests in the pelvis, partly protected in the front by the pubic bones. When full it projects up into the abdomen. Urination is controlled by two sphincters, one at the exit from the bladder and the other at the exit from the urethra. It appears that only the latter can be controlled voluntarily. During ejaculation the sphincter vesicae, controlling the exit from the bladder, prevents the escape of urine into the semen and the regurgitation of semen into the bladder.

Urine, kidney disorders

Weightlessness
in space causes gross changes in the bodies of astronauts. Going into orbit induces redistribution of about 4½ pints (2l) of blood and fluid into the head and thorax. This inevitably produces changes in salt and water clearance through the kidneys.

Urine Urine is the raw material of numerous schoolboy jokes and folk remedies. Indeed it has been surrounded by almost as many fables and mysteries as blood. It was once taken orally to initiate monthly periods and to relieve toothache, and applied externally for chilblains and chapped hands. In Britain during the 16th century the so-called Piss Prophets claimed that they could diagnose disease by holding up a phial of urine to the light. And even today urine is one of the simplest and most revealing of diagnostic pointers.

The fact that urine is available in abundance and does not have to be extracted forcibly from the body like blood adds to its advantages as a diagnostic aid. Consisting of 96 per cent water and 4 per cent dissolved solids—the water is merely the transport medium for the solids—urine is usually straw-coloured. However, colour and contents can vary with food, with liquid intake and with health. Foods like blackberries and beetroot can alter the colour of urine, as can a disease such as blackwater fever, which produces brown urine. In jaundice bile pigments from the liver can produce a dark-coloured urine. In some other diseases the urine may become red due to the presence of blood in the bladder.

Drinking more fluid than normal dilutes urine, making it paler. During fever we sweat more and produce less urine, meaning that the fluid which is excreted is more concentrated, and therefore looks darker in colour.

Kidney disorders There are many different kinds of kidney disease, all of which are potentially serious in view of the kidneys' important role. The most common disorders arise from infection, various types of inflammatory disease, obstruction of urinary flow from the kidneys and inadequate blood flow to the kidneys.

Surprisingly many produce remarkably little disturbance of kidney function, but sometimes the kidneys may fail completely, leading to death within a few days. In some patients the damage is reversible (acute renal failure) and recovery may occur in a week or two provided the cause is corrected and the patient is kept alive by dialysis in the meantime. More often, however, the damage proves to be permanent (chronic renal failure) and the patient requires either long-term dialysis treatment or a kidney transplant.

Renal dialysis
or the mechanical filtration and purification of blood, is expensive, time-consuming and can lead to psychological disturbances. And because it is an intermittent rather than a continuous procedure kidney patients experience large fluctuations in their body chemistry. Kidney transplants and continuous dialysis, using a portable dialiser with a catheter permanently inserted into the abdomen, will eventually supersede machines like this one. One can only marvel at the compact design and complex chemical and pressure mechanisms of the real thing.

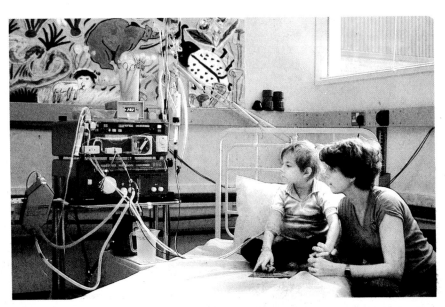

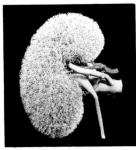

A resin cast
of a kidney, showing the many thousands of vascular bundles which form the medulla. The larger vessels are the renal artery and renal vein, and the ureter, which takes urine to the bladder.

On the road

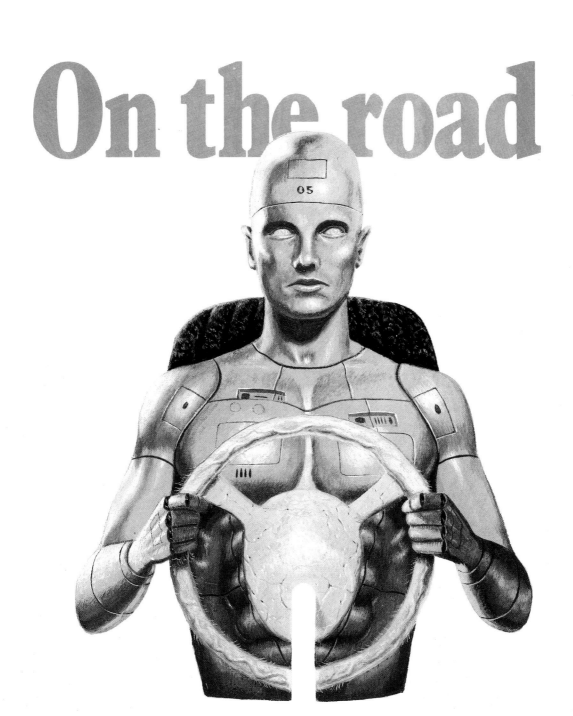

The developing foetus

The time of prenatal development is the period of growth about which, inevitably, we know least. Our ignorance begins at the beginning—with fertilisation. We do not know what forces are responsible for selecting, out of millions of sperm, the one which fertilises the ovum. After fertilisation in one of the tubes leading from the ovaries to the uterus, the fertilised egg spends several days in the tube before implanting in the wall of the uterus. During this time the cells divide steadily. About 30 hours after fertilisation the ovum divides into two cells; a second division occurs some 20 hours later, giving four cells, and by the time of implantation there are about 150 cells. At this stage the embryo is called a blastocyst. A series of changes affecting the outer layer of the blastocyst bring about the formation of the placenta, the organ which provides the developing embryo with nourishment from the bloodstream of the mother.

A point of incidental interest: blastocysts can be washed out of the tube for implantation in foster mothers. This technique has been used in animals to investigate the effects of different types of uterine environment, and to transport by air the foetuses of large animals packed temporarily in the uteri of small ones.

Spontaneous abortion This is a hazardous time for the developing ovum. Many ova do not develop normally, a greater number in fact than those which do. About ten per cent fail to implant and of those that do about half are aborted spontaneously, usually without the mother knowing.

Most of these losses are attributable to developmental abnormalities either of the embryo or of its nutritive and protective surrounding structures. For example, chromosomal abnormalities are found in five to ten per cent of fertilised ova, but in only 0.5 per cent of newborn infants. A foetus may be abnormal yet still be viable. This may result in a child with Down's syndrome, say, a condition arising from an abnormal number of chromosomes.

Assessing age Traditionally, for want of a better method, age is usually counted from the first day of the menstrual period before conception, on average two weeks before fertilisation, hence the term 'postmenstrual age'. Thus the most frequent 'age' at birth is 280 days or 40 weeks (38 weeks of true foetal age).

From embryo to foetus The embryonic period starts two weeks after fertilisation and ends six weeks later, by which time the child, now known as the foetus, is about 1¼ in (3 cm) long and recognisably human. The foetus has a nervous system which shows the beginning of reflex

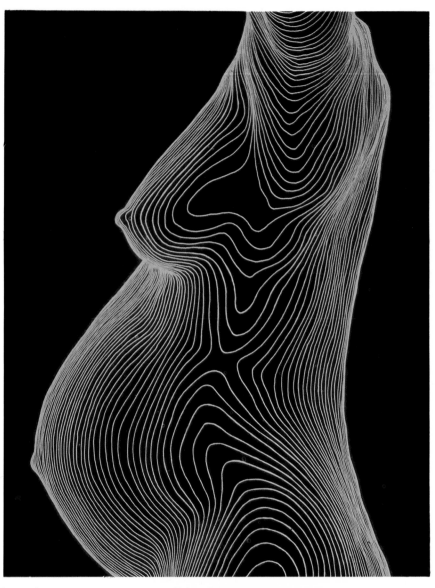

Stereophotogrammetry
This striking contour map of a full-term pregnant woman was produced from two photographs, each taken while parallel bars of light were projected onto her.

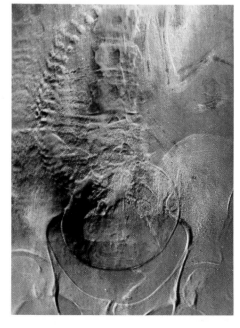

Radiography
showing the position of the foetus towards the end of the eighth month. The spinal column and skull can be clearly seen, the latter having already dropped down into the pelvis in the correct position for a normal birth.

Cross references
Fertilisation 20
Heredity 14
Genetic control of cell division 244
Cell differentiation 244

responses to tactile stimuli, a beating heart, arms and legs, and other organs such as the intestine, liver and kidneys, are also taking shape, as are the eyes, ears, mouth and nostrils.

Each area of the body is moulded into a different shape by a process called cell migration or morphogenesis; this lasts into adulthood and indeed in some parts of the body into old age. But most cell migration is complete by the eighth postmenstrual week.

Never again does the human body grow at such a speed as in this early dynamic phase. The pace of development is set by the speed of cell division or replication. As the foetus develops the proportion of cells undergoing division falls. Few if any new nerve cells (as distinct from the cells that support them) are believed to form after 30 postmenstrual weeks. Similarly, only a small proportion of new muscle cells form after this time. In appearance foetal nerve and muscle cells bear little resemblance to those of a child or adult; they contain a far higher proportion of water than mature nerve and muscle cells. In later foetal and postnatal growth the concentration of water falls and the cells enlarge.

During the first 24 weeks in utero (in the uterus) accumulation of protein accounts for most of the rise in foetal weight; thereafter the foetus stores considerable amounts of energy in the form of fat in preparation for the post-birth period. Analysing 36 foetuses of this age, Drs D. A. T. Southgate and E. Hay found that fat increased from 1⅛ oz to 15 oz (30 to 430 g) between about 30 and 40 postmenstrual weeks.

It seems that the pace of foetal growth slows down from about 34 weeks onwards as available space in the uterus fills up. This braking mechanism ensures that a large baby in the uterus of a small mother can be delivered successfully.

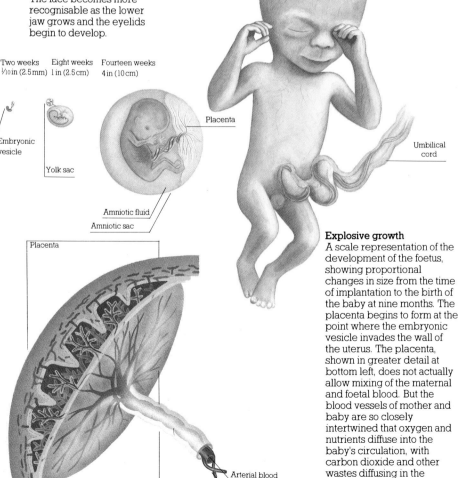

Three months old
and all the main organs and tissues have differentiated. The foetal circulation has been established and the intestinal loops are present. The face becomes more recognisable as the lower jaw grows and the eyelids begin to develop.

Two weeks
1/10 in (2.5 mm)

Eight weeks
1 in (2.5 cm)

Fourteen weeks
4 in (10 cm)

Embryonic vesicle

Yolk sac

Amniotic fluid

Amniotic sac

Placenta

Five and a half months
12 in (28 cm)

Placenta

Umbilical cord

Explosive growth
A scale representation of the development of the foetus, showing proportional changes in size from the time of implantation to the birth of the baby at nine months. The placenta begins to form at the point where the embryonic vesicle invades the wall of the uterus. The placenta, shown in greater detail at bottom left, does not actually allow mixing of the maternal and foetal blood. But the blood vessels of mother and baby are so closely intertwined that oxygen and nutrients diffuse into the baby's circulation, with carbon dioxide and other wastes diffusing in the opposite direction.

Arterial blood
Venous blood

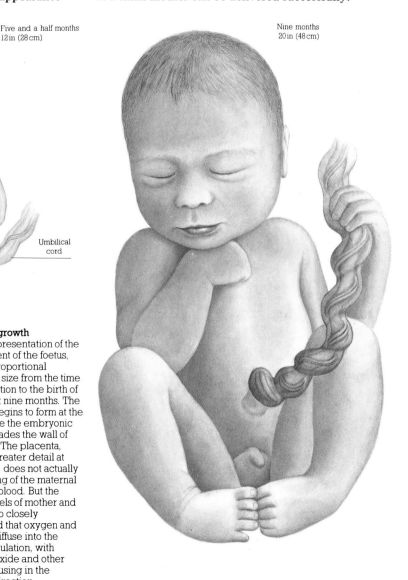

Nine months
20 in (48 cm)

Babies born before term

'Premature' babies We have noted already that the average length of gestation (from the first day of the last menstrual period) is 280 days or 40 weeks. Even allowing for errors and inaccuracies there are considerable variations, so much so that babies born between 259 days (37 weeks) and 293 days (42 weeks) are regarded as 'normal' or, to use the accepted jargon, 'term' babies. Babies born earlier are 'pre-term', those born later 'post-term'.

Until recently all babies weighing less than 5½ lb (2,500 g) at birth were known as 'premature', regardless of their physiological health and/or length of gestation. Now babies who are less than 5½ lb (2,500 g) at birth are known as 'low birthweight babies'.

Take the cases of baby Leonard and baby Peter. Baby Leonard, born at 36 weeks, weighed 5½ lb (2,500 g), a perfectly normal weight for his gestational age. Baby Peter also weighed 5½ lb (2,500 g) but he was born at 40 weeks, and his weight was outside the normal range for his gestational age.

Babies like Leonard catch up perfectly well without showing any adverse effects from their earlier exposure to the outside world. In fact, the development of a baby weighing 2⅕ lb (1,000 g) after birth at only 28 weeks can be maintained quite normally with concentrated milk preparations and intravenous nutritional supplements; the baby goes home eight or ten weeks later at the normal weight for a full-term infant.

However, so-called 'small for dates' babies, on average, do not catch up with babies in the normal range, though they may close the gap a little. Some fail to grow as tall as other children and may also be mentally impaired to varying degrees.

About a third of the babies born in Britain are both small-for-dates and pre-term; the lower the birthweight, the bigger the deficit between later size and ability. Babies who are between 4½ and 5½ lb (2,000–2,500 g) at full term show only a slight size deficit and little sign of impaired ability, whereas a significant number of babies under 4½ lb (2,000 g) have a neurological or mental problem.

Several different causes seem to account for small-for-dates babies. Malnutrition of the mother is one, though this has to be extreme to have any effect on the baby since the foetus tends to be protected at the expense of the mother.

Small-for-dates babies can also arise from maternal illness, particularly rubella or German measles. In some cases it is the foetus itself which is unable to grow normally.

Smoking mums Smoking in pregnancy results in a reduction of 5 oz (180 g) in full-term foetal weight on average, and a 30 per cent rise in perinatal deaths (deaths within 24 hours of birth). Some babies fall into the small-for-dates category as a

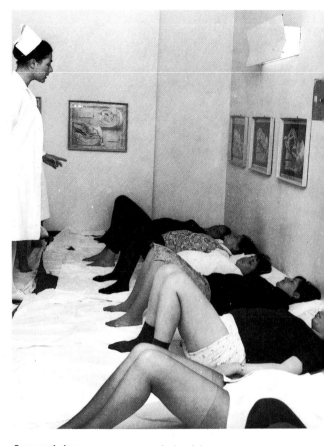

Antenatal classes are useful for exercising correctly to strengthen the back and abdominal muscles which come under particular strain during pregnancy. They are also important in teaching mothers to relax between contractions and to breathe correctly during labour. Research has shown that relaxation combined with mental rehearsal of the birth increases tolerance towards pain.

result of smoking-induced weight loss. The association between smoking in pregnancy and reduced birthweight is not fully understood, but it is believed that smoking affects placental blood flow and foetal nutrition. It is also possible, though less likely, that smoking has a direct action on the foetal cells.

Alcohol Alcohol may also affect foetal weight. Excessive consumption can lead to what is known as the 'foetal alcohol syndrome'. Described by Professor David Smith and colleagues at the University of Washington, Seattle, this is associated with characteristically poor development of parts of the upper lip, nose and eyes.

Ultrasound We know that the outlook for a small child following normal-length gestation is different to that of an equally small child who has had a shorter gestation period. We also know that early exposure to the outside world is not in itself necessarily harmful, and that an underweight

Cross references
Women and smoking **204**
Computer scanning **214**
Alcoholism **206**

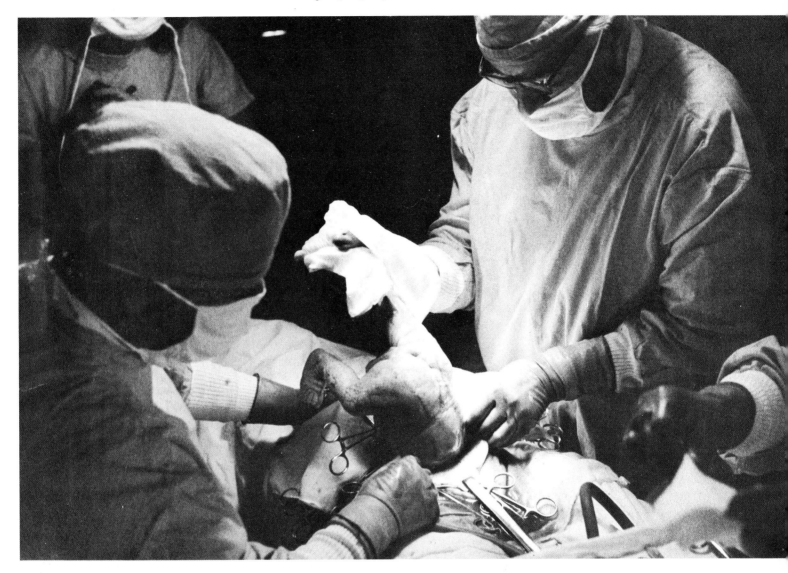

A Caesarean section, surgical delivery through an incision in the abdominal wall, is necessary when natural childbirth may jeopardise the survival of the baby or the mother. In such cases the baby may be too large to pass through the birth canal; be facing the wrong way (breech presentation); the placenta may obscure the birth canal; the baby may be suffering from lack of oxygen; the mother may be exhausted by a long labour and be too weak to continue without help.

full-term baby is less likely to achieve his or her full potential. And we also know that the worst time for small-for-dates babies is the tail-end of pregnancy when growth should be rapid. Many doctors are now recommending induction of such foetuses at 36 weeks, or 34 weeks in some cases. But how can such babies be identified?

The most effective means known is through ultrasound. This technique can be used to determine growth trends at any stage of pregnancy. Very high frequency sound waves—so high that they cannot be heard—are beamed at the foetus and echoed back. The time taken for the echo to return is measured. The size of the foetal head can be measured by scanning with a number of beams and feeding the findings into a computer. The print-out provides a kind of map. Similarly, though with less accuracy, ultrasound is used to measure foetal abdominal circumference and length from head to rump. Although it is a relatively new technique, ultrasound has already made a major contribution to our understanding of foetal growth.

It seems that more than 90 per cent of small-for-dates babies could be detected if all babies were measured from crown to rump between the age of 6 and 12 weeks, for head width between 13 and 20 weeks, and for abdominal circumference at 32 weeks.

At King's College Hospital, London, Professor Stuart Campbell, one of the pioneers of ultrasound, and his colleagues, followed up some 60 small-for-dates babies for an average of four years; foetal head growth had been followed from 30 postmenstrual weeks or before. The findings were unequivocal. At follow-up, babies whose head growth had been normal, or in whom rate of head growth had started to fall only after 34 postmenstrual weeks, were either normal in body size or very close to it, and normal in intellectual development. In contrast, babies whose head growth rate began to slow up before 34 weeks and continued thereafter were much smaller at follow-up and were found to be less well endowed intellectually.

Goodbye to the womb

Birth How does a baby react physiologically to the process of birth, an experience which for his or her mother can be one of the most fulfilling and exciting experiences of her life? There is no one simple answer to this question. Strange as it may seem to us in the outside world the experience is, as far as some physiological functions are concerned, an incident without special significance. It marks just another part in a steadily changing programme of events regulated by biological clocks. For example, the maturation of the nervous system seems to be unaffected by birth, judging by brain wave activity as measured by electroencephalograph (EEG). The EEG of a baby born at 30 weeks will be much the same five weeks later as that of a baby born at 35 weeks.

Similarly, the experience of pre-term birth does not precipitate any switch-over from 'foetal haemoglobin' to 'adult haemoglobin' (haemoglobin is the pigment which gives blood its red colour and is the means by which oxygen is carried from the lungs to the cells; foetal and adult haemoglobin have different molecular structures). This switch normally occurs in about the 36th week in preparation for birth, but it is not triggered by birth; the percentage of foetal haemoglobin is high in pre-term babies and low in post-term ones.

Cardiovascular and respiratory systems are the ones most altered by birth. Failure to breathe normally in the crucial period just after birth is a common cause of neonatal death and of brain injury among survivors. However, contrary to popular opinion, the newborn infant is better able to withstand oxygen deprivation than children or adults. Many neonatologists are inclining to the view that any failure to start breathing arises from pre-existing brain damage.

Following a study—one of the most comprehensive of its kind—throughout childhood of small-for-dates babies in Scotland, Dr C. M. Drillien commented that the most severe defects arise usually at an early stage of foetal development, rather than from damage during the last three months of pregnancy or during delivery.

However, it was also found that the behaviour of some children subjected to certain obstetric hazards differed from those who were born without difficulty. This might have been wholly or partly due to minimal brain damage sustained during delivery. Forceps are used five times as frequently in induced as in 'natural' births.

It should also be remembered that painkillers and anaesthetics taken by the mother during birth all pass through the placenta to the baby in greater or lesser amounts. This can result in a baby who is irritable and less alert and responsive to particular stimuli, which could be vital.

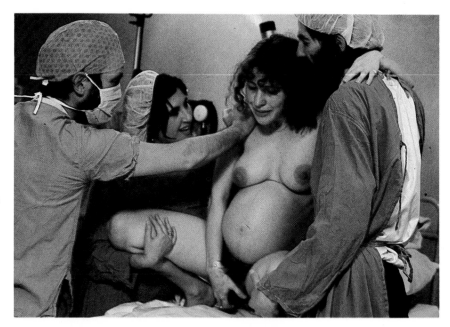

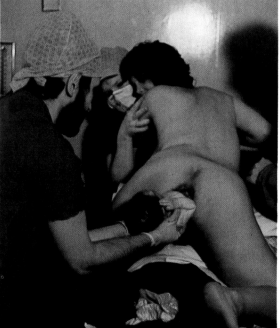

Giving birth sitting
or, better still, squatting, is now generally accepted as being easier for both mother and baby. Gravity helps the birth canal and cervix to widen, and also helps the uterus to expel the baby. An added bonus is that the mother can see the baby being born.

Less conventional
positions are always worth a try. Many doctors now think a woman should be allowed to give birth in the position she finds most comfortable. In past centuries women usually gave birth squatting or standing up. The supine position so widely adopted in hospitals is really for the convenience of hospital staff; for example, a forceps delivery is easier if the woman is on her back.

Birth is hard work
for the baby too. Some obstetricians insist that the trauma of birth should be alleviated by treating the baby very gently once it has been born. In some clinics dimmed lights, soft voices and soothing immersion in warm water greet the newborn.

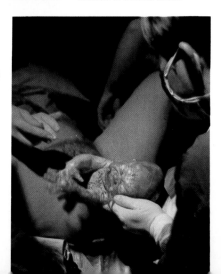

Cross references
Studying the brain **52**
Respiratory system **114**
Heart **81**
Blood **100**

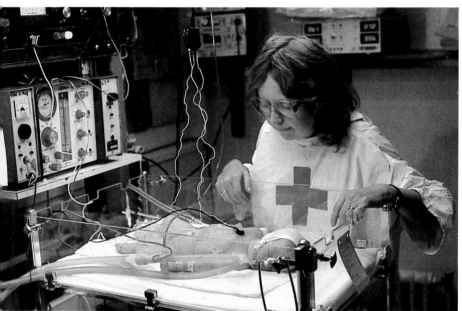

A premature baby
sometimes needs
specialised care to survive.
It is tube-fed on breast milk,
usually the mother's, and
kept warm in an incubator.
Its breathing and
temperature are also
monitored. Mothers are now
encouraged to cuddle even
very sick premature babies
as much as possible.

Having a baby
is just as important an
emotional experience for
the father, and most
hospitals encourage fathers
to see their babies being
born. Many fathers say they
feel much closer to their
wives and children
afterwards. They can also
give practical and emotional
support to their partner
during labour.

The first twelve months

Is he developing normally? Shouldn't he be walking by now? Questions like these are common and often reflect distressing parental concern. Parents may worry about a less than average rate of physical development or be proud about rapid development in one area. But differing rates of progress do not necessarily signify much—every normal child gets there in the end.

Growth is a target-seeking process. The passage of a child along his or her 'growth curve' is comparable to that of a missile directed at a distant target. Just as two missiles may follow slightly different paths and both hit the target, two children may have slightly different courses of growth but both end up with almost the same physique.

This self-correcting capacity was once thought to be a very special property of living things, but we now know that it is a property even of lifeless substances. The ability to return to a preordained growth curve after being pushed off trajectory, so to speak, persists throughout the growth period. If a young animal's growth is temporarily inhibited by starvation, development will speed up and overtake the normal rate when normal feeding is resumed. Rapid growth after a period of restricted growth is known as 'catch-up' growth.

Differences in rate of maturation are apparent even before birth and may be especially marked during adolescence. Some children play out their growth allegro, others moderato, a few lentissimo. It seems that heredity is to a large extent responsible for setting the metronome, but as we explain later, environmental influences also play their part.

Does growth occur in spurts or is it a smooth continuous process? Except during adolescence, which is marked by a dramatic growth spurt, development is more continuous than sporadic. This applies as much to motor development (crawling, walking, and so on) as to mental ability. This is why it is unwise to set hard and fast standards of growth and development.

The first year Never again will a baby grow so quickly as during the first year of life. Birth weight usually doubles within six months and triples within a year. In this short time the infant passes from a state of being unable to make any distinction (as far as we know) between himself and the rest of the world, into a smiling, playing, observant being.

This phase marks the beginning of a long period of dependence upon adults. Compared with other species—even with our closest primate relatives, the great apes—this period is exceptionally long. Indeed anthropologists have postulated that it is the key to human evolution and 'the cradle of culture'. In infancy and childhood we are far more receptive to learning than in adult life, and so by extending childhood more can be learnt.

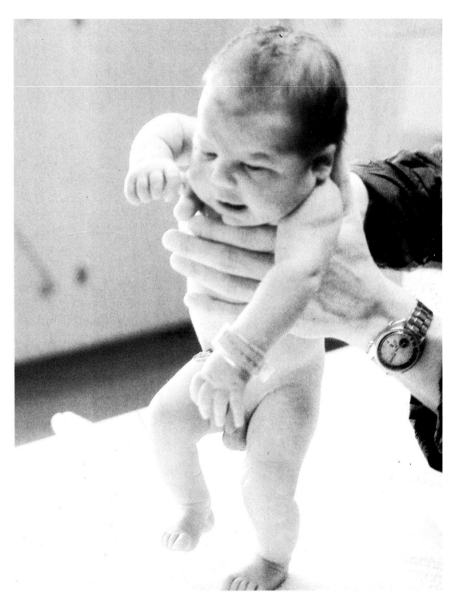

Human babies, of course, have far more to learn than dogs or cats, which master basic social skills within a matter of weeks, or newly born guinea pigs, which can run around and are almost sexually mature as soon as they are born. Such rapid development allows little chance for the passing on of skills from parent to offspring. By contrast human infants are endowed with very sophisticated learning abilities and if these are developed properly they form the basis of lifelong learning of new skills.

It is, above all else, our brain power which distinguishes us from other creatures. While maturation of the human brain is slower than that of other species, the brain develops earlier than most other organs. From early foetal life its weight is nearer to its adult value than that of any other organ except the eye. At birth the human brain averages about 25 per cent of its adult weight; at six months nearly 50 per cent; at two years about 75

The walking reflex
If a newborn baby is held upright with his feet touching a flat surface he will take deliberate steps, placing one foot before the other as long as his weight is supported. Within a few days, however, this reflex is lost and he forgets the motions of walking until months later.

Cross references
Heredity **14** Brain **50** Pituitary **66** Taste **65** Hearing **60** Seeing **58**

per cent; at five years 90 per cent; and at ten years 95 per cent. In contrast, the weight of the whole body at birth is about 5 per cent of young adult weight, and at ten years about 50 per cent. However, brain growth is not a uniform process—different parts grow at different times, which partly explains why development is quicker in some areas than in others.

Distinctions are often made between the development of motor skills, like crawling and grasping, and mental and perceptual abilities. But these things are closely related. An infant cannot reach out for an object until he has the visual capacity to do so, and until he can coordinate muscular movements. We are conditioned to think of our minds and bodies as separate entities and this mode of thinking is reflected in the way we evaluate childhood development.

Developing senses As the brain develops and the cerebral cortex increases in size, more areas of the body, and the visual and auditory areas, come under greater control.

Very early in life objects about 8 in (20 cm) from the eyes are seen most clearly—this is about the average 'face to face' distance when an adult holds a newborn baby. At the age of one month a baby looks at mother's face with increasing alertness during feeding; at three months the eyes follow slowly moving objects held 6–12 in (15–30 cm) from the face; at four months full 'accommodation' or focussing occurs; at six months objects are watched until they disappear from the field of vision and are then immediately 'forgotten'; at 12 months familiar people within a range of 20 ft (6 m) are recognised, and vision in all directions is well coordinated.

A newly born infant will 'corner' his eyes towards sounds. Experiments have shown that babies are far more receptive to the sound of human voices than to pure tones and household noises like gushing taps. In other words, they already possess special selective ability.

In his book *Infancy: world of the newborn*, Dr Martin Richards comments: "Selective attention to speech sounds has great advantage for infants because it leads them into our dominant mode of communication. Without this ability an infant would be truly a blank slate and it is hard to see that an infant would ever learn to speak and to understand speech. It would be a monumental task to sort out which sounds are part of human communication and which are irrelevant. A blank slate baby would be as likely to sing like the family budgerigar or bark like a dog as utter words in the second year of life."

Sweet tastes can be distinguished from sour or salty ones right from birth, although sweet ones are preferred (breast milk is sweet). Similarly, the sense of smell is well developed at birth.

Motor development Hold a newborn baby over a table and allow his feet to touch the surface and he will lift each leg up in turn and place it in front of the other, as if trying to walk. This is known, appropriately, as the walking reflex. Of course a newborn infant cannot walk because he cannot support his own weight, but he instinctively has the right idea—for a little while. Interestingly, these early movement patterns are difficult to elicit after a few months, and do not reappear again until the baby prepares himself for real walking. A baby may take his first steps as early as nine months or as late as 18 months. In this, as in any other area of development, the term 'normality' covers a very wide spectrum.

Between 16 and 28 weeks the most pronounced physical development is in the muscles supporting the head and moving the arms. By this age a baby may be able to sit unsupported for increasing periods, and can reach and grasp objects. Once again this is not a sudden development, but the culmination of practice in 'swiping' at things within close range.

Muscular development also encourages crawling and by 40 weeks most babies have refined a highly effective crawling technique which opens up new frontiers for exploration.

If handled too roughly your baby will snatch at your arms and his legs will curve upwards. This 'Moro' reflex is of no practical use to the human baby because there is such little muscle development, but it may be a legacy from our ape-like ancestors who may have clung to their mother's belly fur in the same way as this baby orangutan does.

Learning to speak

The importance of the establishment of the maternal bond early in life cannot be over-emphasised. A baby deprived of love, it seems, may grow up unable to respond to the demands of parenthood with love and affection. Studies of parents who physically abuse their babies often reveal the tragic effects of early maternal deprivation.

The confidence shown by a normal healthy one-year-old is determined in no small part by the strength of the maternal bond, and indeed by the paternal bond, but probably to a lesser extent. A one-year-old separated from mother for a long period tends to become withdrawn.

First words Strictly speaking infancy ends with a child's first word—the Latin word *infantia* means inability to speak. As the end of the first year approaches an infant produces his first recognisable word. Very often this is the name of one of the more significant figures in his social world. At first he produces words as if they were an optional extra to gestures and non-language sounds. 'Cat' may mean any animal with fur and four legs. 'Mama' may refer to any adult who seems friendly. Quite frequently the meaning of first words goes through a three-stage evolution; at first they are used very specifically, then they are generalised very widely, and finally the meaning is narrowed to the usually accepted adult meaning. Knowing just what an infant means when he utters a word is a complex question. If he says 'cat', is he saying 'there is a cat', 'where is the cat?' or 'I want a cat'? In fact it may be a mistake to try to place too precise a meaning on what a child says at this stage. As with earlier non-language communication, the point may be to socialise and to keep adults talking and reacting. At this age the infant is trying out the effect of saying things.

The magnitude of the learning process of which this is the first step is truly staggering—the number of possible word combinations in the English language is around 10^{20} (10 followed by 19 zeros). Noam Chomsky, the doyen of psycholinguistics, has suggested that humans have an innate capacity for grammatical construction, which saves us the trouble of having to learn all the possible combinations of words. In fact the grammatical structures we develop as young children are not only quite different from the actual grammar we use as adults, but also remarkably similar throughout the world. In short, children appear to speak according to fairly universal grammatical rules of their own. It also seems, from studies of the very small number of children who have grown up without human contact and have subsequently proved unable to learn language, that there is an optimum time or critical period for language learning, beginning around the age of 12 months.

The close contact between mother and child is seen by most psychologists as the basis for all future relationships. If the mother herself has been deprived of maternal warmth and affection, her baby may suffer in the same way. The maternal instinct is not totally automatic.

Bathing junior Baby's bathtime can be a high spot in the day, and a chance for fathers to become involved. But daily immersion in soap and water is not essential for an infant; the essential areas to clean thoroughly are the eyes, face, hands and bottom, the traditional 'topping and tailing' technique.

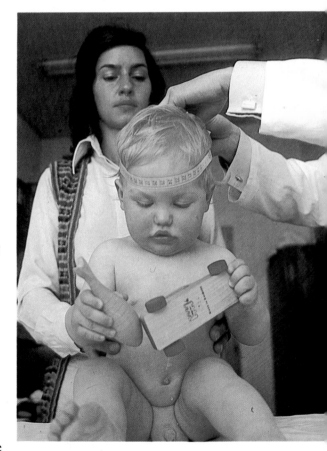

Head circumference is usually recorded three or four days after birth, and serves as a baseline for assessing growth and detecting abnormalities. Average head circumference at term is 14½in (35cm), though it can vary from 13¾in (33cm) to 15¾in (38cm) depending on the baby's weight.

Cross references
Studying the brain 52
Nervous system 48
The developing nervous
system 146

Joining the celebrations
A young boy in the ritual costume of the Mt Hagen tribesmen of New Guinea. But as many child psychologists have observed, children throughout the world have a great gift for inventing rituals of their own, and peopling them with imaginary beings . . . and all before the age when they begin to talk coherently.

A Camopi Indian mother breastfeeding two babies at once. In some countries where breast milk is the only available food for infants for the first two or three years, malnutrition of both mothers and babies can be very severe. In some countries late weaning is used as a method of birth control, though an unreliable one; lactation inhibits conception.

Child development and the environment

By the age of 12 months an infant usually weighs three times his or her birth weight, and average head to toe measurement is about 28½ in (72.5 cm). In the second year there is an average gain of 4½ in (11.5 cm) in height, and weight increases to about four times birth weight. The tail-off in growth rate becomes even more marked after that until the adolescent growth spurt. Each year height increases by some 2 in (5 cm) and weight by 5–6 lb (2.3–3.0 kg), though after the age of three or four the rate of increase is slightly less each year until puberty begins.

From birth to maturity there are considerable changes in body proportions. At birth a baby's head is a quarter of the size of the body. By the age of two the head accounts for about one-fifth of body size, by the age of six about one-sixth, and by the age of 15 about one-seventeenth. These are the visible signs of growth, but what about the unseen growth which enables the child to run and jump, and think and reason?

Developing nervous system Studying a process called myelinisation in the brains of deceased children has made it possible to estimate the development of different areas of the brain. Myelin, a grey fatty substance which forms a sheath around certain nerve fibres, speeds up the rate at which messages are transmitted along nerves. Myelinisation is incomplete at birth, but advances rapidly during the first few months of life. But in some areas of the brain myelinisation is still in progress at the age of 10 and even as late as 30.

At birth the most advanced part of the cerebral cortex, the outer layer of the forebrain, is the primary motor area—it contains the cells responsible for initiating most body movements. The next area to develop is the primary visual area in the occipital lobe, and then the primary auditory area in the temporal lobe. All the 'association areas'—these are areas of the brain where primary impulses are compared and integrated with other impulses—lag behind the corresponding primary ones. Association areas enable us to determine if a touch is friendly or hostile; they also enable us to link certain visual images—of a parent, say—with a feeling of warmth or love.

Nerve fibres associated with the acoustic system, with receiving and interpreting sounds, myelinate as early as the sixth foetal month, but they do not complete the process until the fourth year, a tempo presumably linked with the development of language skills. In contrast the nerve fibres of the light receiving system or optic analyser begin to myelinate just after birth.

Fine control of movement A number of nerve tracts do not complete their myelinisation until three or even four years after birth. For example,

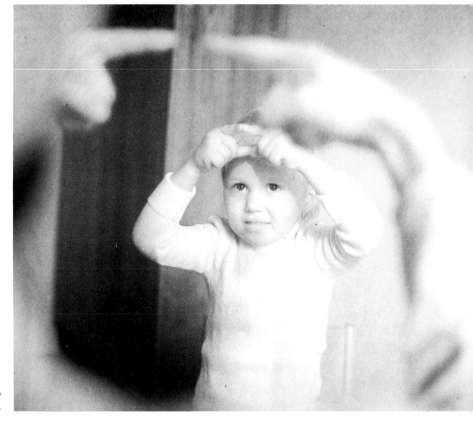

the fibres linking one area of the brain with another and responsible for the fine control of movement do not acquire their full quota of myelin until the age of four. This is why nursery school children tend to be slightly awkward in their movements compared with children of elementary school age.

Neuromuscular development progresses from the trunk outwards to the limbs and finally to the hands and feet. Watch a three-year-old throwing a ball and you will see that control of the arm and shoulder is far more advanced than that of the wrist and fingers—these still lack fluency.

Myelinisation is generally completed in the parietal and frontal areas of the cerebral cortex between the age of six and ten. The frontal area has been identified as the area responsible for planning, amongst other things. It seems that myelinisation of this area is the equivalent of developing foresight and a sense of responsibility.

Heredity and environment Growth is a product of both heredity and environment. To say that 'height is inherited' or that 'intelligence is the product of social forces' is misleading. What is inherited is the DNA in the genes. Everything else is developed.

Take, for example, two children with different genotypes (sets of genes) brought up in a well-off home in New Orleans. Child A grows 4 in (10 cm) taller than child B. Now let us imagine that these same genotypes are inherited by two children exposed to chronic infections and recurrent famine

Developmental test
This little girl is showing that she can coordinate her movements well enough to put her two forefingers together. All children should have regular developmental tests to make sure they are growing properly.

A temper tantrum,
a fact of life for most small children. Tantrums can be frightening for parent and child but are simply a sign of the child's emotional immaturity. However if the parent always gives in to displays of temper the child quickly learns that being obnoxious pays. The trick is to spot when the tantrum is being used as a lever.

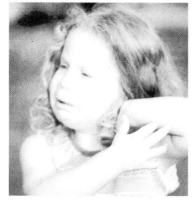

Painting is fun,
but a child learns all sorts of skills as he paints. Not only must his co-ordination improve if he wants to use a special colour or draw a special shape, but he also begins, unconsciously, to use symbols.

In full control
of their young bodies. At two years old most of them would not have been able to stand on one foot!

in Southern India. Child B may be the same height as or even taller than child A in this different environment, because his genes may be more suitable for the regulation of growth in more unfavourable circumstances.

Urban versus rural life Urban children in developed countries are usually bigger and show a quicker tempo of growth than children living in villages and rural areas. This is attributable to regular and varied food supply, health and sanitation services, and educational, recreational and welfare facilities. In countries like Finland, Poland and Greece, for example, the difference is quite considerable; town boys are between 1 and 2 in (2–5 cm) taller than those living in the country.

Why this difference? Theories abound, with improbable explanations ranging from greater exposure to artificial light to greater exposure to

sexual stimulation! A more plausible explanation might be that rural children burn up more energy in physical activity than urban children, as well as consuming fewer calories. Strenuous exercise and high calorie consumption do not necessarily go together.

Psychosocial stress Psychological stress can inhibit growth by inhibiting secretion of growth hormone (GH); remove the stress and GH secretion resumes, resulting in 'catch-up' growth as described earlier. However, *most* children continue to grow normally even under severely stressful circumstances, provided they have enough to eat. In some boarding schools boys have been known to grow more slowly in term time than during holidays at home. Conversely, a friendly boarding school may stimulate 'catch-up' growth in boys whose growth has been stunted.

Some social comparisons

Social class Children of professional and managerial fathers tend to be taller than those of manual workers. In Britain, for example, the difference is about ⅘ in (2 cm) at the age of three, rising to 2 in (5 cm) at adolescence. A British National Child Development Survey, a nationwide sample of children born in the United Kingdom in the first week of March 1958, showed an overall difference of 1⅓ in (3.3 cm) between seven-year-old children of managerial and unskilled workers. A similar contrast emerged from a national sample studied by the National Center for Health Statistics in the USA; children aged between 6 and 11 were about 1¼ in (3 cm) taller in rich families.

Some of this difference is due to the faster growth rate fostered by affluent environments, but it seems to persist into adult life. For example, the tallest students at the University of Paris in the 1960s were those of parents in non-manual and intellectual professions.

Tall boy meets tall girl Differences in childhood growth patterns have far-reaching implications. For example, a study in Belgium by R. L. Cliquet showed that young men entering more prestigious occupations than their fathers were taller as well as cleverer than their peers who stayed in occupations the same as or similar to their fathers.

A similar trend was seen in Aberdeen in Scotland in the 1950s. Girls entering non-manual jobs were taller than those entering manual ones. However, the taller girls more often married men in non-manual jobs, and shorter girls those in manual ones.

Height and the classless society If one abolished socio-economic differences, would such trends continue? There is one pertinent reason for posing this question, namely the experience of the Swedes. In a recently published study Dr Gunilla Lindgren of the School of Education, Stockholm, observed no variation in height between children from different social backgrounds (this finding was restricted to urban children). Similarly, there is now no difference in height associated with the social origins of men conscripted for military service in Sweden. Perhaps uniform childhood growth will develop with the classless society.

Height and mental ability In view of what we have already said, it will come as no surprise to learn that there is a relationship between height and mental ability. In all countries students represent the tallest population group, averaging some ⅘–1¼ in (2–3 cm) taller than the average for the total population. At the other extreme the UK National Child Development Survey showed that children requiring places in schools for the educationally subnormal were 1¼ in (3 cm) shorter at the age of 11 than children with normal IQs.

Fresh air and exercise really do help the body to grow better. Sunlight is needed for the production of vitamin D, vital for strong bones. Exercise releases bodily and emotional tension, and also encourages healthy appetite.

An abacus helps a child to get a concrete idea of what numbers mean. Numbers themselves are an abstract concept which a young child cannot grasp. An abacus, or any group of identical objects such as spoons or sweets, demonstrates the reality behind the abstraction.

Sex interests children from very early on. Young children have sexual feelings and are curious about the differences between the sexes. But they are often confused by comparisons between their own bodies and those of adults of the same sex. Telling a small child, simply, about sex and conception will help him or her later on. Interest in sex usually fades between five and puberty, Freud's 'latent' period of psychosexual development.

Adolescent girls
in New Guinea. Many tribes have complicated rituals to mark the transition from childhood to adulthood. A child is indulged in many cultures, but an adolescent is expected to start assuming adult responsibilities. In many cultures girls are treated as women, and expected to marry, as soon as menstruation begins.

Tall girls marry tall men.
This makes sense in that few girls want to look down on their husbands, though we're still sexist enough to think the reverse situation quite normal! Height and intelligence appear to be linked. So the mutual attraction of like for like is more than skin deep.

Puberty: the adult in bud

Most teenagers are eager to act independently, but they still need the support and approval of their peers. Cult movements associated with motorbikes, music, sport . . . play a fleeting part in the lives of most teenagers, but for a few they provide an off-the-peg identity which continues for several years.

Out in the big bad world cultural and religious traditions can provoke ridicule and hostility. Will this Jewish boy continue to conform to tradition or will he take what he needs and invent the rest?

"Fifteen years old! This was indeed the most memorable day of my life, for on that evening I began to think about myself, and my thoughts were strange and unhappy thoughts to me—what I was, what I was in the world for, what I wanted, what destiny was going to make of me! . . . It was the first time such questions had come to me, and I was startled at them. It was as though I had only just become conscious; I doubt that I had ever been fully conscious before . . ."
Far Away and Long Ago, W. H. Hudson

At no other time, from the age of two onwards, does the individual experience so much change as during adolescence. The adolescent faces an ever-changing physical image in the mirror, and is haunted by new sexual awareness and a desire to establish just who he or she is. Let us look first at the physical changes that mark this period of bewildering alterations.

Puberty

The growth of the younger child is gradual. Not so that of the adolescent. At a biologically ordained time, which varies from person to person, the hypothalamus, an important co-ordinating centre in the brain, signals the onset of puberty, the first phase of adolescence when sexual maturation becomes apparent and the adolescent growth spurt occurs.

The hypothalamus stimulates a gland just below it, the pituitary, to secrete hormones (chemical messengers carried in the blood). These are carried to other hormone-secreting glands. In their turn these release other hormones which regulate physical growth and development.

Boys The first sign of puberty is usually an increase in the size of the testicles, accompanied by changes in the colour of the skin and in the texture of the scrotum, the loose bag of skin containing the testicles. A little later the pubic hair appears and the penis begins to grow. These changes may occur at 13 in one boy, 14 in another and 15 in another. Such variations at this self-conscious time can distress late developers and sometimes early maturers as well. However, the sequence of events is much less variable than the age at which they take place. It is as if there is a series of clocks, each one of which is linked to the next and has to run its course before the striker falls.

The spurt in height and other body dimensions starts about a year after the testicles begin to enlarge, reaching a peak later, when the penis is growing maximally. Acceleration of penis growth starts around the age of 12½ on average, but may occur as early as 10½ or as late as 14½. This means that late-maturing boys do not begin this phase until the early maturers have completed it. The process is completed, on average, by the age 14½, and in early maturers by 12½ and in late ones by 16½ years old.

The prostate gland and seminal vesicles, where sperm is stored and various substances are added to it, enlarge at the same time as the penis. Prostate secretion makes up most of the seminal fluid, so no true ejaculation occurs before puberty.

Initially seminal fluid seems to carry fewer and less viable sperm than in early adulthood; thus in boys (as well as in girls) there may be a temporary period of reduced fertility.

The first spontaneous ejaculation of seminal fluid usually occurs about a year after the beginning of penis growth, often in a 'wet dream'. This can be an alarming experience, especially for a boy who has masturbated previously without ejaculation but with accompanying pleasant sensations. He may fear that he is 'leaking' in some abnormal, horrific way. Such fears should be forestalled by adequate information. Even in this allegedly sophisticated age ignorance is a long time dying and parents should not assume that boys understand the significance of what is happening to them. Wet dreams can worry adolescent boys so much that they become afraid to sleep in strange beds or even in their own for fear of tell-tale stains. They may also feel guilt or confusion if their dreams are accompanied by erotic fantasies.

Growth of hair on the face usually follows a set order: it appears first at the corner of the upper lip, then above the whole upper lip, then on the upper cheeks and the mid-line below the lower lip, and finally along the sides and lower border of the chin. At the same time as the moustache emerges hair starts to grow on other parts of the body, a process which continues for a considerable time after puberty. Heredity seems to determine how 'hairy' men are.

The breaking of the voice, occurring relatively late in puberty, marks the virtual doubling in size of the vocal chords following growth of the larynx. This is another phase which can cause worry or embarrassment. It can take as long as two years for the average boy to gain full control of this change, during which he may alternate between a shrill squeak and a deep bass. Making fun of him will not help and can be harmful.

Some temporary and some permanent changes are seen in the breasts of adolescent boys. The diameter of the areola, the pigmented skin around the nipple, doubles in size (it triples in size in girls). Studies suggest that the breasts of between one-fifth and one-third of boys enlarge midway through adolescence; especially pronounced enlargement is known as gynaecomastia. Usually this enlargement subsides spontaneously within a year; if it does not the tissue can be removed surgically. Again this phase demands tact and

Cross references
Hypothalamus **66**
Pituitary, thyroid, parathyroid **68**
Hormones and sexuality **72**
Biological clocks **76**

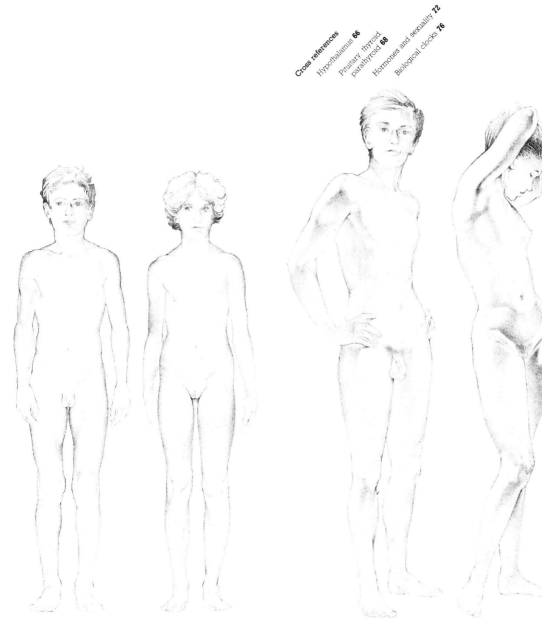

The rapid bodily changes and emotional turmoil of adolescence are often ignored or made fun of. The boy's testicles become fully developed and his voice and musculature change. The girl develops breasts, menstruates and ovulates. Her pelvis changes shape to prepare her for child-bearing. While all these physical changes are taking place the adolescent needs a relatively stable emotional base from which to go out and find his or her independence and sexual identity.

understanding from adults. Reassurance helps boys who fear that their masculinity is threatened.

Girls The advent of the breast bud, the rudimentary swelling of the breast, is usually the first sign of puberty in girls. Among North American and European girls 'budding' occurs, on average, at the age of 11, but it can become apparent as early as 9 or as late as 13. In most girls pubic hair appears later. However, in a third of girls pubic hair arrives first.

Menarche, the first menstrual period tends, to occur at a relatively late stage in puberty. It almost invariably occurs after the peak of the 'height spurt'. Amongst populations in northern and central Europe and in North America the average age of menarche varies from 12¾ to 13¼ years.

A girl does not usually attain full reproductive capacity with menarche. In the early menstrual periods, which may be irregular, an egg is not always shed from one or another of the ovaries. So-called adolescent or partial sterility tends to last for 12 to 18 months, but not all girls are affected.

Attitude to menarche both among adolescents and parents varies widely. Some girls await it eagerly, seeing it as a sign of maturity; others dread it, envisaging cramps, abdominal pain, headaches and so on. Such prophecies can be self-fulfilling and once again one must underline the need for parental understanding and encouragement. How many fathers behave like one described by the author Wardell Pomeroy: "[He] observed the occasion of his daughter's first menstruation by bringing her flowers and making a little ceremony of the fact that she had become a little lady". That daughter, as Pomeroy added, felt proud and good about this important milestone in her life.

A mother should explain about menstruation before menarche to avoid the shock and fear that can accompany the sudden appearance of menstrual blood. Again, ignorance takes a long time to die. Our children are not nearly as knowledgeable as we like to assume, and if something dramatic happens to them it is to parents that they should be able to look for advice and reassurance.

Growth spurts and emotional development

Girls tend to have their height spurts considerably earlier than boys. In fact, in girls the beginning of puberty is often accompanied by a seldom noticed increase in height. In contrast, in boys the height spurt is never an initial sign of puberty. This is an important finding in that late-maturing boys can be reassured that their height spurt is yet to come if genital development is not far advanced, while girls concerned about being too tall can be reassured that their height spurt is nearly over if they have started to menstruate.

Boys are only slightly taller than girls before puberty, but after it the difference averages 5 in (13 cm). During puberty shoulders and muscles develop more in boys and hips more in girls. Thus boys are better suited to heavy physical work and can run faster and further.

We have mentioned already how the growth rate falls continuously from birth onwards. Just before puberty it reaches its lowest point. In the year before his adolescent spurt an average boy grows only 2 in (5 cm), although a gain of only 1½ in (3.5 cm) is within normal limits. What this means—yet another source of worry and confusion—is that the late maturer may see his friends shooting up all around him, while he seems to get no taller.

Once it starts the spurt is dramatic. The average boy grows 3 in (7 cm) during the first year, 3½ in (9 cm) in the second and 3 in (7 cm) in the third. There is a further of 1¼ in (3 cm) the year after and ⅘ in (2 cm) the next. In the average girl the gains are 2½, 3¼ and 2½ in (6, 8 and 6 cm) respectively.

In North America and Europe the average adolescent growth spurt reaches a peak by the age of 12 in girls and 14 in boys. But once again there is considerable variation. An early maturing boy, for example, may begin to shoot up at 10½ and peak only 18 months later. The late maturer, who begins to spurt at 14, usually takes two years to peak.

Howzat for teeth!
This young male orangutan is demonstrating a response to testosterone which human males have lost. At puberty most primate males develop longer, stronger canines along with their secondary sexual features.

Order of growth Acceleration of trunk length accounts for more of the growth spurt than the legs, but the legs usually grow first, some six to nine months ahead of the trunk. This is why boys stop growing out of their trousers a year before growing out of their jackets.

Adolescent children, particularly girls, worried by large hands and feet can be reassured that after the growth spurt their hands and feet will be a little smaller in proportion to arms, legs and height.

In most adolescents the diameter of the head grows as the skull bones thicken by some 15 per cent. Growth of the brow ridges and the air sinuses behind them make the forehead more prominent, producing a straighter profile and a more pointed chin. Facial muscles develop at the same time. These changes are emphasised more in boys than in girls. In fact, in some girls changes in the face are hardly detectable.

The spurt in hip width in girls is quantitatively as great as that in boys, while nearly all other skeletal changes in girls are less marked. The shoulder width spurt is especially marked in boys. Hormones account for these changes. In girls cartilage cells in the hip joints respond to oestrogen; in boys cartilage cells in the shoulder region respond to male sex hormone.

In the course of evolution specialised reactions to hormonal activity have been lost as well as won. The fighting ability of most male apes and monkeys is enhanced by large canine teeth which normally develop at puberty. They will grow beforehand, however, in response to male hormone. In humans the canines are slightly bigger in males than in females, but they have lost most of their ability to respond to the stimulus of male hormone.

A Ovary
B Primary follicle
C Graafian follicle
D Released ovum
E Corpus luteum
F Remains of corpus luteum
G Body temperature
H Oestrogens
I Progesterone
J Uterine wall

Menstrual cycle
The ovaries produce oestrogen from puberty to the menopause. Part of the follicle left behind every month as the ripe egg is released develops into a miniature gland, the corpus luteum; this secretes progesterone, a hormone which prepares the walls of the uterus for pregnancy. Body temperature and oestrogen levels are highest at ovulation, which occurs half way through the menstrual cycle. Progesterone levels are highest seven days later. As these levels fall, and conception does not occur, the uterine wall breaks down and menstruation begins.

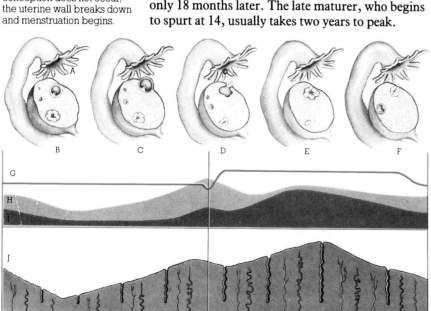

Days   7   14   21   28

Cross references
Pituitary 66
Growth: dwarfs and giants 68
Sex hormones 71
Hormones and sexuality 72

The adolescent spurt is responsible for far-reaching changes in body composition, and these are far more pronounced in boys than in girls. However, since the spurt tends to occur earlier in girls, they have, for a short time, more muscle than boys. The subsequent greater strength of boys seems to arise from changes in the structural and biochemical nature of muscle cells induced by male sex hormone.

As well as larger skeletal muscles boys develop bigger hearts and bigger lungs. They acquire a greater capacity for carrying oxygen in the blood and are better able than girls to neutralise the chemical products of exercise. In adolescence the quantity of red blood cells and the amount of haemoglobin (the oxygen-carrying pigment) increases in boys but remains the same in girls.

Throughout adolescence athletic prowess and physical endurance progress rapidly. 'He's outgrowing his strength'—this is what many parents say of their adolescent sons, but this idea has little scientific support. Indeed, if a boy becomes weak and easily tired during adolescence, it is usually for psychological reasons, not physiological ones. There is however a period, usually of about six months, when the length of the trunk increases relatively to that of the leg. At this time the muscles have yet to reach their full size and strength; this can sometimes create problems with balance.

Emotional development

There is very little solid information available about the relationship between emotional and physiological development in puberty, but what there is supports what our commonsense tells us, namely that being an early or late maturer has repercussions on behaviour. In the tooth and claw world of the small boy physical power means prestige as well as success. Follow-up studies in the USA, where most if not all such work has been done, suggest that early maturers develop into more stable, less neurotic, and more successful adults. More so than at any other stage of life—unless he becomes a dancer or an athlete—the adolescent boy regards his body as an instrument. The arousal of the sex drive only makes him more acutely conscious of his body.

The psychological effects of early or late maturing do not impinge as much on girls as on boys. Nevertheless a girl's physical development inevitably affects her personality and relationships with the world. In one American study early maturing girls were considered more grown-up and were accorded higher 'social prestige' than late maturers of the same age. However, this finding was restricted only to girls aged 12 and over. Eleven-year-olds gave premenstrual girls higher prestige ratings. In other words both very early and

very late maturers are likely to have a tougher time than average girls. A girl whose breasts are beginning to bud before those of her classmates may develop a slouch in order to disguise her embarrassing new endowments.

Who am I? In contemporary industrialised societies the adolescent is expected to master many complex tasks in a very short period of time. To meet these challenges the adolescent must develop a sense of his or her own identity, a philosophy of life, a coherent view of the world, a set of guiding moral beliefs and standards.

Many adolescents find themselves playing roles that change from one situation to another and from one moment to another. They worry about which, if any, is the 'real me', and self-consciously try out different roles in the hope of finding one which somehow 'clicks'.

But to say that the problem of identity is a central one in adolescence does not mean that the task of 'identity formation' either begins or ends in one's teens. The process starts in infancy and continues through all the partial identifications that a child forms with parents, peers, siblings and non-familial adults, well into mature life. All such identifications are part of the maturing process.

Emotional stability
means a successful transition from a parent-oriented to a partner-oriented world. For most people this transition is at best frustrating and at worst very painful. Many of us get confused and hurt by several relationships before we find and commit ourselves to one partner.

Illness and physical change

Every stage of life has its hazards, but looking across the whole age span the human machine is most vulnerable when it is very young and very old. Here we survey some of the avoidable and unavoidable risks of late 20th century living.

The lottery begins in the womb, at the drawing board stage. At conception we are irrevocably saddled, barring accidents, with 46 chromosomes bearing an assortment of genes. Either the ovum, with an X chromosome, unites with a sperm carrying another X chromosome, to produce a female, or with a sperm carrying Y, to produce a male. Around the sixth or seventh week of life the genes trigger differentiation as a male or female. But for a few individuals this sex determination process is only partially successful. One in every few hundred people could be described as being of intermediate sex. Though they may marry as males or females, they are usually sterile, or the characteristics which emerge at puberty are in conflict with those evident at birth and on which their upbringing was based.

Occasionally an abnormal egg or sperm gives rise to an embryo with a complement of 45 or 47 chromosomes; the former is not viable and usually aborts spontaneously, but the 47-chromosome or 'trisomic' embryo can survive to birth as a mongol. Faults like this can now be detected before birth using techniques such as ultrasound and amniocentesis. The latter involves withdrawing a small sample of fluid from the amniotic sac surrounding the foetus; levels of tell-tale substances such as alpha-fetoprotein will indicate whether the foetus is developing normally or not.

The short trip from the relatively secure environment of the uterus to the outside world is the next hurdle for the developing individual. If a baby has suffered physical damage during labour and delivery, it may not be able to inflate its lungs properly. The state of a baby at birth will also be affected by anaesthetics and other drugs in the mother's circulation, and in the case of Rhesus incompatibility by a negligible or marked degree of anaemia. Drugs taken during pregnancy, especially the first eight weeks, can affect physical and neurological development.

Like many new machines immediately off the production line, many of us are born with slight faults or blemishes, most of which can be corrected shortly after birth. Some conditions the doctor knows we will grow out of; others such as squints or hearing defects he will want to detect as soon as possible to have the best chance of correcting them. Defects of a more serious nature, for example a perforated heart septum, can be corrected surgically within weeks of birth.

But a new baby, with an immature metabolic system and immune system, is especially vulnerable to infections such as pneumonia and gastroenteritis. Later one or more of the childhood fevers—German measles, chickenpox or whooping cough—may be contracted, though nation-wide vaccination programmes have done much to reduce this possibility. Diseases like diphtheria, whooping cough and polio are only uncommon today because of vaccination. For some parents, however, the risk of vaccine damage to their child is unacceptable; if this trend continues it could mean the resurgence of diseases which have lain low for 20 or 30 years. Once again the risk of death from childhood diseases could outweigh the risk of vaccine damage.

Nutritional childhood diseases are now rare in the West, but in the Third World rickets (vitamin

D deficiency causing defective bone growth) and kwashiorkor (lack of protein and vitamins causing severe malnutrition with oedema or pot-belly) are still endemic. The poor hygiene which contributes to child deaths from water-borne infections in developing countries is rarely seen in the developed ones. Fungal and parasite infections (ringworm, lice, scabies) in the child populations of the developed world have been largely eradicated thanks to school health services.

As body metabolism and the immune system mature serious illness becomes rarer. Cuts, grazes and burns are the lot of every child—nervous coordination and muscular strength take time to develop and so does a sense of danger. In fact impulsiveness and recklessness represent a greater hazard to the healthy older child than disease.

Adolescence marks the end of the assembly line. Our reproductive equipment is fully functional. Our intellect is as good as it ever will be. We are ready for road testing. The ailments peculiar to adolescence are few, and due to major gear changes on the part of the endocrine glands. Acne is the norm rather than the exception in adolescents, and is due to overactivity of the sebaceous glands; sebum blocks the pores of the skin, providing breeding sites for bacteria.

It is no accident that motor insurance companies ask high premiums of teenage drivers; they do get involved in more accidents than older drivers. New-found freedom and lack of experience leads to mistakes, sometimes fatal ones. Most teenage pregnancies are mistakes, in the sense that they are unwanted or unintentional. Sexually transmitted diseases start to figure as a hazard too.

In the average adult the years between 20 and 45 are relatively trouble free. Blood pressure and weight usually increase, but without ill effects. The wear and tear of over-indulgence in food, alcohol or tobacco, or of too sedentary a lifestyle, is insidious. Viruses and bacteria make little headway against the immune defences of a healthy adult. Attack comes mainly from stress. Depression and nervous breakdown begin to emerge in the late 20s and 30s as the workload of parenthood, home ownership and carving a career take their toll. Stress mainly affects the circulatory system – which is why deaths from coronary heart disease and stroke top the mortality league table in most developed countries. Cancers, particularly of the lung, stomach and breast, are the next most common cause of death. Next on the list are diseases of the lung (bronchitis, pneumonia, asthma), followed by conditions of the digestive system (peptic ulcers, cirrhosis of the liver).

The shadow that haunts most people in their old age is the prospect of dependence and senility, which is hardly surprising. We spend all our lives building our self-respect on our ability to fend for ourselves or care for others, and health is an important part of independence. Senility, clinically, is due to cerebral arteriosclerosis (hardening and narrowing of the arteries that serve the brain) leading to senile dementia (widespread atrophy of cells in the brain cortex). Typically there is progressive loss of brain function, expressed as lapses of attention and memory, and perseveration. The label 'senile' is particularly destructive and is often misapplied to people whose problems are physical or emotional rather than mental. Frequently the signs of senility disappear rapidly when the physical or emotional problem has been attended to.

What is ageing?

Theorist Roger Gould classifies the changes after adolescence thus:

Age 16–18 Yearning to escape parental dominance; the future is distant and unknown.
Age 18–22 Transfer of dependence on family to a group of friends to achieve independence.
Age 22–28 Confidence and self-reliance develop as we begin to establish ourselves in the world.
Age 29–44 Self doubt. Life is passing us by. We seem to be missing out on important experiences.
Age 45–50 The mellowing phase. We come to terms with ourselves and what we have achieved.

Of course, all ways of dividing up our lives are more or less arbitrary. Shakespeare did it one way, with his seven ages of man. Biologists have their own divisions—infancy, puberty, prime of life, senility. Sociologists do it by stages linked to the cycle of social institutions such as school, family and occupation, marriage, parenthood, and retirement. In her lively book, *Passages*, the writer Gail Sheeny divides life into decades entitled Pulling Up Roots, The Trying Twenties, Catch Thirty, The Deadline Decade, and so on.

The boundary lines between these divisions are blurred by individual variations. Furthermore, as Gail Sheeny implies, each stage has its problems. It is fashionable to talk about a 'mid-life crisis', but in most cultures and among most people, adult life consists of coping with a series of changes which may or may not be perceived as crises.

The ageing process

Age is implicated in our journey through adulthood. But what is meant by 'ageing'? An international swimming star may be past her sporting prowess by the age of 18 or 19. A professional footballer's playing days are usually over by the age of 35. Yet at 55 or 60 an international statesman is still considered 'young for the job'.

Maybe we should define more clearly what we mean by ageing. James Birren has classified three types of functional ageing: biological, psychological and social. The more all three dimensions are apparent in any one individual, the less 'old' he or she is. In one major study the functional age of more than a thousand American service veterans is being assessed through repeated clinical and laboratory tests. The men taking part are healthy volunteers of all ages, and the idea is to build a profile of biological, psychological and social ageing. Preliminary findings show that the participants have a variety of functional ages.

The peak of physical prowess occurs early in life when we produce our children and when we are at our most energetic. By this time the process of biological ageing has already begun. In fact, even in adolescence individuals may start to lose a little

visual acuity—before he or she has reached physical maturity.

However, as we see ourselves visibly ageing we may well improve in some aspects of mental functioning. For example, in a verbal comprehension study it was found that 30- and 40-year-olds performed better than 20-year-olds, while 50- and 60-year-olds did even better. Work like this suggests that some aspects of mental functioning actually improve in the second half of life. The old idea that we reach an intellectual peak in adolescence or by the mid-20s seems to be over simple. All too often we equate physical decline with mental decline. The two do not necessarily go hand in hand. Many people continue to develop throughout their lives using their wide experience and sense of perspective to master new challenges. This is why compulsory retirement between 60 and 65 seems particularly hard to some people.

A common complaint of old age: arthritis. Here it is the hands that are affected but the disease can strike any or every joint in the body. Some, but not all, joints can be replaced by prostheses. It is now believed that some forms of arthritis are hereditary.

Cross references
Skeleton 33
Arthritis 35
Joints 35
Skin 42

Premature ageing
has made this five-year-old an old woman. This very rare condition is hereditary. Affected children appear normal at birth but most die before adulthood.

A sexy old age
is often a state of mind. A lifetime of experience and mutual affection can sustain physical desire. The advancing years need not preclude sexual activity nor diminish the attraction between the sexes.

The old are neglected
because we expect them to be slow and unassertive. Depression will go unnoticed. Senility is a label which is too often applied; confused behaviour may be the result of anxiety, loneliness or an unexpected reaction to a drug.

An 80-year-old athlete
from Hungary who would put many younger people to shame. His muscles have shrunk and his skin has lost much of its elasticity. Yet the muscles he has are clearly very efficient. Ageing need not mean catastrophic decay.

Physical change

The far-reaching effects of physical change underline the need for healthy eating habits and flexibility of outlook. Let us look more closely at some of these physiological changes.

Height Older means shorter. A study of 23,000 Canadians, the largest investigation of its type, showed that old men were, on average, 3 in (7.5 cm) shorter than young men; old women were 2⅕ in (5.4 cm) shorter than younger women. Shrinking is not usually apparent until the age of 50. It occurs because the posture-supporting muscles and the discs between the spinal vertebrae shrink. Effects are more pronounced in those with poor posture.

Skin Look carefully at the skin of a healthy 30-year-old and you will probably see wrinkling due to a loss of fatty tissue under the top layers of skin and from sunlight exposure. The tendency to wrinkle becomes more marked as we age, showing how ageing is not a sudden, dramatic phenomenon but a gradual process, a slow tide rather than an enormous wave. In old age it may become difficult to adjust to temperature changes; skin condition can inhibit the body's sweating capacity.

Bone Bones tend to lose calcium and become more thin and brittle in old age. This increases the risk of injury and decreases the capacity to make a quick recovery from breaks and fractures.

As we pointed out earlier in the book, we become increasingly prone to osteoporosis as we age. The body is held together by various types of connective tissue, one of which, collagen, helps us to perform stretching movements. In old age, stretching ability is reduced, making movement more taxing.

Alterations and expectations

The generation gap need not exist. The old, while sharing their experience and knowledge, can still learn new attitudes from the young. Mental agility is a positive way to fight senility.

Muscles Although an old person with good general health is likely to be equal to most muscular tasks, the number and size of muscle fibres throughout the body falls with age. However, muscle degeneration is more likely to reflect poor nutrition, poor circulation, or lack of use, than old age itself. If there is a weakness it does not necessarily mean that the muscles are to blame. The problem may stem from faulty coordination of muscular activity by the central nervous system.

Cardiovascular system The old saying that 'a man is as old as his arteries' is supported by many scientific studies. In old age the circulation cannot work as efficiently as in earlier years because the arteries harden and become partially obstructed. This can result in high blood pressure, one of the serious ailments of old age. High blood pressure is associated with strokes and with heart and kidney failures. Typical Western-type diets and stress also appear to be linked to high blood pressure. The native populations of the Fiji Islands and New Guinea are not prone to the kind of blood pressure rises one sees in middle-aged Western Europeans and Americans.

Respiration Moving air in and out of the lungs demands more effort as we grow older. This is believed to be because the absorption surface of the lungs decreases, as does their capacity for elastic recoil. Declining respiratory function has repercussions on the rest of the body, because every cell depends on oxygen supply and the removal of carbon dioxide.

The brain As we observed earlier we are born with all the neurons or nerve cells we will ever possess. It seems that neuron loss may account for the slow-down in electrical activity in the brain detectable in even the healthiest old people. It also seems that signals governing coordination of the various body systems take longer to reach their targets—to put it another way the brain is not as finely tuned as it used to be.

When people stress the importance of body maintenance, great emphasis is put, quite properly, on the heart. By looking after your heart, you may also help to preserve brain function. Because high blood pressure, arteriosclerosis and other common ailments affect the circulation, they can reduce oxygen supply to the brain.

Sight and sound The first special sense to show the effects of ageing is usually eyesight. We may get spots before the eyes, or take longer to adapt to light changes; our visual field shrinks, and visual acuity declines.

Hearing, especially in the higher frequency band, diminishes; we can no longer appreciate the full range of sounds from a good hi-fi system. Hearing loss tends to be more pronounced in men than women, perhaps because of more exposure to industrial noise. Ageing people of both sexes living and working in quiet places seem to be less prone to hearing loss.

Similarly, our sense of smell and taste are not as sharp. This can lead to under-nutrition which in turn can cause other problems. Elderly people should plan their meals carefully.

Sleep As we grow older we do not always sleep as soundly, yet a good night's sleep is vital to overall functioning and contributes towards general wellbeing. Research has shown that the amount of

Cross references
High blood pressure **98**
Brain **50**
Seeing **56**
Hearing **60**
Sleep need **194**

REM sleep (rapid eye movement or dreaming sleep) declines in old age. Healthy tiredness arising from exercise can promote sleep.

Attitudes and expectations

The visible evidence of biological ageing affects psychological and social ageing, inevitably. In societies like ours we are acutely conscious of chronological age; we start school at a certain age, and we retire at a certain age.

Chronological age also shapes attitudes and expectations. In his book, *Growing old: years of fulfilment*, Dr Robert Kastenbaum comments: "Our society usually calls upon children to live up to expectations, but upon old people to live down to expectations. If we do not expect a person to keep up with current events, to make responsible decisions, to continue learning, to create and innovate, then why should he expect this of himself? The 80-year-old may have nourished for many decades the expectation that 80-year-olds do not think very well or enjoy life very much. He becomes the victim of his own expectations. It is the rare individual who can transcend the climate of such attitudes.

"But there is no reason to suppose that this effect starts in old age. How many people continue to expect creative thoughts from themselves and others in middle age? Does our family life, our work, or culture in general reward us for reflective thinking, for innovation? Looking back even further, do we leave school more interested in learning than when we entered? It is possible that the mentally inert old person is victim of experiences throughout his life rather than his old age?"

Anthropologist Renaldo Madure gives a sharp example of the effect of cultural expectations on

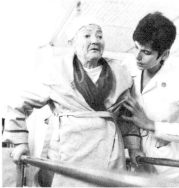

Sick old people
need exercise as much as their fitter contemporaries if they are to regain their independence. The symptoms of old age are depressing enough without the added burden of immobility.

Jazz ballet in the 80s
Octogenarians exercising in a dance class. One of many ways of keeping physically fit, this kind of energy in old age follows on from an active adult life. Mental agility, too, can be linked to an alert lifestyle. An old mind is still capable of learning if it has had a lifetime of 'exercise'.

Capacity for learning

Contentment and dignity
are not easy to achieve at any age. And the forces which tend to isolate a person from the community—poor health, depression, a dwindling circle of contemporaries, stubborn clinging to independence—are sometimes strongest in old age. We too readily label old people as eccentric, senile, or mentally ill.

Underdeveloped countries
often have a more compassionate and caring attitude towards old people. They remain an integral and useful part of the family and the community. A cynic might say that there is no social welfare system to absolve the family of responsibility, but such a system would not be welcomed.

Age is a stigma,
or at least this is often the attitude that seems to prevail in the dynamic, youth-oriented cultures of the West. With money, one can appear younger longer; cosmetic surgery, used here to lift and smooth the wrinkles of the face, is a staggeringly profitable branch of medicine.

intellectual functioning in old people. He found that the oldest members of a painters' colony in Northern India were also the most creative and were expected to advance both themselves and their art throughout their lives. In the West, in contrast, we reach our peak quite early and then, as Kastenbaum puts it, "more or less hang around".

There are, of course, many Western people who stoutly defy popular expectations and cultural stereotypes; these are the people who adapt, so to speak, by re-wiring their brains. To what do they have to adapt? In old age the pace of living slows down as a result of what psychologists call a reduction in 'psychomotor speed'. This is, quite simply, the rate at which we do things, react to changing circumstances, devise strategies to contend with change and so on. Yet reduced

psychomotor speed does not necessarily indicate a decline in intelligence. What it does do is to put old people at a marked disadvantage in tasks that place a premium on speed. But it does not affect learning ability.

Two researchers, George Naylor and Elsie Harwood, set out to establish the learning potential of a group of 80 'old' people by teaching them German. The group had an average age of 70 (youngest 63, oldest 91) and an average IQ of 118, considerably above average, although their scholastic experience was well below—half the group had only primary school education, and only a quarter had completed secondary school.

Schoolchildren take three years to prepare for the formal examination which half the group passed in only *three and a half months* of once-a-week lessons. In that short time just under half the group attained the 16-year-old matriculation standard.

Said Naylor and Harwood: "It is no exaggeration to say that the attitude of the majority of our students underwent a revolution. So widespread and deep rooted has the 'old age' stereotype become in our society that it has been widely accepted by the elderly themselves. Those of them who had smiled disbelievingly at assurances of their capacity to succeed . . . could not escape the impact of their progress."

The ghost
in the machine

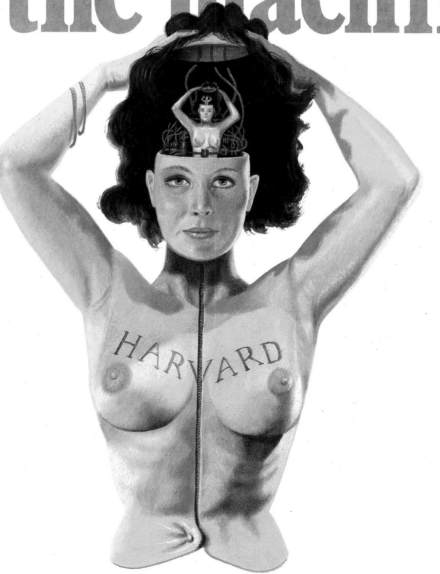

Stress: physical and mental

Is living bad for you?
Stress is an inevitable part of living. No man or woman alive is capable of drifting through life without change, challenge or opposition.

"Everybody has it, everybody talks about it, yet few people have taken the trouble to find out what stress really is. . . . Nowadays we hear a great deal at social gatherings about the stress of executive life, retirement, exercise, family problems, pollution, air traffic control or the death of a relative. . . . The word 'stress', like 'success', 'failure' or 'happiness' means different things to different people, so that defining it is extremely difficult." *Stress without Distress*, Dr Hans Selye

"Anxiety seems to be the dominant fact . . . and is threatening to become the dominant cliché . . . of modern life. It shouts in the headlines, laughs nervously at cocktail parties, nags from advertisements, speaks suavely in the board room, whines from the stage, clatters from the Wall Street ticker, jokes with fake youthfulness on the golf course and whispers in privacy each day before the shaving mirror and the dressing table. Not merely the black statistics of murder, suicide, alcoholism and divorce betray anxiety . . . but almost any innocent, everyday act: the limp or overhearty handshake, the second pack of cigarettes or the third Martini, the forgotten appointment, the stammer in mid-sentence, the wasted hour before the TV set, the spanked child, the new car unpaid for." *Time Magazine*

Drive a family saloon at 50 miles per hour (80km/h)

in second gear and the engine will scream under the strain. Engage third and then fourth gear and the engine will perform smoothly and efficiently. But if you drive at 20 miles (32km) per hour in top gear the engine will judder and splutter. There is a limit to how long an automobile will continue to function if it is driven in the wrong gear. The body machine is just the same.

The terms 'stress' and 'strain' are often confused. In physics and mechanical engineering stress is the force exerted on a physical object and the strain is the internal reaction of that object to that stress. To take a very simple example, if you attach a weight to a rope, the rope will stretch in proportion to the weight, the weight being the stress and the stretching the strain.

Assessing the stress an automobile will tolerate is obviously a major part of the designer's job. Some models have a greater resistance than others. So it is with the human body. Some of us are grand prix racing models, but most of us are comfortable estate wagons or family saloons.

Engine breakdown

The body maintains a relatively constant internal environment through a process known as homeostasis which regulates vital bodily functions like respiration, circulation of the blood and body temperature. Regulation of the volume and

concentration of body fluids is an especially important part of homeostatic function. A 10 per cent loss of water creates a serious medical problem, but a 20 per cent loss usually causes death. However, long before we reach this stage homeostatic mechanisms encourage us to drink to restore our body fluids to the optimum level.

Investigating the homeostatic mechanisms related to 'fight' or 'flight' reactions to stressful stimuli in the early 1920s, physiologist Walter B. Cannon observed changes in the adrenal glands and in the sympathetic nervous systems of animals and humans exposed to painful stressors, such as extreme cold, lack of oxygen and emotional disturbance. Cannon believed that homeostasis counteracts the adverse effects of painful stimulation and restores the equilibrium of the internal environment. He concluded that when homeostatic balance was upset, his subjects were in a state of stress. In other words stress represented a homeostatic disturbance.

Gearing up to stress

Hans Selye, a great pioneer of psychosomatic medicine, describes the physiological response to stress in three phases, which he christened the General Adaptation Syndrome (GAS). This concept evolved from a series of famous experiments in which Selye subjected animals to various stressors, including starvation, extreme heat or cold, loss of blood, and surgical trauma. He found that response to stress tended to be the same in all animals regardless of the stressor.

Alarm phase The hypothalamus, the coordination centre in the brain, triggers a complex chain of neural and biochemical processes. It activates the autonomic nervous system, which mobilises the body, and it also sends a chemical messenger to the pituitary gland lying directly below it. In turn the pituitary releases adrenocorticotrophic hormone (ACTH) into the blood. Stimulated by ACTH the adrenal cortex releases corticoids and other biochemical agents into the blood; these also help to mobilise the body. Heart rate is increased to pump more oxygen-rich blood to the brain and muscles; breathing rate quickens to meet the greater demand for oxygen; blood vessels close to the skin constrict, and clotting time shortens so severe bleeding from wounds is less likely; muscles tighten to prepare the body for fight or flight.

Resistance phase The symptoms of the first phase subside as the body develops resistance to the stressor. Since it absorbs energy which may be needed for other physiological functions, this adaptive change is of limited duration.

Exhaustion phase Signs of the alarm reaction may

reappear, and resistance weakens. The flow of hormones from the pituitary and the adrenal cortex is insufficient to meet the body's demands. Sustained stress leads to the atrophy of the endocrine glands, eventually culminating in death.

Studies of physiological reactions to stress have shown that similar body symptoms—decreased electrical resistance of the skin, faster brain waves, faster heart beat and respiration—are associated with widely differing emotional states.

So how do the physiology of stress and the psychology of stress tie up? Are physiological stress and psychological stress the same thing? Does one foreshadow the other? The questions may sound sensible and straightforward but in practice it is impossible to separate mind and body in this way.

Mental processes

Professor Richard Lazarus of the University of California, a major contributor to our current understanding of stress, emphasises that it is cognitive appraisal, the way in which we see and interpret threatening stimuli, which determines our response to stress. The process of appraisal is a two-stage one. First, we evaluate the situation: is it threatening or not? Second, we weigh up alternative ways of coping with it. The process of coping is also a two-stage one. One either reacts directly, by fight or flight, or one reappraises the situation, perhaps seeing it as less of a threat.

So there is an interplay between cognitive appraisal and emotional reaction. Cognition is a convenient umbrella term for all mental processes—perceiving, remembering, appraising, imagining, reasoning, etc. Inevitably cultural norms affect these cognitive processes. To what extent, for example, is your sense of self-worth based on the value society places on your job?

These prisoners of war are suffering from chronic stress. Studies have shown that prolonged anxiety and deprivation do permanent psychological damage. Even ten years after their release, nearly half the survivors of Nazi concentration camps still suffered from depression, nightmares and other disturbances.

In a dangerous situation like this relaxation is entirely inappropriate. Fear and anxiety can be lifesavers—they concentrate the mind and prepare the body for action. Physically and psychologically we are better equipped to deal with emergencies than with prolonged stress.

Who is prone to stress?

Since everyone's cognitive processes are different it follows that no two people interpret or react to objective stress in exactly the same way. So personality is an important element in the stress equation. Researchers have found, for example, that the fear and apprehension of patients awaiting surgery is less directly related to the seriousness of their operation than to their personality and cognitive style. In American space-training programmes it was found that some astronauts' fear of failure, failure to accomplish their mission, overshadowed all other dangers including death.

There are a number of factors crucial to the way individuals interpret and react to stress.

Degree of threat There is a direct relationship between the actual degree of threat to life or ego and the degree of primitiveness with which one responds; the greater the threat the more 'animal-like' one's reactions.

Duration of threat There is also a correlation between the length of time a known threat hangs over one and the stress one experiences. Prolonged threat can lead to a state of mental exhaustion.

Resources for coping The more resources one has—previous experience of coping, the opportunity to change or divert the threat, the opportunity to escape or to 'halve' trouble by sharing it—the more adequately one copes.

Imminence of threat The nearer the threat in time the more intensely it is felt. In one study in which volunteers were asked to walk blindfold towards a precipice, those who had been led to believe they were in danger of falling over the edge judged the time it took to walk towards the cliff face as being very much shorter than those who anticipated no such peril!

Helplessness Apprehension and fear of threatening situations is at its most intense when no active preparation is possible, when nothing one does can avert or palliate a forthcoming disaster.

Pinpointing the source of threat Psychologist Bruno Bettelheim illustrated this phenomenon by pointing out that concentration camp prisoners blamed journalists for the reprisals inflicted on them by their Nazi captors following a newspaper exposé of their appalling living conditions. Presumably the prisoners coped better with the stress inflicted on them by blaming it on a distant source, the journalists, rather than on the immediate and true source, the Nazis.

Ambiguity of threat Ambiguous situations mean two things: either you are uncertain as to the true nature, or imminence, or intensity of the threat; or you are in a quandary about what action to take. In such a situation the stress experience depends on the interpretation of related cues.

Predicting reactions to stress

Different threatening situations—whether long-term/short-term, intense/weak, or clear-cut/ambiguous—elicit different reactions from different people. Nevertheless, one can make a number of general predictions about a person's reaction to stress based on his or her motivation, intellect and education, and self-opinion.

Someone with strong incentive to cope and great certainty about the rightness and value of holding on and winning through will cope better than someone who lacks incentive or motivation. People of limited intelligence and education tend to mis-appraise threats, either vastly overestimating them or underestimating them. In 1947 H. Cantril, analysing the panic that hit large sections of the American population following Orson Wells' 'Invasion from Mars' radio broadcast, found that the least intelligent sectors of the population were the most panic stricken, despite the early information that the broadcast was a hoax. Nor is it surprising that people lacking in self-esteem are more likely to succumb to stressful circumstances than those who have a high opinion of themselves. Similarly the stronger your ego, your sense of being in control, the more positive your response to a stressful situation

A most essential element of coping is confidence. Being confident of one's ability to cope becomes a self-fulfilling prophecy. Confidence is based on past experiences of coping successfully, not necessarily on experiences of identical situations. Obvious familiarity with a moderate recurrent stress breeds, if not contempt, at least a fairly high tolerance threshold towards stress provoking events..

Though avoidance may in some instances be an entirely appropriate coping strategy, one cannot always give stress the slip. We have to learn how to deal with stress, survive it, build on it if possible. There will always be certain tasks to do, certain changes to be adapted to.

Yet the facts indicate that we aren't doing too well. Probably about half of all patients who consult their general practitioner have symptoms which can be traced to psychological stress. Emotional factors have been clearly shown to dispose a person to ulcers, high blood pressure, colitis, migraine, back pain, dermatitis, asthma, obesity and many other ailments.

Some cardiologists, notably the Americans Dr Meyer Friedman and Dr Ray Rosenman vehemently argue that there is a strong correlation between coronary heart disease and stress. For research purposes they classified men into two

Agoraphobia
Agoraphobics cannot tolerate the stress of being away from home. They find public places, like the shopping centre depicted here, threatening and terrifying. Those who seek help are usually encouraged to confront feared situations in their imagination first and then in real life, progressing through a hierarchy of increasingly threatening situations. Cue exposure, as this method is called, is painful at first but becomes less so as the phobic realises that his or her fears are unfounded.

An Encounter group
The Encounter Movement was pioneered by American psychologist Carl Rogers and is particularly strong in the United States. The goal of Encounter therapy is to learn more about oneself, how to express thoughts and feelings more openly, how to communicate better. Those who attend Encounter groups are usually quite normal—they are not suffering from major psychological problems.

A crowded street
can be a lonely place—our private space is invaded, our identity becomes insignificant, and we find it more, not less, difficult to communicate.

groups, A and B. As are hard driving, aggressive and prone to what can be described as 'hurry sickness'. They demonstrate extraordinary physical and mental stamina, always playing to win, both at work and at home. In short, they are workaholics. Bs on the other hand are more relaxed and often more efficient than As, especially in tasks demanding patience or methodical application. Bs are also more likely to think a situation through more thoroughly before making big decisions and they avoid snap judgements, unlike As.

An eight-year study of 3,500 men by Friedman and Rosenman suggest that type A are twice as prone to coronary heart disease as type B, and five times more likely to have a second myocardial infarct. In an earlier study they had also found that cholesterol levels among As were higher than among Bs, 253 mg per 100 ml of blood compared with 214 mg per 100 ml. This difference could not be accounted for by difference in diet, since the intake of the two groups was similar both in fat content and total calorie intake. Also although there were no significant differences in the number of smokers within the two groups, As tended to smoke more, averaging 23 cigarettes a day compared with only 15 a day among the Bs. Evidence such as this certainly tends to support the idea that a stressful lifestyle can kill.

Situations that cause stress

Despite the fact that there are potentially as many forms of stress as there are individual personalities, is it possible to pinpoint those situations which cause the greatest intensity of stress among a majority of people?

Thomas H. Holmes and Richard H. Rahe of the University of Washington attempted to do just this. They noted a strong correlation between significant life events and the onset of illness. All of the life events listed in their major stress chart below require some measure of readjustment. The more readjustment needed, or the bigger the scale of impact, the more susceptible we become to illness. Illness follows lowered body resistance, and lowered resistance follows adaptive efforts by the individual which run counter to the way the body usually operates.

To use the chart below, check the events that have occurred to you in the past 12 months and then add up your score.

Events	Score or scale of impact
Death of spouse	100
Divorce	73
Marital separation	65
Jail term	63
Death of close family member	63
Personal injury or illness	53
Marriage	50
Fired at work	47
Marital reconciliation	45
Retirement	45
Change in health of family member	44
Pregnancy	40
Sex difficulties	39
Gain of new family member	39
Business readjustment	39
Change in financial state	38
Death of close friend	37
Change to different line of work	36
Change in number of arguments with spouse	35
Mortgage over $10,000	31
Foreclosure of mortgage or loan	30
Change in responsibilities at work	29
Son or daughter leaving home	29
Trouble with in-laws	29
Outstanding personal achievement	28
Wife begins or stops work	26
Begin or end school	26
Change in living conditions	25
Revision of personal habits	24
Trouble with boss	23
Change in work hours or conditions	20
Change in residence	20
Change in schools	20
Change in recreation	19
Change in church activities	19
Change in social activities	18
Mortgage or loan less than $10,000	17
Change in sleeping habits	16
Change in number of family get-togethers	15
Change in eating habits	15
Vacation	13
Christmas	12
Minor violations of the law	11

Holmes and Rahe calculated that a score of 150 based on events in the past year would point to a 50-50 chance of developing an illness or 'health change'. A score of 300 would increase the chance of a health change to nearly 90 per cent.

Rahe tested the scale on 2,500 officers and enlisted men aboard three US Navy cruisers. In the month following the test the 30 per cent with the highest life change scores developed almost 90 per cent more 'first illnesses' than the low scorers.

In another study in which they investigated 84 resident physicians, Holmes and Rahe extended the timescale used for life changes to 18 months. Nearly half the physicians in the high risk group (scores of 300+) developed illness, compared with only a quarter of the medium risk group (scores 200–299) and only nine per cent of the low risk group.

Convincing as this might sound, no investigator would pretend to be able to predict disease on the basis of measuring psychosocial stress alone. Indeed as a measure of psychological and social proneness to stress-induced illness the Holmes-Rahe scale is relatively crude. 'Divorce' may have little impact if both partners have been separated for any length of time. 'Moving home' may create more or less turmoil depending on local amenities, one's financial state, one's attachments to material things, and so on. And some people are genetically more prone to disease than others, regardless of life events. A man with a family history of heart disease, for example, may be more at risk than others.

Minor stresses

These are what Professor Richard Lazarus calls the everyday hassles—commuting on a crowded train, contending with a snarling boss, wondering how to keep on the right side of a fussy husband or a bossy wife. Such hassles are minor only in that they do not immediately transform our lives as the death of a spouse or a jail sentence would. Indeed Lazarus believes that daily hassles have a far bigger impact than the life events listed by Holmes and Rahe. He and his colleagues even drew up a 'daily hassle measure'. Testing it on 100 people aged between 45 and 65 they found it to be a more sensitive indicator of vulnerability to disease than the scale drawn up by Holmes and Rahe.

There are different kinds of 'minor' stress, some ephemeral, some naggingly persistent. They are an inescapable part of daily living and in combination and over a relatively short period can weaken our resistance to illness.

Good stress

Yet stress is not all black, not all 'distressing' to use Hans Selye's terminology. Some forms of stress are immensely stimulating. Selye coined the word

Cross references
Anxiety neurosis **170**
Predicting reactions to stress **165**
Use of tranquillisers **174**

Bereavement
is one of the most stressful events in most people's lives. 'Dying of a broken heart' is more than a romantic idiom; statistics show that there is a greater incidence of fatal heart attacks in the months immediately following bereavement of a close relative or friend.

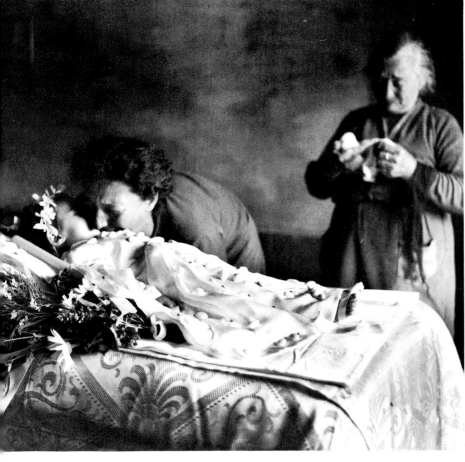

Stressful occupations
are by definition those that demand a high level of alertness and concentration for long periods. Air traffic controllers, aware of the appalling consequences of even small errors, are particularly prone to stress diseases. So are doctors whose responsibility for others' lives is a heavy burden.

'eustress' to describe constructive and enjoyable stress. Sexual intercourse, for example, can be extremely stressful if one measures its effect on adrenaline flow, heart rate and so on. An athlete or a parachutist subjects himself to stress—stress is part of winning, of experiencing one of life's ultimate sensations. Karajan conducting the Berlin Philharmonic through a Beethoven symphony is under stress—sweat pours off his face, adrenaline pumps around his circulation, his heart pounds . . . Yet this is the human machine seen at its best, at the very peak of creative coordination. This is the kind of intense short term stress which evolution has equipped us to cope with.

The lingering effects of acute stress

Despite the note of optimism sounded in the paragraph above, there is evidence that extremely harrowing experiences which have apparently been assimilated and forgotten may give rise to what Professor Irving Janis of Yale University has called 'latent traumatic neurosis'. The effects of trauma linger and reverberate, bringing about episodic or permanently incapacitating personality changes. A latent traumatic neurosis may go undetected for many years until a new crisis revives the feelings and ideas related to the original trauma; at this point all the former acute symptoms come flooding back. Many psychologists agree that people with a past history of traumatic stress experiences are likely to react adversely to similar future stress encounters. They are likely to demonstrate far more anxiety, greater physiological stress reactivity and poorer intellectual functioning under new yet similar traumatic circumstances than people with no such experiences.

American psychologists R. L. Leopold and H. Dillon demonstrated this by conducting a study of survivors of a particular maritime explosion, focussing solely on those who had shown anxiety symptoms after the tragedy but who were assumed to have completely recovered. Examining them some four years after the explosion, they discovered that 70 per cent continued to exhibit typical traumatic neurosis symptoms. The same kind of results emerged from studies of survivors of the Holocaust and Vietnam. Studies of American World War II victims examined after 20 years of civilian life also showed that the majority (70 per cent) still suffered from the anxiety symptoms which had incapacitated them under combat conditions. The assumption that they had recovered from their harrowing wartime experiences was disproved.

Sadly, therefore, we must assume that in many cases the disappearance of acute anxiety and stress symptoms merely masks certain permanent personality changes in the form of lower tolerance to stress and greater vulnerability to anxiety.

Who is normal - society or the individual?

Most of us at one time or another have seen someone whose behaviour in public is both eye-catching and grossly abnormal. Behaviour that is obviously peculiar presents us with the only observable evidence of abnormality or pathology. Yet it is often difficult to decide for certain when someone's behaviour actually is bizarre: not all aberrations from the 'normal' can be labelled 'mad'. Suppose a usually warm and outgoing friend becomes progressively withdrawn and suspicious. You may feel that he or she needs professional help but at the same time you would hesitate to use the description 'insane' or even that frequently misapplied word 'neurotic'.

There are two methods of looking at abnormality and various diagnostic criteria are derived from them. First, there is what is known as the *evolutionary* definition of abnormal behaviour which describes it as 'maladaptive for the individual and ultimately for mankind as a species'. This definition can be extended by the argument that behaviour is abnormal if it interferes with a person's, or a society's, chances of complete well-being. This definition is influenced greatly by the World Health Organization's definition of 'health' formulated in 1960, namely "a state of complete physical, mental and social well-being and not merely the absence of disease and infirmity".

Second, there is the *statistical* definition of abnormality which classifies pathological behaviour by setting the standards of the particular society we live in against the way we as individuals act. According to this definition, very uncommon behaviour is abnormal because 'normality' is closely equated with conformity; given such a definition a genius may be regarded as so 'different' from other members of society as to be 'mad'; on the other hand a soldier who, as a part of a common standard, may have to kill is accepted as perfectly normal. Social conformity too varies from culture to culture: in some cultures it is common and acceptable for people to go into a trance-like emotional state; in Western countries many psychiatrists would associate this same state with catatonic schizophrenia.

Many psychologists and psychiatrists adopt a strictly pragmatic approach: anyone seeking help is regarded as a candidate for therapy. Labels such as 'abnormal' may then be seen as unnecessary. The goal of therapy is not simply to get rid of odd behaviour but also to foster the fullest development and most wholesome awareness possible.

This does not help to diagnose actual mental illness which is not necessarily the same as abnormality. Somebody has actually to decide whether the person is mentally ill or not. For many years this decision conformed to the 'medical model' built into psychiatry. Mental disturbances, in this model, are thought of as primarily caused by genetic or organic malfunction; abnormal behaviour is therefore a symptom of underlying causes and diseases are treated in hospitals by doctors and psychiatrists.

This medically-orientated approach has been severely criticised by radical psychiatrists such as R. D. Laing and Thomas Szasz. Laing has criticised the traditional concept of mental illness and the authoritarianism of traditional psychotherapy. He has also criticised psychiatric wards and mental hospitals, electro-convulsive shock therapy and the use of drugs in psychiatry. Instead of seeing abnormal behaviour as the result of a person's past history or disease, Laing sees the cause of abnormal behaviour as the current breakdown of his or her ability to interact and adjust. Szasz believes that the relationship between a hospital psychiatrist and a patient is similar to that of master and slave rather than physician and adult patient. This radical school argues that it could be postulated that so-called 'mental illness' is simply a healthy response to a sick society. Instead of treating the 'mentally ill' as passive patients, such radical psychiatrists believe that patients themselves should assume some active degree of responsibility for their behaviour management. Some psychiatrists regard 'mental illness' simply as deviant behaviour.

In a notable challenge to the conventional diagnosis and treatment of mental illness in 1973, David Rosenhan and seven of his associates adopted false identities and had themselves committed to various mental hospitals in the United States. They falsified certain information about their supposed complaints, claiming that they heard voices and so on, but gave truthful reports on their past histories and current circumstances. At 11 out of 12 hospitals these would-be patients were diagnosed as 'schizophrenic' and committed to psychiatric wards on the strength of their simulated abnormalities. Once inside, however, Rosenhan and his colleagues stopped simulating psychiatric symptoms and behaved as normally as possible in every way. Yet despite their public display of sanity, these pseudo-patients remained undetected. Each of them was eventually discharged with a diagnosis of 'schizophrenia in remission' after having been hospitalised for an average of 19 days. At no time did any hospital staff member realise that an admissions error had been made or that a perfectly normal person was being kept in an asylum for the insane. It was left to husbands, wives and colleagues of the pseudo-patients to secure their release.

Reassuringly, however, even during the last few years there has been a major change of ideas within psychology and psychiatry about concepts such as 'normality' and 'insanity'. Contemporary mental

Cross references
Stress 162
Tranquillisers and sleeping pills 174
Mental processes 163
Antidepressants 176

health specialists are working on fresh and effective approaches toward diagnosis and treatment.

Psychological discomfort can arise in many ways. Examples include guilt caused by an illicit love affair, tension in times of crisis, hopelessness in time of loss, or anxiety caused by work situations. One way of losing the discomfort may be simply to give up what is causing guilt or anxiety; another method may be to seek the comfort of religion during times of loss and crisis, though religion is no longer the powerful solace that it once was. But few people actually want to change their living situations. They would far rather turn to medically-prescribed drugs which make them feel better without having to relinquish the cause of stress or else wait for nature to take its course.

Sadly the taking of tranquillisers or sleeping pills has become a dominant part of life for an increasing number of people. Such people use drugs to stay awake, go to sleep or as a general aid for everyday living. For these people the net result is that feelings of self-control abate, there is a loss of self-confidence and the continuous use of drugs becomes the central reinforcer in their lives. Once this pattern becomes well established, behaviour routines are organised around it. Problems are no longer confronted and coped with but are set aside and left unresolved. Even non-addicted people who lean on temporary psychological props during recovery from an emotional upheaval such as the end of a love affair or a divorce, often find it difficult to break the pillpopping habit.

Society defines
what is normal and what is abnormal. In some cultures nakedness is considered offensive—the people in this picture have committed the 'crime' of sunbathing in the nude. The 'naked savages' of Africa were considered 'ungodly' by the missionaries who came to convert them and were compelled to wear European clothes.

Neurosis: loss of joy in living

When a person feels persistently threatened by the potential dangers of life and unable to cope with them he or she may gradually come to rely to a large extent on a neurotic defence pattern. Such a pattern is characterised by a loss of meaning and joy in life. The neurotic typically feels helpless and useless and acts in such a way as to lessen discomfort or 'unpleasure' rather than strive for positive accomplishment.

Anxiety neurosis This is the most common of the neurotic responses. Throughout the Western world tens of millions of people suffer from anxiety neurosis. One in six readers of this book may well have consulted a general medical practitioner about the problem, which manifests itself as an overwhelming feeling of anxiety. Medical examinations reveal no organic causes and the individual is pronounced perfectly healthy. But neurotics know and feel otherwise. They fail to cope with their overwhelming anxiety and their minds are continually churning. They perspire, have heart palpitations, muscular pains and continuous attacks of breathlessness. A declaration of 'no known medical cause' simply feeds the cycle of anxiety which, in turn, entrenches feelings of helplessness.

This phenomenon is known as 'free-floating anxiety' because it does not appear to be anchored to a specific source. Psychotherapy is used to try and identify the source of the problem and institute a reasonable way of handling it.

Phobias By contrast a person with a phobia attaches this 'free-floating anxiety' to a specific object in the environment. Typically such objects are not a source of physical harm or danger. Phobics realise the irrationality of their reaction but this realisation serves only to make their anxiety worse. There are many theories about phobias but one way of explaining the phenomenon is that a phobic tries to handle serious internal conflicts by externalising them. If the object is external the phobic can attach his anxiety to it and avoid it. But in reality it is the 'self' which is being avoided. Self-confrontation is usually too painful, so the external object epitomises all that should be avoided. The prospect, for example, of going outside, crossing the road, seeing a bird or a spider, may terrify phobics to the point of total incapacity, which may be, of course, what they want.

Behavioural psychologists have, however, successfully treated large numbers of phobics. Fear of travel, for example, is a common phobia. Treatment begins with subjects taking a train journey in a group together with a therapist. Subsequently they travel without the therapist but with the members of the group able to comfort one another along the way.

Down and out
and nowhere to sleep but the street. Every city in the world has its quota of destitutes, many of them ill in body and mind—alcoholism and schizophrenia are not uncommon. Because such people rarely go to the doctor's, their condition stays untreated, often until they are admitted to casualty after collapsing or injuring themselves.

Vincent van Gogh suffered from depression hallucinations and epilepsy. In 1890 he attempted suicide by swallowing paint; three months later he shot himself. The tortured state of his mind can be guessed at from his brushwork. This painting, done towards the end of his life, shows the garden of Docteur Gachet, a friend who gave him psychiatric treatment.

Obsessive compulsive neurosis Also a form of neurotic behaviour, this is thought to stem from guilt feelings and repressed desires. It incorporates two separate reactions which occur together so frequently that they are regarded clinically as two aspects of a single behaviour pattern.

Most people have recurrent nagging thoughts like worries about leaving the car lights on or locking the door of the house. But such niggling thoughts are trivial when compared to neurotic obsessional thoughts which can disable an individual completely. Such neurotics cannot concentrate on anything but their obsession.

Hysterical neurosis Everyone tries to avoid unpleasant situations. But when this type of defence is taken to its extreme and includes an actual loss of motor or sensory function, it is known as a hysterical neurosis.

An example of hysterical behaviour is that of a husband who, on his way to the hospital to see his baby for the first time, was involved in an automobile crash. Although quite uninjured he

Cross references
Stress 162
Tranquillisers and sleeping pills 174
Antidepressants 176
Responding to emergencies 74

stumbled away completely blind. Intensive opthalmic investigation revealed no organic reasons for his blindness. Four months later, a clinical psychologist solved the mystery: the man was bitter because his wife had conceived under false pretences. It was suggested to him that he may have deliberately crashed the automobile and that he became blind so that he would not have to set eyes on his child, the source of his resentment. Offered this interpretation, the man regained his sight almost miraculously.

This particular example is of conversion hysteria and it is not an isolated case. Cases of sudden paralysis or loss of speech, sight, hearing or feeling, all without medical foundation, are well documented. Hysterical symptoms last as long as the underlying conflicts remain unresolved.

Amnesia This is another means of wiping out a system of failed 'coping processes' and an unhappy past. The amnesiac 'disowns' himself to avoid unbearable conflict. In doing so he gives himself a fresh start to a new life.

Hypochondria This is yet another sort of neurotic response. Most people have been jokingly accused, or have accused others, of being hypochondriacs. Clinical hypochondria, however, is a serious problem—the victims are really ill. Typically the hypochondriac has a morbid preoccupation with every minor bodily ailment, believing it to be the first sign of a very serious disease. Some psychologists feel that hypochondriacs enjoy their so-called poor health as a means of gaining 'secondary attention' in the form of sympathy and favours from others.

Depressive neurosis This is characterised by distortion of reality, the over-exaggeration of problems, pessimism, and intense sadness for an abnormally long period of time. Together with this morbid state go such complaints as irritability, boredom, lack of concentration, loss of sleep and appetite, a poor self-image and eventually poor physical health.

Neurotic depression usually emerges after the loss of someone close, a failure of some sort, or even as a result of constant frustration. There is little or no connection between the reality of what has happened and the individual's subjective evaluation of it. To the depressive, subjective reality is the only reality and it is always tinged with fatalism, unhappiness and pain. Many depressives take either drink or drugs just to keep going.

Manic depression This manifests itself as fits of severe depression alternating with periods of mania. In some cases, however, only one of these conditions may manifest itself. Manic-depression is

not in most cases a continuous illness; about 50 per cent of those who have it suffer only a single attack but some may have repeated attacks.

The manic phase is characterised by lively behaviour, enthusiasm, much movement, great self-confidence, and increased alertness and sharp sensory perceptions—lights for example may look brighter or noises sound louder. These symptoms may indeed sound very desirable but their tolerable form can give way suddenly to acute mania in which there may be confusion, delusions of omniscience and omnipotence, insensitivity to others, aggressiveness, especially in response to criticism, and hallucinations. This phase may be an attempt by the sufferer to stave off the depressive part of the cycle and it intensifies as desperation sets in.

The alternate phase, depression, produces feelings of hopelessness and inability to derive pleasure from anything and such feelings can grow progressively worse. Characteristically depressives sleep for only four or five hours a night. As a result of this sleeplessness and consequent fatigue, the sufferer may lose all power to act although he may, curiously, rally at about five o'clock every afternoon. The sufferer may become obsessed with thoughts of sin and death. Suicide is a real risk, especially after the trough of depression has been passed and some energy returns. Before that it is possible to be too depressed to take suicidal action.

Many cases of manic depression are now thought to be due to biochemical imbalances and they may even be partly hereditary. But it can also be associated with an overload of responsibility during childhood. Manic depression is often treated successfully with drugs.

Illegal drug taking
is a serious and still growing problem. Drug abuse is greatest among young people, many of whom reject and feel rejected by society. It is not only 'hard' drugs that are misused: illegal use of benzodiazepine tranquillisers is increasing.

Biofeedback
This man is attempting to control his migraine by reducing his skin temperature. The machine buzzes when his skin temperature rises, and he has to try to stop the machine buzzing. With feedback it is possible to control reactions which are not normally under voluntary control. Similar techniques have been used to control heart rate and blood pressure.

Psychosis: adrift from reality

According to an old joke a neurotic knows that three and three make six, and worries about it; a psychotic knows that three and three make seven and is quite happy about it. But psychosis is no laughing matter; it is far more deviant and pathologically intense than neurosis. Psychotics lose touch with reality as they act out their fantasies in life, and are usually quite barren of emotion and appear shabby and disorientated. Since they do not differentiate between their own (subjective) reality and the real (objective) world around them, they do not understand that their behaviour is in the least unusual or bizarre.

A psychosis is not simply an extension of a neurotic illness; in fact neurotics do not ordinarily become psychotics. Instead the dividing line between the two is stark and dramatic.

There are two main categories of psychoses, organic and functional. If a psychotic reaction is caused by some physical ailment such as brain damage or biochemical imbalance, it is called an organic psychosis. In contrast functional psychoses have their roots in a breakdown of behavioural function. The functional psychoses include three well-known psychotic states: paranoid reactions, affective reactions and schizophrenic reactions.

Paranoid reactions Although no laughing matter, the delusions which characterise paranoid reactions can best be illustrated by another joke. Two psychotics are having a heated argument in their ward about which one of them is Moses. "I know I'm Moses. God told me so!" says one with conviction. A third patient interjects "Not true, not true. I never told you anything of the sort." Here the delusions are delusions of grandeur. Another sort of delusion common in the paranoid state is that of reference. When this takes hold,

Spider phobia

A phobia is an intense, irrational fear of a particular object or situation. Phobias persist mainly because phobics invest such a lot of effort in avoiding the things they fear. So far, behaviour therapy offers the most successful treatment: the phobic is progressively 'desensitised'. The psychoanalytic view of phobias is that they are inner anxieties which become attached to external objects.

Trance and ritual

propel the mind into an abnormally suggestible state. The participants in this voodoo ceremony in Haiti are totally under the influence of the *bocor* or witchdoctor and will do all manner of things at his command, and not remember them afterwards. Trance is one of 20 different states of consciousness studied by psychologists.

Electronic circuits

are a good analogy for the structure of the brain. The brain contains about 10,000 million cells, each one making contact with hundreds, if not thousands, of others. If any part of this intricate circuitry is damaged or disconnected—as the result of accident, poisoning, heart failure, stroke, or neurological disease— faculties may be impaired and behaviour may change.

Cross references   Antipsychotic drugs **178**   Chronic schizophrenia **179**   Dopamine and schizophrenia **180**

psychotics see everything that happens around them as being aimed against them. For example, two old people sitting innocently on a park bench may appear to the tormented psychotic to be plotting his or her death. Delusions of persecution are similar to those of reference. The typical sufferer complains that everyone dislikes him.

Intense inferiority complexes and unrealistically high goals are thought to be among the precipitating factors of paranoid reactions.

Schizophrenia About one person in 100, in any culture for which figures are known, will develop schizophrenia. The current interest in schizophrenia can be ascribed partly to R. D. Laing who claimed that the schizophrenic reaction was the only sane way of dealing with an insane world; so-called normal people are mad because they have not adjusted to the craziness of life.

Whatever the merits of Laing's theories, the description of the condition is not in dispute. Characteristically the schizophrenic's way of thinking does not match the reality the rest of us know. Disordered perceptions and emotions mean that he or she respond to stimuli in what appear to be quite inappropriate ways. Extreme withdrawal is a common feature of schizophrenia.

Variations of schizophrenia range from the simple, with less obvious symptoms and a gradual withdrawal from people, to the 'silliness' and giggling and regressed mannerisms of the hebephrenic. A paranoid schizophrenic usually has persecutory or grandiose delusions and hallucinations and is frequently aggressive and hostile. Catatonic schizophrenia is characterised either by the assumption of fixed postures or trances for hours on end, or excessive and sometimes violent activity and excitement.

Adolf Hitler
and other charismatic leaders exert an influence on their followers that is in many ways similar to that of the voodoo *bocor*. Personal judgement is suspended and obedience given, regardless of the consequences. In a famous series of experiments psychologists found that perfectly ordinary people were prepared to administer lethal electric shocks to people just as ordinary as themselves when persuaded to do so by an authority figure. Those who disobeyed showed every sign of acute stress.

Managing anxiety and insomnia

Opium, an ancient remedy for monotony and boredom. For thousands of years man has used psychotropic substances to escape into a world of fantasy and illusion. The cultures of ancient America had their 'sacred mushroom' (*Psilocybin mexicana*) and mescalin (from the cactus *Lophophora williamsi*); their 20th century descendants hallucinate with 'angel dust' (phencyclidine) and the fumes of glue and aerosols.

Reasons for drug abuse are much the same the world over; here the drug is opium, elsewhere the drug is alcohol or nicotine. We have a deep-rooted tendency to opt for the quick solution, to want more than humdrum reality, to obliterate identity when the going gets tough. But the price may be enslavement.

Macbeth	Canst thou not minister to a mind diseas'd;
	Pluck from the memory a rooted sorrow;
	Raze out the written troubles of the brain
	And with some sweet oblivious antidote,
	Cleanse the stuff'd bosom of that perilous stuff
	Which weighs upon the heart?
Doctor	Therein the patient must minister to himself.

Macbeth, Act 5, Scene 3

Aldous Huxley wrote in *The Doors of Perception* that the urge to escape from selfhood and the environment is in almost everyone almost all the time. Mind-affecting drugs provide a vehicle of escape. Drugs that soften the sharp edges of reality have been used throughout history and by most cultures. The effects of alcohol and opium were known in Neolithic times. In 1680 Sydenham regarded opium as the most universal and effective of the remedies "which it has pleased Almighty God to give to man to relieve his sufferings". More recently alcohol, tobacco and caffeine have been used widely in European culture. Other intoxicants, stimulants and hallucinogens such as cannabis, cocaine and mescaline, have been employed on a large scale in many other parts of the world.

Such use is primarily *social* rather than *medical*. This distinction is both important and topical, for pharmacological developments over the last 30 years have made available a new range of drugs for the treatment of dis-ease (as opposed to disease) and mental illness.

Have people come to regard these psychotropic or mind-altering drugs as a universal panacea for a wide range of emotional and social problems? It seems they have. In his report 'The prescribing of psychotropic drugs in general practice', the British researcher Professor Peter Parrish wrote: "Psychotropic drug medication is expected to provide happiness when we are sad; energy when we are tired; sleep when we are wakeful; and clear thinking when our minds are cloudy."

There are dangers in using drugs as a comforting means of escape from painful realities because unhappiness is not a wholly negative emotion. It provides us with an incentive for taking stock of our problems and doing something positive about them. That is not to deny the enormous importance and benefits of drugs in modern medicine.

Tranquillisers and sleeping pills

Tranquillisers and sleeping pills are the most widely used of all prescribed medicines. Tranquillisers, sometimes called sedatives, are used to allay people's anxieties, to calm them and help them deal with stress. Sleeping tablets are similar, but are given at night to induce sleep, especially in anxiety sufferers. In fact most tranquillisers taken in a single large dose at night act as sleeping tablets, conversely sleeping tablets taken in small amounts during the day have useful tranquillising effects.

Tranquillisers comprise many different groups of chemical compounds, but the benzodiazepines are the most commonly used. Now regarded as obsolete because of their various drawbacks, the barbiturates are being phased out and replaced by the benzodiazepines. The only current usage of barbiturates (apart from phenobarbitone in the treatment of epilepsy) is for severe intractable insomnia.

Use of tranquillisers Tranquillisers are used to lessen anxiety in whatever context it arises.

Most prescriptions for tranquillisers are for patients who develop symptoms of anxiety in response to relatively minor stresses, sometimes no more than the usual wear and tear of everyday life. Problems pile up, the person despairs of ever coping with them, and anxiety symptoms may develop. Sometimes such anxiety feelings are entirely in the mind—a sense of apprehension, a fear of dying, irritability, intense pressure of thought, and so on. Many other symptoms are bodily and can affect almost any system in the body—palpitations, sweating, stomach upset, diarrhoea, trembling, faintness and the urge to urinate are the commonest. Sometimes these bodily symptoms dominate the clinical picture so that the patient complains primarily of palpitations or shortness of breath rather than of anxiety; his general practitioner may even refer him to a heart specialist to exclude the possibility of heart trouble.

Many patients with anxiety attacks recover within a few weeks as the stresses lessen and as they learn to cope both with the stresses and with their anxiety feelings. But it is doubtful whether tranquillisers hasten this process, though they certainly lessen the severity of the symptoms in the interim. Tranquillisers are invaluable in lessening anxiety to manageable levels.

Some individuals suffer from chronic anxiety; they have been anxious all their lives, anxiety is built into their personality. For some of these people tranquilliser drugs become 'chemical crutches' for years on end.

Use of sleeping tablets The function of sleep is ill-understood; the harmful effects of insomnia can only be related with certainty to feelings of tiredness the next day. Sleep requirements vary from person to person: some require 10 hours, others five or even less; the average is between seven and eight. Elderly people require less sleep than they did when younger. Also many people have unreal expectations of sleep and worry about the occasional broken night's sleep.

A few special causes of insomnia exist but almost

Cross references
Anxiety neurosis **170**
Depressive neurosis **171**
Stress **162**
Sleep need **194**

always sleep difficulties can be traced to underlying anxiety or depression, or to wrong expectations of sleep. People who are depressed sleep for only a few hours and wake up very early. The insomnia can be treated by treating the depression. Patients with insomnia due to anxiety have problems getting off to sleep. Once asleep, they generally sleep well unless wakened by nightmares. This type of insomnia can be treated by giving a large dose of a long-acting tranquilliser before sleeping.

Long-term use Both tranquillisers and sleeping tablets tend to lose their effectiveness after a time. There is little evidence that tranquillisers remain effective beyond six months or a year of use, though some individual patients report continuing benefit. With sleeping tablets, the effects also seem to wane. Thus, everyone who has been on such treatment for several months or more should be assessed from time to time by their doctor to confirm that some benefit is being maintained. Too often prescriptions are renewed automatically.

Other uses Drugs like diazepam (Valium) are used in contexts other than the psychiatric, as an intravenous injection before dental procedures, for example. They are useful relaxants of muscle spasm and so have wide use in treating orthopaedic injuries involving muscle spasm, slipped discs and painful muscles. They are less useful in treating muscle spasm in cerebral spastic patients.

Tranquillisers are used by doctors in all specialities to treat patients who seem anxious about their symptoms or where no definite cause of the symptoms can be found.

Side effects All drugs have unwanted side effects and the tranquillisers are no exception. However, benzodiazepines such as diazepam have few side effects, apart from drowsiness and lassitude.

Uncommon but more serious reactions are forgetfulness and aggressive impulses. Typically, such lapses occur when a patient is starting on tranquillisers or shortly after an increase in dosage.

Sudden aggressive outbursts, often totally out of character, are a somewhat paradoxical reaction to tranquillisers. Some baby-battering by mothers has been associated with the prescription of tranquillisers. Often a reduction in dose reduces aggressive feelings. That said, most patients on tranquillisers find themselves less aggressive.

Overdose Unfortunately many people at the end of their tether seek escape by taking overdoses of drugs. With barbiturates this can be exceedingly dangerous: 20 times the usual dose can be fatal. Benzodiazepines such as diazepam (Valium) are much safer except in very young children. An overdose simply causes a deep sleep.

Psychotropic drugs are drugs which affect perception, mood and emotion, and they are prescribed for one in seven people in Europe and the United States each year. Antidepressants, tranquillisers and hypnotics are taken more by women than men, and more by old people. And they are not only prescribed for psychiatric problems. Just as often they are given to relieve the tensions and worries of being physically ill.

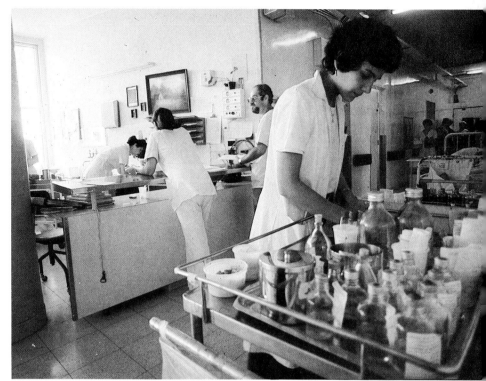

Drugs like this, bought from a chemist or even a supermarket without a prescription, are often taken by people with emotional and psychological problems. Every year vast quantities of analgesics, laxatives and tonics are taken in the mistaken belief that such problems are physical. It is not uncommon for depression and anxiety to be experienced as aches and pains.

Managing depression

Drug addiction
Dependence on narcotic drugs—those derived from opium and synthetic drugs with similar action—is a major problem in many countries. This picture shows a heroin addict 'mainlining', injecting the drug directly into a vein. Opiates and opioids mimic the effect of naturally occuring substances in the brain called enkephalins.

Over a period some patients on barbiturates or benzodiazepines edge up to ten or more times the usual dose. Having become tolerant to these large doses, they do not appear unduly sleepy or unco-ordinated. When they stop taking the drug, severe withdrawal symptoms occur, including anxiety and insomnia, trembling, weakness, aches and pains and general upset, and even occasionally epileptic fits or hallucinations. Even patients who have been on normal doses of benzodiazepines for six months or more can show mild withdrawal symptoms. Patients who have been taking sleeping tablets for a long time often have difficulty stopping because their sleep may remain disturbed for several nights after discontinuing the tablets.

Extent of usage Use of tranquillisers is increasing gradually. About one in five women and one in ten men take them at some time during the course of a year. About one in 40 adults takes these drugs *every* day of the year. Usage is greater among the elderly than the young.

Much concern and misgiving has been expressed over the magnitude of tranquilliser use. Generally the argument is that tranquillisers are over-used to assuage mental symptoms arising from poor social and economic conditions, and that attempts should be made to correct the underlying problems instead. The problem of dependence may be more widespread than than we realise. There is evidence that people taking tranquillisers all the time may be functioning below par intellectually.

We have not yet developed the perfect tranquilliser, and even if we did, it might be better to develop alternative methods of treating anxiety and insomnia.

Antidepressants

Antidepressants (better termed 'antidepressives') are drugs used to treat people with depressive illnesses. They are distinct from drugs like the amphetamines, which merely fight fatigue and perk you up but do nothing about the depression.

Depression as a mental condition ranges from the normal sadness which we all experience from time to time, to severe and even life-threatening 'lows'. The most typical depressive reactions follow bereavement or physical illness. The intensity and type of depression in such reactions is readily comprehensible to an outside observer—it's only natural, we say. Such reactions usually lessen and disappear as the person comes to terms with his loss or illness; drugs are neither necessary nor advisable.

In non-situational depression, usually of greater severity, the person's reactions are more morbid in character; he mulls over his past, blames himself for his predicament, can see no future and may contemplate suicide. The depressive emotion is anguishing in nature and permeates all the person's thoughts and actions: actions are slowed and

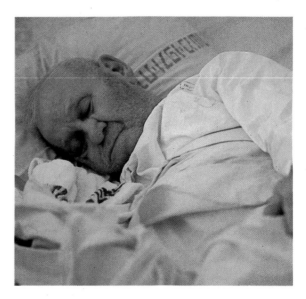

lethargic, it becomes difficult to concentrate or remember things, life loses its sparkle, relationships and friendships become meaningless. Bodily reactions may include poor sleep with early morning wakening, loss of appetite and weight, frigidity or impotence, and a general running down of bodily function. Depression is often worse in the morning than in the evening. People who are depressed not only look depressed, they look physically debilitated as well.

Very severely depressed people can become so retarded that they neglect themselves or present a high risk of suicide. Electroconvulsive therapy (ECT) is usually highly effective in such cases. The patient is given a general anaesthetic and a drug which relaxes all the muscles, then a brief electrical pulse is passed across the head which induces electrical discharges in the brain. When the patient wakes, he feels muzzy but usually less depressed. A course of six treatments is usually adequate. Full discussion of the pros and cons of ECT with the patient and his relatives is essential. Used sparingly in severely depressed patients ECT can be life-saving. Used on less ill patients, the response is not so satisfactory.

Depressive illnesses are often accompanied by some degree of anxiety which may need treatment in its own right. Contrary to popular belief, patients who talk about committing suicide are *more*, not *less*, likely to make the attempt than those who deny such intent. Drug overdose is the most frequent method.

Tricyclic antidepressants These are the most commonly used antidepressants today. They have complex biochemical actions but essentially they increase the concentrations in the brain of 'neurotransmitters', chemical messenger substances which connect nerve cells and thereby increase brain activity. Patients with depression

Hypnotic drugs
induce sleep and improve
its quality, important in
recovery from many
psychiatric disorders.

An alternative to drugs
This Thai girl is being
treated for opium addiction
by a native healer. We in
the West prefer to rely, and
almost certainly over-rely,
on chemotheraphy.

Physical violence,
especially in a family
context, is usually the result
of emotional disturbance,
but not necessarily of
adverse social conditions.
Baby battering and wife
bashing are not symptomatic
of any one class or income
group. Some psychotropic
drugs, especially the
benzodiazepines,
occasionally cause violence.

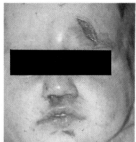

appear to have low levels of these substances.
However, the biochemistry of depression is little
understood at present.

Patients who respond best to tricyclic
antidepressants are those with depressive illnesses
of moderate intensity associated with bodily
changes such as weight loss. More severely ill
patients respond better to ECT, the less ill to
counselling and reassurance. Typically, a
depressive patient is started on a low dose of
antidepressant, especially if he is elderly, because
the side effects are often unpleasant (see below).
The dose is then slowly increased until the
depression starts to lift. This may take up to four
weeks to occur and about one in five patients do not
respond satisfactorily. The first signs of response
are usually an improvement in sleep and appetite,
and arrest of weight loss. Then the patient begins
to feel more active and alert, can concentrate and
remember things better, and begins to take an
interest in life again. Good days may be
interspersed with occasional bad days when the
depression and gloom return, but gradually his
mood lifts. Full remission of symptoms may take
several weeks or even months. At this juncture the
dose of antidepressant is usually lowered to about
half the therapeutic dose. Patients are then
maintained on this reduced dose for several more
weeks or months because relapse can supervene if
medication is withdrawn too soon. This suggests
that the therapeutic action of antidepressants is not
to *cure* depression but merely to hold the symptoms
in check until the illness lifts of its own accord.

Side effects The major problem with
antidepressants is that they have a range of
unpleasant side effects. Many are very sedative,
producing drowsiness and torpor, others less so,
though sometimes their sedative action is useful in
treating patients who are both anxious and
depressed at the same time.

Other side effects include a very dry mouth,
constipation and blurring of vision, effects which
can be intolerable especially in the elderly, though
some of the newer antidepressants are less
distressing in this respect. Side effects like these
often lead to patients refusing to take any
medication or taking it erratically, though most
people find that if they persist with their treatment
these effects wear off.

Tricyclic antidepressants are dangerous in
over-dosage so care must be taken in prescribing
them to patients who present some risk, however
slight, of suicide. The best strategem is for the
doctor to give the drugs into the care of a
responsible relative or friend.

Antidepressants do not cause dependence or
addiction, which is fortunate since chronic
depressive illnesses require long-term therapy.

Antipsychotic drugs

Monoamine oxidase inhibitors These antidepressants (MAOIs for short) are much less commonly used than the tricyclics because they have severer side effects and are generally less effective. They are useful in patients who suffer from somewhat untypical depressive illnesses, characterised by excessive anxiety or preoccupation about bodily functions such as bowel action. The two most commonly used drugs in this group are phenelzine and tranylcypromine. Dosage at the start of treatment is usually low but is then increased steadily. Even so, a delay of four weeks or even more is seen before response occurs. Patients feel dizzy if the dose is too high, or may develop swelling of the legs.

The major problem with the MAOIs concerns their interaction with some foods and some other medicines. Monoamine oxidase is an enzyme which breaks down and so inactivates chemical messengers in the brain. By destroying this enzyme, MAOIs prevent the breakdown of these substances and so increase their concentration. But monoamine oxidase is also present in the gut and liver where it inactivates harmful substances in the food preventing them from getting into the blood stream. Destroy monoamine oxidase in the gut and the body's defences are breached. Patients taking MAOIs must not eat foods which tend to ferment during digestion (some cheeses, yeast extracts, some wines). The chemist who makes up their prescription usually gives them a full list of foods to avoid. If eaten inadvertently, severe headaches and dangerous rises in blood pressure may ensue. Other drugs such as cough medicines and nose drops may also interact.

Because of these complicating restrictions on diet, MAOIs are popular neither with doctors nor with patients, but they are useful when the occasional patient fails to respond to a tricyclic antidepressant.

Other antidepressants Several other substances have been used as antidepressants with some success. One of the most interesting is tryptophan. This is natural amino acid, one of the building blocks of protein, and also changed into one of the chemical messengers believed to be deficient in depression. It is fairly effective in milder cases of depression and, as it has few side effects, is well tolerated especially by the elderly.

To summarise, then, the antidepressants are useful and effective drugs which curtail depression in the majority of patients, although treatment may need to be continued for some time. Their side effects are a major disadvantage but compounds currently being developed and introduced are less culpable in this respect.

Antipsychotic drugs

Antipsychotic drugs are used to treat the symptoms of psychotic illnesses such as schizophrenia and mania. They come into the category of 'major tranquillisers', which is a little confusing, because they differ fundamentally from the tranquillisers used to treat anxiety. They are also known as 'neuroleptic' drugs, in acknowledgement of their neurological side effects. The main use of antipsychotic drugs is in the management of schizophrenia, the most serious of the common psychiatric disorders. The first drug of a whole generation of similar antipsychotics was chlorpromazine, introduced in 1953.

Non-psychiatric uses The antipsychotic drugs have a wide range of actions, some of which are useful in non-psychiatric conditions, in preventing nausea, vomiting, and some forms of vertigo, for example. They also are useful in tranquillising patients with severe pain, although they do not affect pain directly as morphine does.

Use in acute psychoses The antipsychotic drugs are used to treat patients with overactive, disturbed, or aggressive behaviour, whether this is associated with schizophrenia, mania, or brain disorders of known origin. High doses may be needed but the dosage varies with the patient.

Use in acute schizophrenia The effect of antipsychotic drugs in schizophrenic patients seems rather more specific than a general tranquillising action. Many of the symptoms of schizophrenia not obviously related to overactivity also respond to them, in particular hallucinations and delusions. Even so, it may take several weeks of treatment combined with expert nursing before the symptoms subside sufficiently for the patient to be discharged from hospital. Many symptoms do not disappear completely but persist in a minor and muted form.

Schizophrenia is typically a relapsing illness with long periods of relative normality punctuated by acute episodes. The antipsychotic drugs lengthen the intervals between relapses, provided they are taken regularly. It is probable that complete prevention of relapses cannot be achieved but they can be postponed for long periods of time. On occasion, an incipient relapse can be aborted by a temporary increase in dosage. Schizophrenic patients are often reluctant to take medication indefinitely, or may stop taking their tablets without telling their doctor. In this context long-acting injectable antipsychotic drugs are particularly useful; if the patient fails to turn up for his injection, at least the doctor knows about it.

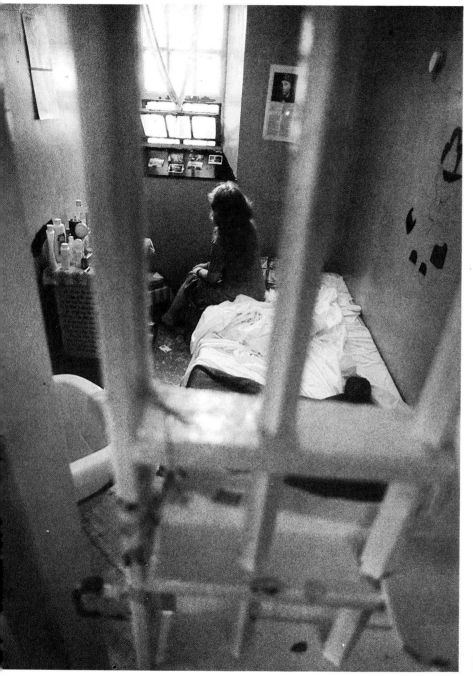

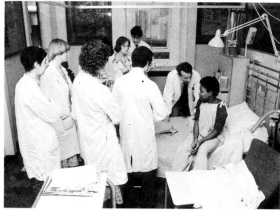

Psychological factors are important in physical disease. They may be part of the cause, or they may interfere with the process of recovery. Equally they can retard the progress of a disease or cure it. The 'will to live' can be vital for recovery.

Schizophrenia
The bizarre thought processes typical of schizophrenia are usually impossible for anyone else to follow, though they may appear completely logical to the person concerned. Schizophrenics are not withdrawn and inaccessible all of the time however; at intervals they behave quite normally. Drug treatment and expert care can bring great improvement, but drugs must be continued after recovery to reduce the risk of relapse.

Chronic schizophrenia Many patients become chronically socially incapacitated to the point where they must live either in a mental hospital or in some form of sheltered home or community. Their symptoms persist in a less severe form but seem rather less responsive to antipsychotic drugs than the more acute symptoms. Though symptoms of overactive brain function (hallucinations and delusions) often improve, signs of underactivity (lack of energy and initiative) may not.

Another form of chronic schizophrenia, which is milder and onsets in later life and is characterised by delusions of persecution, usually responds well to antipsychotic drugs.

Young children at home make a woman more vulnerable to depression. Many mothers tied to the home, often isolated, often resentful of their role and aware that their talents are under-used, turn to tranquillisers to help them through the day.

Dopamine and psychotic behaviour

In psychiatric hospitals today patients receive drug treatment, psychological treatment and expert nursing care. Since one of the main aims of treatment is to get patients well enough to return to a normal life as soon as possible, stays in hospital are usually short. The dangers of institutionalisation are now well recognised.

Side effects The commonest side effects with antipsychotics come under the general heading of movement disorders. Soon after starting treatment, acute spasms can occur necessitating a reduction in dosage. Another reaction is intense nervousness and restlessness of the limbs; again the dosage is reduced. The commonest such side effect is drug-induced parkinsonism. The patient becomes stiff, has an expressionless face, and develops a coarse tremor of the fingers, a condition closely resembling spontaneously occurring parkinsonism in old age. The dose of antipsychotic drug is reduced or an additional drug—an antiparkinsonian agent—given to combat the symptoms. However, the condition tends to diminish of it own accord.

The most troublesome effect of antipsychotic drugs is tardive (delayed) dyskinesia, characterised by repetitive twitches or twisting of the tongue, lips, mouth, face or limbs. It onsets after months or even years of antipsychotic treatment and tends to worsen gradually. In a few cases, serious complications arise, such as difficulty in swallowing food. In about half the number of patients so affected, dyskinesia persists even when medication is reduced or discontinued. Patients with this condition look unsightly, which makes their rehabilitation into the community more difficult. Because no drug treatment of tardive dyskinesia is satisfactory, it may be better to attempt to prevent the condition by periodically taking patients off

maintenance therapy for a month or two.

Antipsychotic drugs have a range of other side effects including dizziness, palpitations, dry mouth, blurring of vision, hormonal upsets and jaundice. Some of these are troublesome but most are relatively mild or uncommon. Each drug varies, and a patient inconvenienced by the side effects of one may be more comfortable on another.

Dopamine and schizophrenia Dopamine is one of the chemical messengers in the brain and is found particularly in areas of the brain concerned with the control of movement and emotional response. The antipsychotic drugs all share the ability to block dopamine action. This has given rise to the proposal that schizophrenic illnesses are associated with an excessive level of dopamine-controlled activity in the brain. Research is proceeding actively along these lines with encouraging results.

In conclusion, the antipsychotic drugs lessen the symptoms of psychosis whatever the cause. They are particularly effective in combating the symptoms of schizophrenia, especially those related to overactive brain function, but they do little to alter the long-term outlook for the condition. More research is needed to elucidate the biochemical mechanisms in the brain associated with schizophrenia. Also new drugs are being sought which will lessen psychotic symptoms without inducing movement disorders.

Body
maintenance

Health habits and longevity

An automobile performs better and lasts longer if it is driven carefully and serviced regularly. The body machine is the same. Yet it is often said that we take more care of our automobiles than we do of our bodies.

We service our automobiles regularly to prevent breakdown, knowing that the engine will seize up if the oil is not changed regularly, if the spark plugs are not renewed, and so on. We also recognise the importance of using the right kind of fuel to increase performance and prolong engine life.

How should we service our bodies? Before answering that question, let us look at the way we regard health. When we talk about it, we tend to think about sickness rather than 'wellness'—in other words, about broken down machines, not well-maintained ones.

When we say a person's health is good, we mean that he or she has no identifiable, serious disease. A nation's health is judged in the same way—by the number of deaths among infants, for example, or by the prevalence of heart disease, cancer and tuberculosis among the middle aged.

In the early part of this century the major challenge in medicine was to overcome diseases in infancy and communicable diseases. As a result, deaths from tuberculosis in the USA, to quote just one example, fell from 119 to 5 per 100,000 of the population between 1920 and 1960. Meanwhile, heart disease, cancer and stroke became the leading causes of death in the USA and Europe, and progress against these diseases was minimal.

Since then substantial gains against several chronic diseases have been made. The number of cases of coronary heart disease (CHD) increased dramatically in the USA up until the 1960s, accounting for more than a quarter of all deaths. The trend has now been reversed. The number of CHD deaths in the 1970s fell by some 2.5 per cent per year. Similarly, the number of deaths from strokes has fallen.

The picture is by no means all favourable. Lung cancer is now responsible for a quarter of all deaths from cancer, and the number of cases among women is now rising rapidly because more women are smoking. For many women sexual equality has become an equal chance to die in a painful, distressing way.

In the USA racial problems are reflected in health as well as in education, employment and other areas. Black people are more prone to premature death from disease and in every measurable way their health continues to lag behind that of the whites.

Yet, it is possible to contemplate a life of 60 or 70 years or more with minimal threat from disease. The character of the mid-20th-century health picture and the promise of what the rest of the century might bring inspired the founders of the

Freeways and skyscrapers are two of the most potent symbols of the 20th century, whose full impact may not be realised for years. How for example, do lack of exercise and psychological stress interact?

World Health Organization to define health in a new way, as "physical, mental and social well-being, not merely the absence of disease or infirmity".

This concept has been criticised as 'woolly'. But is it? We know that the length of our lives is influenced by countless factors, only some of which we control. These range through cataclysms of nature, accidents, epidemic diseases and hereditary endowments, to a host of less obvious and more subtle influences such as environmental pollution, stress and lifestyle. It is lifestyle with which we are concerned principally here because there is a strong correlation between lifestyle and life expectancy.

The Alameda County study

Studies at the Human Population Laboratory of the

Cross references
Coronary heart disease **96**
Lung cancer **121**
Smoking **200**
Women and smoking **204**

Peace of mind
is a precondition for
achieving the famous World
Health Organization
definition of health: 'a state
of complete physical, mental
and social well-being and
not merely the absence of
disease and infirmity'. A
satisfying job in a tightly knit
community, such as on this
Israeli kibbutz, is one way
towards it.

Tension, anxiety
fear, loneliness and loss of
identity, are all part of living
in a big city. Yet all over the
world the rural poor flock to
the cities to seek their
fortune. Many of them end
up in slums and shanty
towns, disillusioned,
diseased, and broken
in spirit.

The antidote to it all
Most people's cherished
wish is to 'get away from it
all'. Antidotes to high-speed
living can range from
passive relaxation, as here,
to dropping out or sailing
round the world.

California State Department of Public Health were
designed to explore the relationship between
health, in broad terms, and lifestyle. There is
nothing new in research like this, but most
programmes have examined small, selected
populations. In contrast, the Human Population
Laboratory surveyed a typical Californian urban
community, Alameda County, in a sample of nearly
7,000 people. These were fully representative of
the general adult population.

The study began in 1965 and follow-up has
shown a strong relationship between physical
health and longevity on the one hand, and what the
researchers called 'the seven health habits' on the
other. These habits were:
☐ Never smoking cigarettes
☐ Regular physical activity
☐ Moderate or no use of alcohol
☐ Seven to eight hours' sleep a day regularly
☐ Maintaining proper weight
☐ Eating breakfast
☐ Not eating between meals

The researchers assessed each and every one of
the sample according to the number of health
habits they practised. Following up the sample in
subsequent years they found a strong relationship
between the seven health habits and longevity.

For example, a 45-year-old man following six or
seven of the habits had a one in two chance of living
to the age of 78; those following four or five habits
of living to 73; zero to three habits of living to 67.
Thus, there was a difference of 11 years' life
expectancy between the first and last groups. In
women the difference was just over seven years.

Staying healthy longer

These are, of course, statistical findings and they do not take into account genetic factors—some people are better equipped than others to withstand the adverse effects of smoking or excess drinking. Nevertheless, follow-up showed that 717 people involved in the 1965 study had died by 1974. The results showed conclusively that subjects who had followed three or fewer health habits were more prone to premature death than the other groups.

The death rate among men following all seven health habits was only 43 per cent that of all men in the survey, and among women 62 per cent.

In every age group those who practised all seven health habits had, on average, better physical health than those who reported six. With one minor exception (the over 75s) there was a consistent progression towards better health at each age as the number of good health habits increased. Remarkably, however, the so-called 'physical health status' of the over 75s who followed all of the good practices was about the same as those aged 35–44 who followed fewer than three.

Let us look at various aspects of these health habits in more detail.

Sleep Respondents who usually slept seven to eight hours a night tended to be healthier than those who usually slept nine hours or more. The least healthy was the group which slept six hours or less. Results were similar for men and women.

Eating Data on eating habits suggest that erratic eaters have poorer health than those who eat regular meals. Those who ate breakfast almost every day or did not eat between meals reported slightly better physical health than those who skipped breakfast or ate between meals.

The population was also grouped according to another indicator of eating habits, the relationship of weight to height in terms of a scale of desirable weights prepared by the Metropolitan Life Insurance Company.

It was found that overweight people were less healthy, especially those who were markedly overweight. Men who were ten per cent or more underweight also reported poor physical health, but underweight women were not at such a disadvantage. Men with the best physical health were those less than five per cent underweight and up to 20 per cent overweight. Women who were underweight or less than ten per cent overweight were slightly more healthy than average.

Physical activity Respondents were given a list of leisure activities and asked; 'How often do you do any of these things?' The list included active sports, swimming or taking long walks, working in the garden, doing physical exercises, taking weekend automobile trips and hunting or fishing.

The urban jogger has become a familiar sight in many parts of the world in the last decade. There is strong evidence that exercising to the point of breathlessness for at least a few minutes each day considerably reduces the chances of a heart attack, and reduces the risk of dying suddenly from a heart attack even more.

Cross references
Sleep need **194**
Diet **187**
Alcoholism **206**
Smoking **200**

Strap-hanging on the train, no longer a mainly male habit in these days of female equality, typefies much that is damaging to health in everyday urban life. Psychological stress, physical strain, passive inhalation of other people's cigarette smoke, lack of active movement—all come together here.

The relaxing apéritif is harmless enough in itself and may even be good for one after a frustrating day. Nevertheless alcoholism is now the fastest growing epidemic in the industrialised world, displacing lung cancer and coronary heart disease as the number one medical worry of the 1980s.

The public washerman is a common sight in many Middle Eastern and Asian countries. This laundry on the banks of the Layari river in Pakistan has changed little in appearance for centuries. The notorious 'dhobi itch', which affects the groin, is spread by laundry infected with skin fungi. *Dhobi* is Hindi for 'washerman', 'washerwoman'.

Those who took part in any of these activities had better physical health than those who did not. However, men involved in active physical sports were healthier than others. Similarly, a difference emerged between women who swam or went for long walks. Frequent working in the garden or frequent physical exercise was also beneficial.

Alcohol Respondents were asked how often they consumed wine, beer and liquor and how many drinks they had at each sitting. The physical health of those who reported five or more drinks at a sitting departed significantly from the average. However it was found that the health of those who did not drink at all did not differ significantly from that of moderate drinkers.

Smoking Not surprisingly it was found that people who had never smoked enjoyed better physical health than present or past smokers.

Working out a diet for today

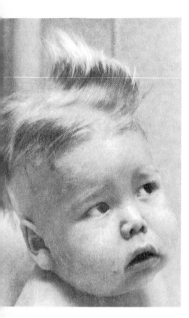

Childhood kwashiorkor
is one of the most pitiful
sights encountered by
tropical health workers.
Essentially the result of too
little protein after weaning,
it overlaps with another
condition called marasmus,
where both protein and
calories are in short supply.
Swelling of the face, mottled
skin, and straight patchy
hair are typical features of
kwashiorkor.

Coronary heart disease and cancer are the principal causes of death in working adults living in Western countries today. Although the causes of these diseases have for some time been believed to be rooted in our modern way of life, it is only in the last 10 to 15 years that their relationship with diet has been explored.

Diet is believed to be one of the three major risk factors for coronary heart disease, the other two being smoking and high blood pressure. Studies in the UK and USA clearly show that giving up smoking and controlling blood pressure markedly reduce risk of heart attacks. But it has also been shown that the incidence of coronary heart disease is low in communities eating a diet low in saturated fats—even where there is heavy smoking, as in Greece, and even where there are very high average blood pressures, as in Japan.

Fats and the heart Between 1968 and 1980 about 37 international committees and expert groups in developed countries around the world studied the evidence relating diet to coronary heart disease. Practically all have recommended a reduction in the total amount of fat we eat; most recommend a lower intake of dietary cholesterol; and many recommend an increase in the consumption of polyunsaturated fats.

Other diseases and diet But coronary heart disease is not the only disease which has been linked with diet. Cancers of the breast and colon have also been linked with a high fat diet. Low intakes of fibre have been linked with diseases of the intestine and with gallstones. A high intake of salt is increasing y being shown to be the principal factor in the cause of high blood pressure. Dental decay is well known to be caused by a high consumption of sugar. Finally, obesity—a cause of much ill health and distress—is another consequence of eating our highly palatable but energy-dense diet, along with a general decline in physical activity.

There is little point in changing what we eat in order to avoid dying of one disease if it means increasing the chances of dying from another. However, more and more evidence is accumulating to show that the dietary pattern typical of affluent countries is linked with many of the major causes of death and disease in the developed world.

A question of balance A high consumption of fat is not the only characteristic of the typical Western diet. It is also very much higher in sugar and animal protein and lower in starch, fibre and vegetable protein than the diets of people in developing parts of the world where diseases like coronary heart disease, cancer, diabetes and obesity are uncommon. As nations become wealthier they

change their eating habits in remarkably similar ways. Records kept by the Food and Agriculture Organization and the World Health Organization (both technical agencies of the United Nations Organization) show that the richer the country the higher the proportion of sugar, meat, milk products and fats in the national diet, and the lower the proportion of cereals, vegetables and pulses. In rich countries it is the adults who are at most risk of disease; the children are healthier and grow taller on this kind of diet. In poor countries many children die from a combination of infectious diseases and malnutrition, but those who survive to adulthood have long life expectancy. The historical and medical evidence therefore suggests that we ought to reverse some of the trends in our eating habits enough to reduce the excesses but not to the extent that we lose the benefits of our present way of eating.

The typical Western diet The average Western man has been estimated to get about 42 per cent of the energy in his diet from fats, 18 per cent from

Positive malnutrition
or obesity is mainly a disease of the richer temperate zones of the world. Though commoner in females than in males, it exacts it severest penalties from the male sex. Hypertension, coronary heart disease, arthritis, gallstones and increased risk of complications after surgery are some of the hazards of eating too well.

The slaughterhouse
is one of the ironies of contemporary civilisation. Gleaming modern technology, watched over by white coated veterinarians and technicians, brings us meat that has been humanely slaughtered, screened for worms and other parasites, and certified free of dangerous bacteria. Yet it is crammed with atherogenic cholesterol and saturated fatty acids.

sugar, 12 per cent from protein, 9 per cent from alcohol and 21 per cent from starch. Individual variations from this pattern can be considerable of course. A frequent recommendation in many dozens of reports on diet and coronary heart disease has been that the proportion of fat in the diet should be reduced from the present 42 per cent to 30 per cent of total energy. This figure is largely arbitrary and no one would claim that eating this or that amount of fat is a copper-bottomed guarantee against heart disease.

Today's diseases—no single cause or cure
Diseases like coronary heart disease are multifactorial, that is they are caused by many interrelated risk factors of which diet is just one. Roughly speaking if you have one major risk factor you are twice as likely as the average man to have a heart attack; with two risk factors the chances are four times as likely; and with three risk factors the chances are eight times as likely. So eliminating one risk factor will help, but will be of limited value on its own. So what should we do?

The chances of research ever being able to identify the exact causes of diseases like heart disease, or to identify with any certainty those people most at risk of a heart attack, are very small. In order to get proof we would need to do experiments covering the complete lifespans of large groups of people under controlled experimental conditions. Since this is impossible we can only follow the judgement of clinicians concerning the facts that are known and the conclusions they draw from them.

Where the experts agree The consensus of world expert medical opinion is that we would all be healthier if we changed our diet so that we ate fewer fatty, sugary and salty foods and drank less alcohol and made up the energy deficit where necessary by eating more foods containing starch and fibre, and fruits and vegetables. Such a diet is advised as part of a general fitness programme.

But what kind of *meals* are we talking about which have a healthier balance of proteins, fats and carbohydrates?

Eating trends and cutting down on fat

Trends in food consumption Over the last 25 years we have been becoming increasingly inactive. This has meant that appetites have grown smaller; we are now eating less than before. However, with the rapid development of food technology, the choice of food available has become much greater. Faced with such an exciting choice, we eat less of what we don't like and more of what we do, less of bulky filler foods like bread and potatoes and the same amount or more of highly palatable foods like meat, cheese, oil and butter. To put it another way, the bread in our sandwiches is getting thinner but the fillings are getting thicker. Instead of 'meat and two veg' we often settle for meat and one veg—the potatoes being optional. The British are eating half the quantity of bread and potatoes they ate a generation ago, and the staple foods of many other Western countries are declining in popularity in a similar fashion.

But simply doubling the quantity of bread and potatoes eaten is not the answer. This would add even more calories to our diet—and most people are eating too much already—and would do nothing about decreasing our high consumption of alcohol and sugar. Also we have got so used to eating potatoes as chips (particularly the thin or crinkle-cut varieties which provide almost twice as many calories as the old-fashioned thick chips) that we would probably increase our fat consumption even further. So, for many reasons, it is not possible to turn the clock back.

Planning meals—East and West Instead we need to fundamentally rethink the way we plan meals. Most Westerners when planning a meal think of the meat (or its equivalent) first, then decide what sort of vegetables to have with it, and lastly throw in the potatoes as an optional extra. If potatoes are eaten they are often cooked in fat; if the vegetables are cooked they are often dressed in butter, or if served as a salad given an oily dressing. The focal point of the meal in poorer countries is very different. In China and India rice is the central part of the meal; soups, meat and fish dishes, and vegetables are appetizing accompaniments to what is essentially a rather bland and boring staple.

Cosmopolitan eating—Western style With foreign travel and migrating populations, foreign dishes such as pizzas, Chinese take-aways, Indian curries, risottos, paella, chilli con carne and Italian spaghetti dishes, are becoming increasingly popular. The trend away from formal meals to snacks also means that we are eating more hamburgers, chips and sandwiches. Inevitably many traditional national dishes are being 'westernised'—spaghetti bolognese frequently means a rich meat sauce and a small helping of pasta, and a Chinese take-away usually means

Bread-eating habits are changing. In line with a general trend towards healthier living, the public is now demanding a wider variety of wholesome bread. Wholemeal loaves made from whole grains of wheat and other cereals offer the best value nutritionally, but granary loaves, with added malt, are also good.

Vitamin C in danger Heat quickly destroys vitamin C, so wherever possible eat fruit and vegetables raw. And don't forget that the skin also contains valuable fibre and minerals.

Eating snacks even so-called junk food, won't do any harm, provided the total diet is balanced.

several portions of fried meats in batter but only one small portion of rice, often fried. Although many of the nutritional benefits of these traditional cuisines are lost in their 'westernisation', the trend towards 'alternative' eating is now fairly well established and has health advantages.

Dietary goals

Eat less fat Fats and oils provide 9 kcal (1 kilocalorie = 1 Calorie) per gram compared with proteins and carbohydrates which only provide 4 kcal. Fats are therefore very energy-dense and so add considerably to the calorie load of any food made or cooked with fat. Fat is also the basic ingredient from which the body makes cholesterol. Some fats—the saturated ones (found in butter, other animal fats, most margarines, fat on meat, meat products and cheese)—significantly raise blood cholesterol. Polyunsaturated oils (good sources are corn oil, sunflower seed oil and soya oil, oily fish and special margarines) have the opposite effect and seem to help lower blood cholesterol. A third group of fats—monounsaturated fats and oils (found in olive oil and some animal fats like pork)—are neutral.

As far as all-round health is concerned it is better to eat less of *all* fats and where fats have to be used in cooking to use a vegetable oil or margarine which is rich in polyunsaturated fats. Simply substituting special margarines and oils for animal fats without reducing total fat consumption is of limited value.
□ Grill instead of fry.
□ Poach onions and other vegetables for stews in stock instead of pre-frying them.
□ Use a non-stick pan—this drastically cuts the amount of fat needed for cooking.
□ Thicken sauces by dissolving the flour in a little milk and water (instead of fat as in a roux) and then add to the hot cooking liquor.
□ Remove all visible fat from meat and skin from poultry, and buy lean mince and stewing steak. Alternatively drain off the fat after cooking.
□ Dry roast joints. A joint or chicken does not need to be larded or covered before cooking; instead put it into the oven unadorned, and preferably on a rack, and allow most of the fat to drip away. Putting roasts in a hot oven for the first 10 minutes keeps in the moisture (the tenderness of meat does not depend on the fat content but on the way it was slaughtered and stored).
□ Omit butter or margarine in sandwiches and use salad ingredients or pickle as a moisturiser instead.
□ Yogurt can often be used in place of cream in recipes—in pâtés, cheesecakes, for thickening sauces and dressings . . .
□ Make your own pâté; shop-bought pâtés and meat products like meat pies and sausages usually have a very high fat content.
□ Avoid biscuits and cakes—these are high in fat

Too many carrots? It would be hard to absorb an excess of Vitamin A, but a man addicted to carrot juice is reported to have turned yellow and died! A good and varied diet provides all the vitamins one needs. Taking extra vitamin pills is about as useless as putting extra oil in an already full sump.

and sugar. Instead eat fatless sponges or yeast buns and cakes which are made with much less fat.
□ Make pastry using one part fat to three parts flour instead of half fat to flour.
□ Use skimmed milk instead of whole milk. If you cannot buy fresh skimmed milk then pour away the creamy top of the milk (most of us drink skimmed milk most of the time without realising it).

Eat less cholesterol Cholesterol is the main constituent of fatty deposits in the arteries. Four-fifths of these deposits come from fat in the diet and only a fifth from cholesterol in the diet. Foods rich in cholesterol are eggs, brains, shellfish and to a lesser extent liver. Studies have shown that eating one egg a day does not raise the blood cholesterol levels of 80 per cent of normal people. However, if you have raised blood cholesterol or a particular passion for eggs, brains or shellfish, it is wise to limit your consumption of these foods.

Kitchen hygiene is very important, even in this age of refrigeration, pasteurisation, sterilisation and preservatives. Meat in particular should not be reheated, and especially not if it has been only partly cooked in the first place. Even the cleanest kitchen is full of pathenogenic bacteria.

More dietary goals

Efficient food
In terms of the amount of energy required to produce them and the amount of energy they contain, cereals such as maize and barley are five to seven times more energy-efficient than meat or poultry. For example, a beef farmer would need 30 times as much land to produce the same amount of protein as a soya bean farmer.

Beef cattle

Soya beans

Addictions and allergies to certain foods are very common. Recent research has shown that people become addicted to food they are allergic to because it gives them a temporary 'high'. Convenience foods, often high in fat and sugar, are particularly easy to become addicted to.

The average man uses 3,000 calories a day. When metabolism is slowest, as in sleep, the body needs calories just to tick over; about 8 hours would use up 500 calories. Work and leisure use up proportionally more. But only 15 per cent of total calorie intake is used in activity. The rest goes towards repairing and renewing body tissue.

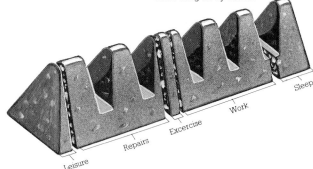

Leisure Repairs Excercise Work Sleep

Eat less sugar Sugar in the diet is the principal cause of dental decay, particularly if it is eaten frequently throughout the day. Saliva has a buffering action but it takes a couple of hours to take effect and so eating sweets or drinking sweetened drinks between meals maintains a continual supply of sugar in the mouth. Bacteria in the mouth turn this sugar into acid, and the acid attacks the teeth. Sugar, like fat, is a highly palatable food. It is easy to eat too much of it and so encourage obesity. Half the sugar we eat comes from jams, preserves and sugar used in beverages and cooking. The other half comes from a wide range of manufactured foods, and not only from biscuits, soft drinks, cakes, puddings and canned fruit; sugar is also added to a number of savoury foods, particularly those containing tomato, and also to many frozen foods.
☐ Make your own meals or read the labels on food so that you can avoid those with sugar in them.
☐ Watch out for foods which say they contain glucose syrup or corn syrup—these are sugars too. Fructose (fruit sugar), honey or brown sugar are no healthier than white sugar.
☐ Use artificial sweeteners in tea and coffee and buy diet drinks rather than sweetened soft drinks.

Eat less salt This recommendation probably only applies to those who come from families with a tendency to high blood pressure. If you already have high blood pressure a low salt diet may be an effective way of controlling blood pressure. The average intake of salt varies between 5–18 g a day. The 1980 Recommended Dietary Allowances from the USA recommend that salt be no more than 9 g a day, all of which can be found naturally in foods.
☐ It is the sodium in salt which is the culprit, so avoid foods which are naturally high in salt or

Cross references
Alcoholism **206**
Large intestine **127**
Liver intestine **127**
Liver **128**
Pancreas **131**

which have salt or any additives with sodium in the name added to them. Salty foods include smoked meats, ham, hard cheeses, bacon, salted nuts and crisps, bread, savoury biscuits. Foods which are naturally low in salt are rice, fruit and vegetables.

☐ Cook you own food without salt and do not add salt at table. It is particularly important that babies in the first year of life should not have salt added to their food.

☐ Potassium seems to have a 'neutralising' effect on sodium's ability to raise blood pressure. Potassium is particularly found in fruits and vegetables but is often lost in the cooking water. Therefore cook vegetables quickly in as little water as possible and eat some raw vegetables or fresh fruit each day.

Drink less alcohol Alcohol provides a generous 7 kcal per gram and so can be very fattening. Alcoholism is a real possibility if you regularly drink more than 80 g of ethanol a day (equivalent to 5 pints or 2.7 l of beer, 5 double measures of spirits, or 1½ bottles of wine). Even 25 g a day (1½ pints or 1 l of beer, 3 glasses of wine or 3 single measures of spirits) have a chronic toxic effect contributing to a wide range of diseases including some cancers, stomach ulcers and mental illness.

☐ If you drink regularly each day stick to one alcoholic drink at a time only.

☐ Respect other people's wishes when they decline the offer of a drink.

☐ Provide a good range of soft drinks as an alternative to alcohol at parties.

☐ If you regularly drink 80 g or more of ethanol a day and are confident that you can 'hold your drink', it is very likely that you are already dependent on drink and might have difficulty giving it up.

Eat more starch Starchy foods have been the traditional way of filling hungry stomachs. Because we take so little exercise starchy foods can provide uncomfortable bulk, yet they are an important source of fibre and vegetable protein, in short supply in many Western diets.

☐ Take more exercise to improve appetite control. A little exercise actually helps keep appetite in check whereas a lot of it increases appetite, in which case bulky, starchy foods are cheap and satisfying fillers.

☐ Eat more dishes where the filler occupies a greater proportion of the recipe (pizzas, risottos, curry, macaroni).

☐ Eat breakfast—breakfast cereals and toast are a valuable way of increasing your starch intake.

☐ Eat sandwiches for lunch, remembering to cut the bread thickly and to keep fatty fillings down to a minimum.

☐ Eat bread and soup before a main meal.

Eat more fruit and vegetables Not only are these good sources of vitamins, minerals and fibre, but most fruits (except avocado pear) and vegetables are bulky, light, and low in calories because of their high water content.

☐ Make soups and sauces out of puréed and chopped up vegetables.

☐ Drink real fruit juice as an alternative to tea and coffee and instead of alcoholic drinks.

☐ Put lots of vegetables into stews and casseroles.

☐ Bake potatoes in their jackets and serve with a dressing of yogurt and cottage cheese mixed with chives or paprika.

☐ Start and finish meals with salads and fresh or stewed fruit. Vegetable soup is a substantial starter and fruit is a light, healthy, sweet alternative to rich desserts.

Eat more fibre If you are eating more fruits and vegetables and starchy foods you will automatically be increasing your fibre intake, even if the bread you eat is white (white bread has a third of the fibre of wholemeal bread, and brown bread comes in between). However, you can increase your fibre intake further.

☐ Eat wholemeal or brown bread.

☐ Eat wholemeal pasta and brown rice.

☐ Eat wholegrain breakfast cereals like Shredded Wheat, Weetabix, oatmeal porridge and muesli. Although sprinkling bran onto food is one way of increasing your intake of cereal fibre it does not provide the starch or vegetable protein that go with wholegrain foods. Also, unless you have constipation or have been prescribed bran for medical reasons, it does not help to balance the diet *as a whole*. The whole diet should be lower in fat and sugar as well as richer in starch and fibre.

Change your protein Most people around the world eat the same *quantity* of protein, but the *kind* of protein they eat is very different. In poor populations four-fifths of the protein comes from plant foods like beans, lentils, vegetables and grains, and a fifth from animal products. In rich countries the figures are reversed: almost two-thirds of the protein comes from foods like meat, milk, cheese and eggs. Unfortunately many animal proteins are also rich sources of fat; for example cheese is a more significant source of fat than protein, although it is often described as a protein food.

☐ Eat more pulses (beans, peas, lentils) by adding them to salads, stews and soups.

☐ Potatoes provide excellent-quality protein, so eat more of them.

☐ Eat low-fat animal protein foods like yogurt, cottage cheese, other low-fat cheeses, skimmed milk, lean meat, poultry (the skin contains most of the fat) and white fish.

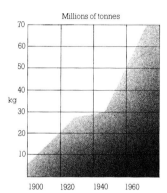

Sugar production
This graph shows the phenomenal increase in world sugar production in the first 70 years of this century. Average per capita annual consumption of sugar in the Western world is over 110 lb (50 kg).

Harvest of the sea
White fish contains less than two per cent fat. Herring, salmon and mackerel contain more fat but also useful vitamins A and D. The bones in sardines, sprats or canned salmon are also a useful source of calcium and phosphorus.

To sleep, perchance to dream...

The body cannot be driven non-stop for 24 hours, day in, day out. We have to sleep. But the body machine is never completely switched off; even when we are asleep the brain remains extremely active. In fact, according to one theory, it is during sleep—when input from the special senses almost ceases—that the brain re-programmes itself, apparently producing new programmes by disposing of out-dated or unwanted information.

It is possible that this re-programming process occurs during what is known as paradoxical sleep. This is one of two physiologically distinct types of sleep. The first, known as orthodox sleep, is characterised by a fall in the metabolic rate, blood pressure and heart rate. It can also be divided into a further two stages: light orthodox sleep and deep orthodox sleep. In light orthodox sleep the body may make up to 40 changes in position per night which helps to keep the circulation on the move and prevent the muscles from seizing up. But in deep orthodox sleep both muscles and brain are at their most relaxed.

Dreaming

During an average night's sleep we oscillate from orthodox sleep to paradoxical sleep about five times. Paradoxical sleep is characterised by irregular breathing and pulse rate and by rapid eye movement (REM). Everyone dreams and dreams occur during REM sleep. Experiments have shown that sleepers can vividly describe their dreams if they are woken during REM sleep. On the other hand, recall is hazy only five minutes after REM sleep, and non-existent after ten minutes. People who claim they do not dream are those who do not wake immediately after REM, but enter a new phase of orthodox sleep. On average, REM sleep lasts for about 15–20 minutes, followed by 60–90 minutes of orthodox sleep. Dreams total as much as two hours' sleep a night, and appear to be important to normal psychological functioning.

Sleepers who have been experimentally deprived of REM sleep—by being woken up each time they enter a period of REM—have become progressively more anxious, irritable and aggressive, and have had difficulty concentrating. Some have had hallucinations. Later they compensate by extra and longer periods of dreaming.

There is experimental evidence to suggest that there is a system in the brain which regulates drive-related behaviours—hunger, sex, aggression—and usually 'discharges' during sleep. If the functioning of this system is disrupted, uncontrolled REM activity occurs in the waking state. This would neatly account for the hallucinations suffered by some subjects after dream deprivation. Now schizophrenics also suffer bizarre daytime experiences, including hallucinations and delusions. In their case a deficiency of a brain chemical called serotonin may be responsible. It seems that in adequate amounts serotonin may prevent REM-type activity from spilling over into the waking state. Cats treated with a chemical compound which blocks the production of serotonin show brain wave patterns similar to those of cats deprived of REM sleep for long periods. It may be that in humans absence of REM sleep disrupts the production of serotonin.

Interpreting dreams The first psychologist to pay close attention to dreams was Sigmund Freud. According to him dreams are expressions, often heavily symbolic, of impulses which are unacceptable to our conscious, responsible selves. One of their functions therefore is to relieve pent-up tensions. Freud also believed that because the watchdog functions of the Superego, our social and moral conscience, are relaxed in sleep, dreams are an opportunity for wish-fulfilment.

However, the manifest content of a dream, the actual scenes and events reported by the dreamer, may be very different from its latent content or underlying significance. Again, this is dreaming seen from the psychoanalytic viewpoint. In his book *The Interpretation of Dreams* Freud suggested that "All elongated objects . . . may stand for the male organ, as well as long, sharp weapons . . . Boxes, cases, chests, cupboards and ovens represent the uterus . . . Rooms in dreams are usually women . . . A dream of going through a suite of rooms is a brothel or a harem dream . . ." One does not have to be too shrewd to realise that Freud saw sex as the source of most dream symbolism. But Carl Jung, an ex-disciple of Freud, downplayed the sexual significance of dreams. In Jungian psychology dream symbols are clues to the dreamer's present life and future possibilities, rather than the unravelling of past conflicts. Jung saw dreams as a descent into the collective as well as the personal unconscious, the collective unconscious being that part of the mind stocked with residues of man's evolutionary experiences. At this collective level we all share certain archetypes or universal symbols related to birth, death, power, resurrection and so on.

Sex differences in dreams In 1966 two American psychologists Calvin Hall and Robert van de Castle developed a method of scoring the manifest content of dreams, and applied it to investigating the dreams of 100 male and 100 female college students. They found that women's dreams tended to take place in familiar, usually indoor settings, men's in unfamiliar or outdoor surroundings. Men dreamed more of groups of people, women of individuals familiar to them. Men's dreams had more aggression, sex, physical activity and success in them; women demonstrated more subtle forms

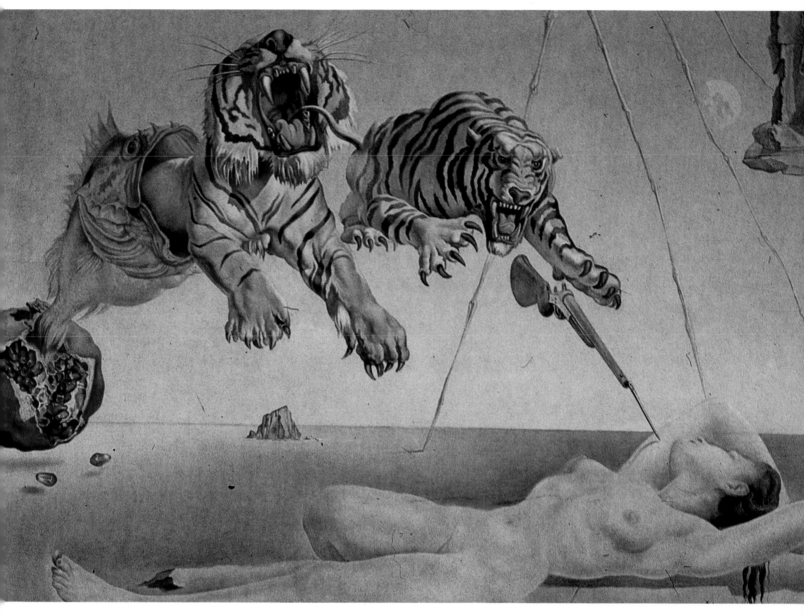

Surrealist painters
like Salvador Dali appear to use dream imagery as a source of inspiration. No doubt a Freudian psychoanalyst would find plenty to say about this particular image! What we commonly call 'imagination' may in fact be the ability to access the less logical strata of our minds.

of aggression, more emotion and more verbal activity. However, the report of a dream is not the same as the experience of a dream—a report can be influenced by current stereotypes of what is acceptably male or female. Perhaps this is what happened in the Hall and Castle study. The great problem with dream investigation is that one can never directly study someone else's dreams; you always have to depend on their interpretation.

Dreams gone wrong Nightmares, according to Freud, are failed dreams. The dreamer wakes because his or her thoughts are so threatening that conscious defences must be mobilised to keep them under control. Physiologically, nightmares are distinct from night terrors. A nightmare may raise your heart rate from about 64 beats a minute to about 80, but a night terror can send it rocketing up to 150. Night terrors are usually considered to

be massive anxiety attacks, and are more frequent in children than in adults, presumably because adults have developed other mechanisms for coping with anxiety.

Sleep and death The quality of sleep declines with age and recent research at the National Institute of Aging, USA, has shown that a link exists between how long you sleep and how long you live. Older people who sleep more than $10\frac{1}{2}$ hours or less than $4\frac{1}{2}$ hours may be experiencing 'pathological sleep', indicating that their health is in danger. This link is supported by evidence that the onset of disease, such as cancer or cardiac disorder, is preceded by abnormally long or short sleeping patterns. Further study of sleeping habits may enable us to relate certain sleep disorders to the development of specific diseases, thus foreseeing and perhaps delaying death.

How much sleep do we need?

Everyone needs sleep
but some need it more than others. Narcolepsy is a sleep disorder in which the sufferer constantly falls asleep during the day, each period of sleep lasting about 15 minutes. Narcolepsy can be treated with stimulant drugs.

Sleep need Though it has clearly been established that no one can dispense with sleep indefinitely, there are some people who manage quite adequately with as little as one or two hours' sleep a night. Scientists investigating the claims of a 70-year-old retired nurse, who said that she had not slept for more than an average of one hour a night since childhood, kept her under continuous observation for five days. An electroencephalogram, which registers and records brain waves, monitored her sleep. During the five days, the minutes she spent asleep were: 1 min, 82 min, 204 min (a record, she said), 19 min, and 29 min—an average of 67 minutes a day. She showed no obvious effects of sleep deprivation during the five day study and remained her usual cheerful self throughout. She clearly had very little sleep need.

Short sleepers tend to share certain features—physical fitness, a tendency to be athletic, and many work and leisure interests to fill their long waking hours. They literally seem not to have enough time for sleep. They rarely complain about tiredness—unlike insomniacs—and are puzzled as to why the rest of us need to sleep so much. In some cases the tendency to be a short sleeper runs in families.

One third of our life
is spent asleep. This man has spent 20 years asleep, five of them dreaming. Rapid Eye Movement sleep, the phase of sleep in which dreams occur, takes up about a quarter of total sleep time.

Cross references
Studying the brain 52
Biological clocks 76
Use and abuse of body rhythms 78
Tranquillisers and sleeping pills 176

Babies and children need more sleep than adults. A newborn baby sleeps for about 16 hours a day, and a two-year-old for about 12 hours. At this age boys spend more time sleeping than girls, though the reason for this is not understood.

The existence of people who function perfectly well on one or two hours' sleep implies that there is a broad spectrum of sleep need, a spectrum which has short sleepers at one extreme, bulges in the middle to include all those people who need the traditional eight hours' sleep a night, and tails off at the other extreme with extraordinarily long sleepers. Both above and below the magic eight hours formula, individuals appear to differ widely in their need for sleep. An unborn baby spends most of his or her time sleeping, while a newborn infant sleeps about 16 hours a day on average. This need gradually diminishes with age, dropping from 10 hours at the age of six to 9 hours at the age of 12. Subsequently the average adult needs about 7½ hours' sleep.

Everyone needs sleep but the specific function of sleep is still debatable. Sleep may be essential solely to enable the brain to re-programme itself. Or it may be that sleep enables the body to re-charge itself like a battery. During sleep there is a rise in the output of growth hormone and protein production—in other words the body services and repairs itself during sleep. However, attempts to measure various physiological parameters have not produced any one biochemical factor to explain sleep. All we know with any certainty is that performance declines if we are deprived of sleep.

Sleep deprivation The Walter Reed Army Institute of Research in the USA, a pioneer sleep research centre, describes the impairment arising from sleep deprivation as one of 'periodic lapses'. Performance deteriorates not steadily like a clock mechanism running down, but in fits and starts like an automobile running out of fuel. But this analogy is of limited value since human beings never run completely out of fuel.

Sleep deprivation studies have also shown that impaired performance is most noticeable when the task being performed is boring or monotonous. No one has yet demonstrated convincingly that one night's loss of sleep adversely affects any exciting or intellectually demanding task. At first sight this may seem surprising—surely the most intellectually and physically demanding projects should be the first to suffer the adverse effects of sleep deprivation. However, it would seem that the tasks most at risk are those which lack interest and immediate incentive, which involve little physical activity, and which require sustained and moderate concentration. Driving along a motorway is a very good example.

In his book *Sleep, Dreams and Arousal*, Edward J. Murray proposes that we have a 'drive' towards sleep, just as we have a drive towards food, sex and other basic requirements. Behaviour, he says, is shaped by the conflict and combination of these drives. Deprive the body of sleep and it will increase its drive towards sleep-attaining behaviour at the expense of all other forms of drive. The weaker drives will collapse first. This is why uninteresting tasks fail first, and why the body seems remarkably able to withstand the effects of loss of sleep when there is a good enough incentive to keep awake.

Insomnia This is a very common complaint which can arise from many different causes. These include physical symptoms such as itching or pain. Other causes may include inadequate bedclothes, anxiety or nervousness, indigestion, excitement, drinking tea or coffee just before going to bed, lack of exercise, an airless bedroom or the need to urinate during the night.

There are other reasons for insomnia, but the relevant point is that insomnia is often easily explained and may then be easily dealt with. If possible, sleeping pills should be avoided. Some alleged cases of insomnia are caused because people confuse sleeplessness with restless or disturbed sleep; a 'bad' night may actually provide a full eight hours' sleep despite periods of wakefulness. However, there is little doubt that worry about not sleeping actually makes sleeping more difficult.

Sleep disorders

Sleep and middle age

After the age of 50 the amount of sleep we take increases. This is not because we sleep more at night but because we tend to take more naps during the day. We seem to need lighter and more fragmented rest as we get older. Complaints about insomnia simply reflect this fact.

Sleepwalking (somnambulism) In this particular disorder the sleepwalker is technically asleep but performs various automatic movements such as walking or talking. These movements are beyond conscious control, and are not remembered on waking. Most sleepwalking episodes pass unnoticed and are benign but some very rare cases end in tragedy. The case of a British woman highlights the potential dangers. She walked free from a British Crown Court, arm in arm with her husband whom she had stabbed 15 times in her sleep. The prosecution brought no evidence against her on a charge of grievous bodily harm; the court was told that her claim that she had been in a state of automatism could not be disproved.

Other examples of the potential dangers of somnambulism include a case in 1967 when a sleepwalking motor cyclist crashed his 650 cc machine into an automobile, and the case of an

11-year-old sleepwalking boy burglar who committed a series of expert thefts. Again, in both instances, the somnambulists were not held responsible for their actions.

Even more alarming, however, are those instances where sleepwalking has resulted in what has been described as 'nightmare murder'. Take the notorious case of a famous French detective; investigating a murder, he found his own footprints on the beach at Le Havre where the victim had been shot—he himself was guilty of the murder.

In another sleepwalking incident, a quiet, retiring Englishman murdered and dismembered his wife while he was asleep. He was so horrified when he woke up that he became severely psychotic and was confined in a mental hospital.

A 16-year-old American girl who was a habitual sleepwalker, dreamt that burglars were in the home. She seized two revolvers, fired 10 shots,

Change in metabolic rate (oxygen consumption)

A Hypnosis
B Transcendental Meditation
C Sleep

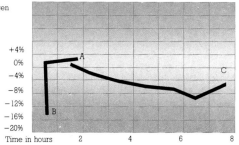

+4%
0%
−4%
−8%
−12%
−16%
−20%
Time in hours   2   4   6   8

Metabolic rate decreases during states of relaxation such as meditation or sleep But if we were able to hibernate, our metabolic rate would drop even further. Biologists have suggested that since metabolic rate appears to be related to lifespan, sleep may be nature's way of ensuring that we live long enough to reproduce, acquire experience and wisdom and pass it on to our offspring.

Cross references
Dreaming 192
Dreams gone wrong 193
Psychosis 172

killed her father and six-year-old brother, and wounded her mother.

These tragedies were recognised as bona fide somnambulism cases, and the people involved treated medically and not punitively. Psychologists believe that somnambulism represents the disassociation of behaviour from consciousness in an attempt to resolve conflicts arising in the unconscious mind during sleep. Psychotherapy may help to pinpoint such conflicts and discover the cause of the sleepwalking.

Children are about twice as vulnerable to sleepwalking as adults. One enthusiastic 12-year-old sleepwalking swimmer 'dived' 60 ft (18 m) to his death from a window of his home. Less tragically, a 14-year-old fell 18 ft (5.5 m) from a window, and continued sleeping, despite a broken foot and severe scratching from a rose bush which had helped to break the fall.

Rocking during sleep Like insomnia, rocking during sleep, and thrashing, grunting, or groaning, are very common sleep disorders. However, people who rock themselves violently to sleep are exposed to physical risk. Children aged between one and two are particularly vulnerable and many have to be cocooned in protective headgear. In his book *Sleep and Wakefulness* Dr Nathaniel Kleitman says: "Sometimes the banging of the head is so violent that the cot vibrates across the room and the whole house is disturbed". Surprisingly, rocking does not interrupt sleep, in fact it encourages it. According to Dr Kleitman, in children rocking is no more pathological than thumb-sucking.

Sleep-talking This is a minor sleep problem. Sleep-talkers fear that they may say something rather too revealing or blunt, but usually their utterances are quite incoherent.

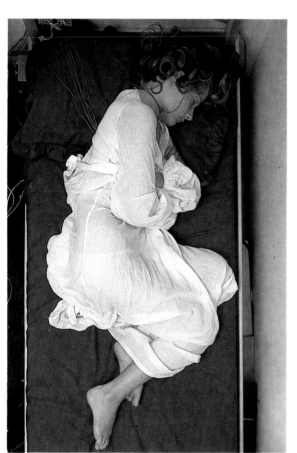

In a sleep laboratory
brain waves, muscle activity and body movements are monitored during the different phases of sleep. Studies like this have taught scientists a lot about how and why we sleep, and how to treat sleep disorders. We know, for example, that sleepwalking cannot occur during REM sleep; although the brain is very active and some muscles twitch, most muscles stay relaxed.

Dreams: another reality?
Freud believed that dreams represent wishes and desires too threatening or too outrageous to be expressed during our waking lives.

Anywhere, anytime,
sleep is possible if the urge to sleep is strong enough. Whereas most adults can manage to stay awake until they find a comfortable place to sleep, young children can sleep almost anywhere, whatever the circumstances—their need for sleep overpowers everything else.

Brain waves in sleep
The deeper the sleep, the slower the brain waves—slow brain waves mean less brain activity. During REM sleep, when dreams occur, the waves are faster, reflecting increased brain activity.

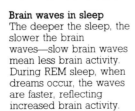

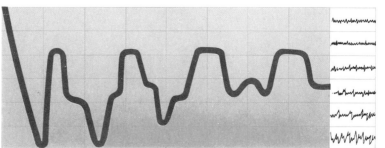

Awake

REM stage

Stage 1

Stage 2

Stage 3

Stage 4

Time in hours   2   4   6   8

How drugs affect body chemistry

Jockey Bob Champion and Aldaniti receive a hero's welcome in the Sussex village of Findon after winning the Grand National in April 1981. In 1980 Champion, suffering from cancer, was given only eight months to live.

First, let us make a distinction between a 'drug' and a 'medicine'; a drug is any chemical capable of altering the function of a living organism, but a medicine is any drug that is taken for its therapeutic effect. So all medicines, whether prescribed by a doctor or bought from a pharmacy, are drugs. But not all drugs are medicines: nicotine, marijuana and heroin are taken for their non-therapeutic effects. And many foodstuffs contain substances that are drugs; tea and coffee contain caffeine which stimulates mental activity, rhubarb and spinach contain large amounts of highly corrosive oxalic acid, and some kinds of cabbage contain thiourea which affects the activity of the thyroid gland.

Research and testing

At one time all drugs were obtained from plants and other natural sources. Today, most drugs are discovered and manufactured in laboratories. Before they can be sold as medicines new drugs go through stringent tests designed to ensure that they are safe and have the effect they are supposed to have. Drug testing is regulated in the United Kingdom by the Committee on Safety of Medicines and in the United States by the Food and Drugs Administration. The chances of another thalidomide tragedy occurring have been appreciably reduced.

The physiological effects and toxicity of a new drug are tested on laboratory animals first, and then on human volunteers, but tests are not carried out on patients in controlled clinical trials until exhaustive research has shown the drug to be safe and efficacious. Not all the patients taking part in a clinical trial are given the new drug; some are given a placebo which looks like the drug. Neither they nor the doctor know whether they are taking the real thing or an innocent substitute. This deception is practiced in order to counteract the 'placebo effect': many people feel better if they think they are taking an active drug, even if it is only a sugar pill, and doctors themselves are also predisposed to see 'improvements' in response to drugs. Clinical trials can only be done with a patient's consent.

How drugs work

In general, drugs work by altering some biochemical or physiological process within the body. Some drugs exert their effect within the cell itself, while others act on the surface of the cell or outside it. Some drugs act only on certain kinds of cell, while others have a more generalised action.

There are four stages involved in the passage of a drug through the body. First, it has to be administered. The most common method of administration is oral; the drug is taken by mouth in liquid or tablet form. Some drugs are administered topically, or applied directly to their site of action—ointments and creams for skin disorders, pessaries for vaginal conditions, and suppositories for anal and rectal disorders, come into the topical category. Some drugs are administered parenterally, by injection into the skin (intradermal), under the skin (subcutaneous), into muscle (intramuscular) or directly into a vein (intravenous) or artery (intra-arterial).

Once administered (unless topically), a drug has to be absorbed into the bloodstream. The rate at which this happens varies widely from drug to drug and from person to person, and depends on the method of administration. A drug taken orally may be absorbed quite slowly—much depends on what else is in the stomach at the time. Absorption after intramuscular administration is quicker, and with intravenous or intra-arterial administration almost immediate. Parenteral administration is often used when quick absorption is essential, or when the drug would be destroyed if taken orally, as with insulin. Some drugs are available in 'depot' form, specially prepared so that they are absorbed very slowly. A patient on a depot drug may require only one injection a week or fortnight.

Once absorbed, a drug is distributed around the body. Some drugs distribute themselves evenly, others become concentrated or deposited in certain organs. For example, some antimalarial drugs become concentrated in the liver. Elimination is the last of the four stages and begins almost as soon as the drug is absorbed. Some drugs are eliminated unchanged, but others are broken down, principally in the liver. The breakdown products are then excreted via the kidneys in the urine, but to a small extent in breath, sweat, faeces and breast milk as well. The speed with which half of a given dose of a drug is eliminated from the body is called the half-life.

Many drugs are only effective if their concentration in the body is kept steady, in other words if the rate of absorption from regular administration roughly equals the rate of elimination. This means that if such a drug is administered too frequently, or if elimination is slower than it should be, the active principle of the drug accumulates, causing unwanted side effects.

Side effects

The majority of people taking drugs experience no unpleasant side effects, and in the small minority who do adverse reactions are unpleasant but usually relatively harmless (nausea, drowsiness, dizziness). Only in rare cases does drug treatment cause serious disease—a small proportion of psychiatric patients treated with chlorpromazine develop liver disease, for example. Treatment-induced ailments are known as iatrogenic ailments.

No drug yet discovered has only one action. It

therefore follows that any drug can cause side effects; for example, drugs used to treat high blood pressure may cause blurring of vision. Babies and elderly people are especially prone to side effects. In babies the mechanisms for metabolising and eliminating drugs have not fully developed and in the elderly these mechanisms are beginning to fail. Idiosyncrasy and allergy also come under the heading of adverse drug reactions. An idiosyncratic reaction occurs in a person who has inherited a deficiency of an enzyme needed to metabolise a particular drug; the deficiency will go unnoticed until the drug is taken. Allergic reactions occur when a person develops antibodies to a drug; a common example here is the rash caused by penicillin allergy. Taking more than one kind of drug at a time can also trigger an adverse reaction. Different drugs can interact with each other, occasionally with dangerous, even lethal, effects.

Drug dependence

Certain types of drug cause dependence and addiction. The World Health Organization recognises seven main categories of drugs of dependence; opiates (morphine) and opioids; barbiturates and alcohol; amphetamines; cocaine; cannabis; hallucinogens (LSD); tobacco and volatile solvents. Drug dependence is as difficult to define as to treat and is a growing health problem.

Families of drugs

ANALGESICS These are pain-killing drugs. Narcotic analgesics, such as morphine, are strong pain-killers but carry a substantial risk of addiction. Antipyretic analgesics, such as aspirin and paracetamol, are weaker than narcotics; they combat inflammation and fever as well as pain.
ANTIBIOTICS These kill bacteria and are therefore used to treat infections. Some antibiotics are broad-spectrum (effective against many kinds of bacteria), while others are more specific. Penicillin, the most commonly prescribed antibiotic, is effective because it destroys the cell wall of bacteria.
DIURETICS These are drugs which act on the kidney tubules and increase urine excretion. They can therefore be used to treat high blood pressure and certain heart conditions as well as kidney failure; because they reduce blood volume the heart has less work to do.
HORMONES These are prescribed as replacement therapy when an endocrine gland stops working. For example, insulin is prescribed when the islets of Langerhans in the pancreas fail and cause diabetes.
STEROIDS These are also hormones, but have a generalised anti-inflammatory action, and are therefore useful in a wide variety of conditions.
PSYCHOTROPICS (see Mind Medicines, pp. 174–80).

VACCINES These give protection against contagious disease, each vaccine being specific for one disease. A vaccine is a weak or inactive form of the culprit virus or bacteria and stimulates the body to produce self-defensive antibodies. Large-scale vaccination programmes can reduce the incidence of disease (tuberculosis, for example) or eradicate it altogether (smallpox).

Ten sensible precautions

If you are taking a drug, it is only common sense to take certain elementary precautions.
☐ Find out the name of the drug.
☐ Know the dose and keep to it.
☐ Find out from your doctor its effects and main side effects.
☐ Tell your doctor about previous adverse reactions before he prescribes.
☐ Find out from your doctor whether there are any restrictions to be observed (e.g. not drinking while taking the drug).
☐ Keep the drug out of reach of children.
☐ Never exceed the stated dose.
☐ Never give your drugs to others, or take theirs.
☐ Never hoard; flush unused drugs down the lavatory.
☐ Never take drugs if you are, or think you might be, pregnant—consult your doctor first.

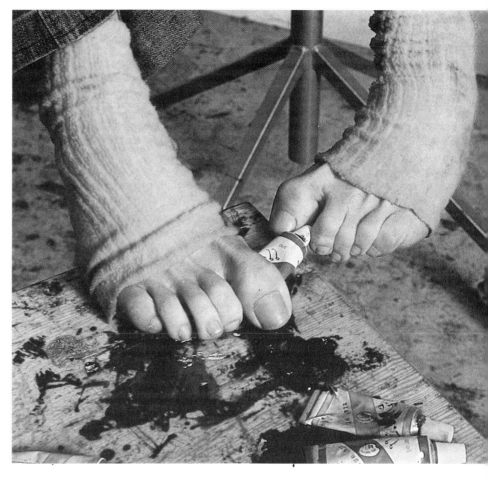

Toes for hands
For many of the victims of the drug thalidomide, introduced in the late 1950s life can never be normal. In every animal test used throughout the drug industry at the time thalidomide was given a clean bill of health.

Nicotine: the 'uncool' addiction

You would not swallow an insecticide—or would you? If you smoke you already do—you take in nicotine, a very effective insecticide, and one of the most powerful poisons known. The nicotine from one small cigar would kill an adult man if injected all at once into his bloodstream. Nicotine is the drug within tobacco which hooks smokers.

Tobacco contains from one to three per cent of nicotine and the average smoker absorbs about two milligrams from one cigarette. A colourless, oily compound, nicotine is a relatively short-acting drug. Levels in the bloodstream fall quickly to about half within 30 minutes of finishing a cigarette and to only a quarter within another half an hour, explaining why so many smokers get through a pack of 20 daily.

Every puff drawn into the delicate capillary beds of the lungs delivers to the brain a small dose of nicotine more rapidly than the dose of heroin the addict injects into his vein.

In their book *Addictions: Issues and Answers* Jerome Jaffe, Robert Petersen and Ray Hodgson, point out that a drug which increases the likelihood of its own self-administration is known by behavioural psychologists as a 'reinforcer of drug taking behaviour'. They add: "There are about ten puffs in each cigarette and a heavy smoker consumes more than 20 cigarettes a day. Even after only a year or two the act of inhalation has been reinforced more than 100,000 times. If physical dependence on nicotine develops, it is likely that each small dose of nicotine produces its own relatively mild reinforcement by relieving the nicotine withdrawal syndrome. This relief may be even more reinforcing than the original effect of the nicotine itself."

The body responds to tobacco in much the same way as an automobile when the accelerator is pressed down. The heart beats faster and blood pressure goes up as nicotine stimulates the production of adrenaline and noradrenaline. These same chemical substances are produced when the body moves into top gear for preparation for fight or flight—in other words, in response to a stressful situation. Thus, smoking is stressful.

So why do cigarettes induce a feeling of relaxation and tranquillity?—as they do. For smokers the answer is simple. The production of adrenaline and noradrenaline is only one of many biochemical responses to tobacco. Another response is increased activity of inhibitory cells in the spinal cord which cause a decrease in muscle tone, thereby inducing a feeling of relaxation.

However, only people addicted to nicotine find smoking relaxing and tranquillising, and much of the apparent pleasure they derive is caused by the relief of withdrawal symptoms and the effects of reinforcement. Alleviation of withdrawal symptoms is in itself liberating and relaxing. But

The feminist response
'Anything you can do I can do better.' Lung cancer, heart disease and alcoholism are soaring amongst women.

Prevention or cure?
The emphasis today is on prevention of smoking by education. This means educating the young not to smoke at all, or to make their first episode of smoking their last.

this not 'relaxation' in the true sense of the word. If you were to check your pulse rate, then smoke two cigarettes, and check your pulse rate again, you would see this for yourself.

Habitual smoking overloads the body—you cannot keep your foot pressed down indefinitely on the accelerator of an automobile and the body

Tobacco growing is an important part of the rural economy of most developing countries.

A search for alternative crops for the small farmer is essential.

Hookah pipe smoking is traditional in many countries in the Near and Middle East. The hookah or narghile is smoked in cafes, in special 'hubble-bubble' houses and at home. The smoke is inhaled by sucking it through a water trap; this removes some, but not all, of the nicotine, tars and carbon monoxide smoke contains. Drugs are often added to the burning tobacco.

machine reacts in much the same way to smoking.

In the USA more than a half a million people die each year from coronary heart disease. Smoking is believed to contribute to at least a third of these deaths. Lung cancer, the next most important health risk associated with smoking, accounts for a further 84,000 deaths. Smokers are ten times more at risk from lung cancer than non-smokers.

Similarly, smokers are also more prone than non-smokers to other cancers, including those of the throat, mouth and vocal chords; to killer respiratory conditions such as chronic bronchitis and emphysema; and to a lesser known but nevertheless painful disease called arteriosclerosis obliterans. This obstructs the arteries carrying blood to the limbs, leading to the development of gangrene and possible amputation, rather than a sudden or painful lingering death.

There are three ways in which smoking causes atherosclerosis, coronary disease, stroke and vascular diseases.

Damage to blood platelets The activity of platelets—substances in the blood which promote clotting by sticking to one another when a vessel is injured—may be damaged by nicotine and adhere to another in the lining of the coronary arteries. This can culminate in the formation of atherosclerotic plaques.

Mopping up carbon monoxide Smokers absorb substantial amounts of carbon monoxide, the poisonous gas emitted in car exhausts. The oxygen-carrying substance in the blood, haemoglobin, has a very high affinity for this gas. In heavy smokers as much as 15 per cent of their haemoglobin may have carbon monoxide attached to it, preventing it from combining with oxygen. This can cause increased production of haemoglobin and red cells, resulting in a thickening of the blood. The combined effect of a weakening in the oxygen-carrying and oxygen-releasing capacity of haemoglobin and the thickening of the blood can have adverse effects on the circulation to the heart. These problems may be compounded by the effects of atherosclerosis.

Interfering with the catecholamines We have already mentioned these. Adrenaline and noradrenaline are catecholamines. As well as increasing the work of the heart they increase its irritability, and this can culminate in serious irregularities.

The strength of the scientific case against smoking is conclusive despite bogus claims made to the contrary. It has been argued, for example, that there is no conclusive evidence that smoking causes lung cancer. And that is true enough. Nobody knows exactly *why* smoking causes lung cancer—but the fact that this painful, killing disease is restricted largely to smokers is more than reason enough for giving up the habit.

Giving up is not easy but in the USA there are now more than 30 million former smokers. A little more than a decade ago about 60 per cent of physicians in the USA were smokers. That figure has fallen by two-thirds because of the weight of evidence against smoking.

A quiz for smokers

Smoke gets in your eyes, but not any more! A gadget like this would give little satisfaction to the smoker who derives most of his pleasure from handling his cigarettes. This lighthearted look at smoking appeared in the magazine *Men Only*. Passive smoking, the inhalation of smoke from other people's cigarettes, is not only unpleasant but dangerous. Particularly menacing is 'side-stream' smoke, more concentrated than diffused smoke. Recent studies in Japan have shown that non-smoking spouses of smokers are more at risk of lung cancer than the partners of non-smokers.

The following test was drawn up with help from the Scottish Health Education Group, and will help you to determine why you smoke, and what sort of smoker you are. The test consists of statements made by smokers to describe their feelings about smoking. To take the test, circle the number that corresponds to the number of times that you have the same feelings; 5 equals always; 4 equals frequently; 3 equals occasionally; 2 equals seldom and 1 equals never. *It is important to answer every question.*

A I smoke cigarettes in order to keep myself 5 4 3 2 1
    from slowing down.
B Handling a cigarette is part of the 5 4 3 2 1
    enjoyment of smoking it.
C Smoking cigarettes is pleasant and 5 4 3 2 1
    relaxing.
D I light up a cigarette when I feel angry 5 4 3 2 1
    about something.
E When I have run out of cigarettes I feel it 5 4 3 2 1
    almost unbearable until I can get them.
F I smoke cigarettes automatically without 5 4 3 2 1
    even being aware of it.
G I smoke cigarettes to stimulate me, to perk 5 4 3 2 1
    me up.
H Part of the enjoyment of smoking a 5 4 3 2 1
    cigarette comes from the steps I take to
    light up.
I I find cigarettes pleasurable. 5 4 3 2 1
J When I feel uncomfortable or upset about 5 4 3 2 1
    something, I light up a cigarette.
K I am very much aware of the fact when I 5 4 3 2 1
    am not smoking a cigarette.
L I light up a cigarette without realising I 5 4 3 2 1
    still have one burning in an ashtray.
M I smoke cigarettes to give me a lift. 5 4 3 2 1
N When I smoke a cigarette, part of the 5 4 3 2 1
    enjoyment is watching the smoke as I
    exhale it.
O I want a cigarette most when I am 5 4 3 2 1
    comfortable and relaxed.
P When I feel depressed or want to take my 5 4 3 2 1
    mind off cares and worries I smoke
    cigarettes.
Q I get a gnawing hunger for a cigarette when 5 4 3 2 1
    I haven't smoked for a while.
R I've found a cigarette in my mouth and 5 4 3 2 1
    didn't remember putting it there.

How to score
In the spaces below enter the numbers you have circled over the appropriate letters. Then total the scores on each line to get your totals. For example, the sum of your scores on lines A, G and M gives you your score on stimulation; lines B, H and N give you the score on handling, and so on. Any score that totals 11 and above is high; any score that totals 7 and below is low.

_____ + _____ + _____ = Stimulation
  A   G   M

_____ + _____ + _____ = Handling
  B   H   N

_____ + _____ + _____ = Pleasurable relaxation
  C   I   O

_____ + _____ + _____ = Tension reduction
  D   J   P

_____ + _____ + _____ = Psychological addiction (craving)
  E   K   Q

_____ + _____ + _____ = Habit
  F   L   R

This test is designed to provide you with a score on each of six factors which describe what it is that people get from smoking. Your smoking may be characterised by only one of these factors, or by a combination of factors.

Three of these factors include the positive feelings people get from smoking; first, a sense of increased energy or stimulation; second, the satisfaction of handling or manipulating things; and, third, the enhancing of pleasurable feelings.

The fourth factor describes smoking as a way of reducing negative feelings such as anxiety or tension. The fifth represents a complex pattern of increasing and decreasing craving for a cigarette—that is called psychological addiction. And the sixth is purely automatic smoking.

A score of 11 or above on any factor indicates that smoking is an important source of satisfaction for you. The higher your score, the more important it is for you to think about that particular factor and try to work out what you can do about it.

Essentially there are only two things that you can do about your smoking. You can either learn to live without a particular source of satisfaction; or find something to put in the place of a cigarette that will give you the same sort of satisfaction. Listed below are certain alternatives to smoking that you can try, according to your score. But only some of these suggestions will work for you, and you may have to find your own 'individual cure'.

Stimulation If you scored high or fairly high on this factor, that is 11 or above, you are one of those smokers who are stimulated by a cigarette; you apparently feel that smoking helps to wake you up, to organise your energies, and to keep you going.
When you feel the urge to smoke, why not:
1 Take a brisk walk
2 Try moderate exercise
3 Drink a mildly stimulating drink such as tea or coffee
4 Breathe deeply. First relax and then go limp. Then inhale slowly and deeply. When you have taken as much air into your lungs as you can comfortably hold, stop, pause, then breathe out slowly until all the air is expelled. At the end of the breathing-out cycle, give an extra push to remove all the air. Repeat this cycle five or six times, slowly.

Handling If you scored 11 or above on this factor, you apparently enjoy opening a crisp new pack of cigarettes, going through the motions of removing a cigarette, perhaps tapping it on your thumb, then striking the match, studying the flame, lighting the cigarette and watching the smoke.
Alternative satisfactions might include:
1 Toying with a pencil
2 Doodling
3 Playing with a coin or piece of jewellery
4 Switching to a pipe. Pipe-smoking too involves a certain amount of pleasurable ritual such as scraping out the bowl, inserting the pipe cleaner, packing the pipe, lighting it, and tamping down the glowing shreds of tobacco
5 Take out a cigarette put it in your mouth but do not light it.

Pleasure It is not always easy to determine whether you use your cigarette to feel good or to keep from feeling so bad. About two-thirds of all smokers score high or fairly high on this factor and about half of those also score high on tension reduction. But if you do get real pleasure out of smoking, an alternative satisfaction might be:
1 Eating, in moderation
2 Drinking, in moderation
3 Community activities, parties or dancing, in moderation
4 Changing your pattern of activity. For example, stop smoking after meals; read a book instead of the newspaper; stop watching your favourite television programmes for a while or sit in another comfortable chair
5 Skipping the coffee break for a day or two particularly if you invariably have a cigarette with that cup of coffee
6 Carrying a little reminder of the nasty consequences of smoking; your problem is convincing yourself that smoking is unpleasant
7 Smoking seven or eight cigarettes in a row, as rapidly as possible, in order to diminish the pleasure

How many cigarettes a day does your child smoke?

When a child breathes air filled with cigarette smoke it can be as bad as if he actually smoked the cigarette himself. Don't smoke when there are children present.

Tension reduction Many smokers use cigarettes as a sort of prop in moments of stress or discomfort, and sometimes they work. But it is both unwise and unhealthy to try to handle personal problems this way. It is far better to face the trouble unaided. Failing that, you could try:
1 Chewing gum, sucking on a mint, or biting a clove
2 Nibbling a low-calorie food (the tension reduction smoker in particular is most likely to gain weight when stopping)
3 Exercising to work out your anger or frustration.

But tension reduction smokers do have a problem, and you will have to make a strenuous effort to eliminate the cigarettes that calm you down. Smoking a cigarette after an upsetting incident will only reinforce your tendency to smoke. Therefore if you want to eliminate an act, you must strive actively to avoid continuing to reinforce it.

Craving If you scored high on this factor, you have a craving for cigarettes that arises solely from not having a cigarette. For you, the craving for the next cigarette probably begins to mount up as soon as you put one out. In order to stop smoking therefore, you have to break the craving absolutely; there are no half measures. We can look at the example of a psychologist who was a heavy smoker; although he claimed that he did not enjoy smoking, he was miserable without a cigarette. In order to stop, he spent three days in a cinema where smoking was not allowed. As a result he stopped smoking, and has not smoked since.

Addicted smokers find it very difficult and unpleasant to stop smoking, but having stopped, they rarely start again. If you are an addicted smoker, you could try to:
1 Develop an aversion to smoking; chain-smoke for two days, or until you cannot bear the thought of another cigarette, and then stay away from cigarettes
2 Switch to a brand of cigarettes that you do not like, and smoke each and every one resolutely; then isolate yourself from cigarettes for as long as possible.

Habit The habitual smoker no longer gets satisfaction from cigarettes. For example, he lights them frequently without even realising it. Stopping is a matter of breaking the habit patterns he has built up. So if habit plays a part in your smoking pattern, you could:
1 As you light up, ask yourself: 'Do I really need this cigarette?'
2 Carry your cigarettes in a different pocket
3 If you have always smoked the cigarette in the left corner of your mouth, switch to the right corner
4 Change the stimuli triggering your need. If coffee for example has always been a cue for a cigarette, change to tea or vice versa
5 Do not carry matches or a lighter
6 If you suddenly realise you have a cigarette in your mouth and you do not remember putting it there, stub it out; do not finish it
7 Try to condition yourself to think: 'Smoking makes me sick today and may kill me tomorrow'
8 Buy ten different kinds of cigarettes and place one of each kind in your cigarette case. Every time you light a cigarette, you will be smoking a different brand. This will make you more aware of your smoking and will also make smoking unpleasant
9 Avoid keeping a supply of cigarettes. Never buy a fresh pack until the old pack is empty. Also keep your cigarettes in an inaccessible place, on a high shelf or in a drawer.

The previous suggestions have concerned those people who want to find satisfaction other than smoking. If, however, you want to stop smoking gradually you should do the following:
1 Do not smoke the cigarette so far down
2 Do not inhale as often. Inhale the first puff only, or every other puff
3 Do not inhale as deeply
4 Smoke cigarettes containing less tar and nicotine
5 Postpone the first cigarette of the day for as long as possible
6 Change to a brand of cigarette that you do not like as much as your favourite brand, then to a brand you like even less, and so on until you arrive at a brand you actively dislike.

Cutting down on cigarette consumption before stopping has an advantage because it means that you are taking less and less smoke into your body. But it offers another advantage too. Once you have cut down by one or more of the above means, you will find it much easier to stop outright.

Whether you are trying to stop smoking completely or just cutting down, give yourself a morale boost—with the money you save, buy yourself a present, such as a new tie or an expensive blouse.

And if you fail to stop smoking after all this then do not despair. Try again and keep trying. You will succeed eventually if you keep trying.

Women and smoking

Through cigarette smoking women have obtained one sort of sexual equality, but a spurious one, an equal chance to become a slave to a highly addictive and dangerous drug. Lung cancer deaths among women in the USA have doubled in the last decade. In fact, if current trends continue, women smokers will soon outnumber men smokers. Consumption has risen sharply among women in semi-skilled and unskilled occupations, and among the younger age groups; girls are taking to the weed earlier and earlier, at the ages of nine, ten and even younger.

Why do women take up smoking? Why are many women beginning to lean as heavily on smoking as on tranquillisers? There are many theories on this.

Weight Men and women want to lose weight for different reasons. Men are more inclined to take action for the sake of good health; women are more often motivated by vanity. It follows that the health-conscious man will be less likely to smoke than the figure-conscious woman. Many women are afraid to give up smoking in the first place for fear they will nibble more and spoil their figures, and many others give up only to start again if they start putting on extra inches.

Isolation Young mums smoke at home while babies sleep. They might be less inclined to smoke in work places and offices, many of which now frown upon smoking. Some offices now have their own 'group therapy' clubs—members encourage one another not to smoke. The housewife marooned at home lacks such moral support, if she tries to break the habit.

Advertisers in some countries are bound by codes of practice but in others they have a relatively free hand. Cigarette (and alcohol) advertisements have been heavily criticised for their sexual overtones. Curiously enough both tobacco and alcohol are potent anaphrodisiacs.

Smoking therapy takes many forms—individual psychotherapy, group dynamic therapy, hypnosis, aversion therapy, and simple supportive help, but results are often disappointing; one large trial reported a 50 per cent relapse rate after six months.

In primitive societies smoking plays an important role in tribal rituals, and is often confined to members of one sex only, in this New Guinea tribe to women. Anthropologists and social psychologists have long been mystified by the reasons for this strange custom. Explanations range from the Freudian (smoking offers a nipple-sucking substitute) to the prosaic (nicotine is a powerful short-acting stimulant).

Anxiety relief Recent research done in Germany suggests that many more women than men use cigarettes as a kind of tranquilliser, as a device for reducing tension. The simple reason for this could be that women are more prone to anxiety than men. According to American health education consultant, Helen Hill, women are also more likely to use cigarettes to combat depression. There are several reasons for this which she told the Third World Conference on Smoking and Health: "Women seem to use cigarettes as coping mechanisms. Thus they can deal with depression, hostility and other negative emotions. Wives and mothers may use cigarettes to mask the resentment of routine housework and caring for young children. This may explain why women who have quit smoking relapse more often than men."

Anti-smoking advertising Women miss out here. Most campaigns are directed at men for the good reason that they are still four times more likely to die from lung cancer. Campaigns for women tend to stress the dangers of smoking during pregnancy. Many women, therefore, resolve to give up smoking only when they become pregnant.

Recent studies show that women who smoke through pregnancy run nearly twice the risk of miscarriage compared with non-smokers. They are also more likely to give birth to smaller babies who, when they go to school, tend to lag behind the children of non-smokers. The children of smokers are also much more likely to need to have their tonsils and adenoids removed. And there are now studies which show that women smokers tend to undergo the menopause earlier.

SMOKING
IS VERY
GLAMOROUS

AMERICAN CANCER SOCIETY

ПЕРЕЕДАНИЕ,

КУРЕНИЕ,

Health education campaigns are being stepped up as governments realise the enormous cost of treating fully developed diseases, such as lung cancer, which are easily preventable. Unfortunately many of us ignore the health educator in favour of the persuasive advertiser.

The health hazards of both smoking and overeating cannot be overstressed. This Russian poster is interesting on two counts: is it a good idea to introduce humour or exaggeration into a desperately serious subject and is the impact of one diluted by the other?

The road to alcoholism

Social occasions
are, for most of us, a time for relaxing and enjoying companionship. But for the potential alcoholic each party or session at the bar is a step along the road from social drinking to anti-social drinking. Sociability ceases to be the rationale for drinking.

Alcohol is basically a stimulant, which in small doses removes social inhibitions and lubricates interpersonal contact. In larger doses it produces unacceptably uninhibited behaviour, and in still larger amounts anaesthesia and coma. Hundreds of thousands, and possibly millions of people throughout the world consume too much alcohol without being aware, until too late, that they have a serious problem.

The sad thing is that such people receive little or no positive help during the early stages of drinking, the countdown to addiction. Alerting problem drinkers to early warning signs of trouble is the biggest single step that can be taken towards eliminating the problem.

The process of becoming an alcoholic can take anything from 2 to 60 years, although 10 to 15 years is the average. You may think you are immune, but do not be complacent. Ask yourself the following questions, replying honestly.
Do you take a drink before facing up to a problem?
Do you drink for the taste or for the effect?
Do you sneak away from work for a 'quickie' before lunch?
Do you drink by yourself?
Do you have memory lapses after drinking?
Do you find other people slow to finish their drinks?

Exercise extreme caution if you have answered 'yes' to one or more of these questions—it could

mean that you are drinking too much. Seek medical advice. You may not necessarily have to stop drinking but you would be well advised to control your consumption.

Never be afraid to consult your doctor about your drinking habits; he would rather see you early on than later when your drinking is threatening your marriage, your career, or both. Likewise do not shield a wife, husband, colleague or friend if you believe that he or she has a drink problem. Initially it is easy enough to disguise a drink problem by refusing invitations to parties or by feigning illness, but lies and deceit will become increasingly difficult and exhausting. As a destructive force alcohol has few equals among common addictive drugs.

A case history The case of 45-year-old David L. is given below as an object lesson. His problem can be charted in four phases.

PHASE ONE Twelve years ago David was a social drinker. Strain and tension at work and at home became an increasing problem, so he began 'relief drinking', learning how to use alcohol to combat stress. Because a certain degree of stress and strain is normal and inevitable he could always justify another drink. No one noticed anything peculiar about his behaviour.

Cross references
Lifestyles 182   Liver 128   Cirrhosis 131   Hypertension 107

PHASE TWO One morning David woke up unable to remember very much about the night before—how he got home was a complete blank. Worried that he might have offended some of his drinking companions, he made a few guarded telephone calls. He had offended nobody and concluded that there had been nothing peculiar about his behaviour. He chose to forget that there was something odd about such a memory blank.

In reality he had suffered his first 'alcoholic amnesia' or 'blackout'. Such blackouts involve loss of memory rather than loss of consciousness. Not all alcoholics suffer from them but David did, increasingly. At the same time he became increasingly frustrated with drinking partners who took longer to drink up than he did and began to drink in secret. From being a man who used to boast how much he could drink, he became a man who insisted that he drank very little.

PHASE THREE David recognised that he had a problem. He found it increasingly difficult to control his alcohol consumption. In company he was still able to stay reasonably sober, reassured by the knowledge that he would be able to drink freely when he was alone. The situation did improve temporarily. He changed from drinking spirits to drinking beer and then stopped drinking for several weeks, only to start drinking again with renewed vigour and intensity, neglecting family, work and food.

PHASE FOUR This was the final chronic phase. By this time David's life consisted of almost continuous drinking. Sometimes he could hardly sign his name or remember where he had hidden his secret supplies of alcohol. On one occasion, late at night, he smashed his automobile and was taken to hospital. The following day he admitted that he was in need of help.

It had taken David L. three years of drinking to become an alcoholic; it took him nearly three years before he could truthfully state that he felt 'cured'—two to three years is about the average. In one sense any talk of 'cure' is dangerous because the alcoholic always remains at risk. There has been speculation about the possibility of transforming reformed alcoholics into 'moderate drinkers', but the consensus among specialists is that rehabilitated alcoholics must never drink again.

Health risks Excess drinking can cause much physical disease. Are the risks involved really worth it?

STOMACH Alcohol inflames the oesophagus and stomach, hence the sensation of nausea the

morning after a heavy drinking session. A stomach lining inflamed by alcohol is super-sensitive to other irritants, aspirin for example. Chronic gastritis (inflammation of the stomach) is extremely common among alcoholics. Gastric and duodenal ulcers are also associated with alcoholism, though the number of ulcers among alcoholics is not significantly higher than among the population taken as a whole.

VITAMIN DEFICIENCY The heavy drinker may find that he needs less food because alcoholic drinks contain sugar and other nutrients. It is now estimated by the British Nutrition Foundation that the average English adult male gets 5.2 per cent of his energy from alcohol.

LIVER Seven out of every ten chronic alcoholics have 'fatty' livers. Amino acids (the basic constituents of protein) usually remove fat from the liver, but fat from the blood accumulates in the liver when there is insufficient protein in the diet.

The combination of nutritional deficiency and the toxic action of alcohol are believed to cause both 'fatty liver' and cirrhosis of the liver. Severe cirrhosis impairs the flow of blood through the liver, putting the victim at risk from haemorrhage. About 20 per cent of alcoholics admitted to hospitals have liver cirrhosis. In Britain between 1962 and 1972 there was a dramatic rise in alcohol consumption and a corresponding 40 per cent increase in cirrhosis deaths. Alcohol is also believed to make the liver more susceptible to damage from other sources of infection.

ANAEMIA Many chronic alcoholics suffer from anaemia. This is attributed to lack of folic acid in the diet, which causes blood deficiencies and difficulties in absorbing food.

BLOOD PRESSURE Recent research has established the first conclusive links between alcohol and high blood pressure. A survey of 84,000 people in the USA showed that people who had two or fewer alcoholic drinks a day had blood pressure readings similar or even lower than those of non-drinkers. In contrast the blood pressure of drinkers who had three or more drinks a day was much higher. The study suggests that hypertension is nearly twice as common among heavy drinkers as among non-drinkers.

A more sensible attitude to drinking must be encouraged, and it is crucial to stop regarding alcoholism as a disease which primarily hits men. It also affects women. In the early 1960s there were 7 or 8 male alcoholics for every 1 female alcoholic; today the ratio is between 4 and 5 males to every female.

The solitary drinker imbibes steadily until oblivion descends. When a person's whole life is devoted to seeking and drinking alcohol nothing else matters, not even family, career, or health. Medical help and lifelong abstention are the only cure.

Tropical diseases: the 'Big Six'

These Masai herdsmen and their cattle are restricted in their nomadic life to areas where the tsetse fly threat is small. The result is often over-grazing of land and the creation of dustbowls.

Elephantiasis is the end result of years of infection with the mosquito-borne filarian worm *Wuchereria bancrofti.* At this advanced state no treatment is possible.

In the mid-70s the World Health Organization, with the purpose of attracting funds from governments and from other international organisations, designated six categories of tropical disease as priorities for action and research: the so-called Big Six. One of the most spectacular achievements of the WHO, founded in 1948, has been the eradication of smallpox; today the virus only survives in a few laboratories.

Malaria In the mid-1960s this most important of the human tropical diseases was thought to be on its way to extinction. Ten years of determined worldwide attack on the vector of the malarial parasites, the female *Anopheles* mosquito, should have paid dividends. Unfortunately *Anopheles* developed resistance to the insecticides used and the health service infrastructure in many tropical areas was inadequate, and so the programme was abandoned. Malaria is now resurgent in many countries where it was previously well-controlled, as in India. To make matters worse human resistance to anti-malaria drugs is spreading.

The most virulent form of malaria, caused by the protozoan parasite *Plasmodium falciparum*, kills 25 to 30 per cent of non-immune persons infected by it and not treated with drugs. The main features of the illness are high fever, chills and sweats, headache and bone pains, and enlargement of the liver and spleen. Death is most commonly due to blockage of the cerebral capillaries by red blood cells containing malarial parasites.

Schistosomiasis The life cycle of the worms responsible for this disease, the second most important of the WHO's 'Big Six', involves freshwater snails as intermediate hosts. The worm larvae parasitise snails first, and then transfer to humans, penetrating even healthy skin if it comes in contact with snail-infested water. Once inside a human host the larvae grow into adults and colonise the bladder (in the case of *Schistosoma haematobium*) or the intestine and liver (*S. mansoni* and *S. japonicum*). Their eggs pass out of the body in the urine or faeces. *S. haematobium* in Africa and the Middle East usually reveals itself in childhood or adolescence by blood in the urine, referred to as 'male menstruation' in many countries when it occurs in boys. In later life, *S. haematobium* can cause kidney failure or cancer of the bladder. *S. mansoni* in the Caribbean, South America, Africa and the Middle East, and *S. japonicum* in the Far East deposit their eggs in the liver, slowly destroying it and eventually causing death.

All forms of schistosomiasis can be cured with drugs, but effective large-scale control also requires the destruction of the host snails.

Trypanosomiasis This is not one infection but a

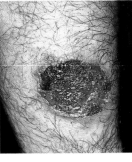

Skin leishmaniasis or oriental sore occurs on any uncovered part of the body from the ankles to the face. It heals slowly by itself, but early treatment speeds up cure and prevents scarring.

The *Anopheles* mosquito, shown here partially engorged with human blood, transmits malaria and sometimes elephantiasis and viruses. Only the female takes blood; the male feeds exclusively on plant juices.

large group of infections found in man and other vertebrates. The culprits in this case are members of the protozoan genus *Trypanosoma*, which multiply asexually in the bloodstream and are transmitted by the bites of bloodsucking insects, tsetse flies in Africa, and 'kissing-bugs' or 'assassin-bugs' in the New World.

AFRICAN TRYPANOSOMIASIS Two forms seriously undermine human health: Gambian sleeping sickness and Rhodesian sleeping sickness. Gambian sleeping sickness is a slow, chronic, and fatal infection if untreated—fever, anaemia, weakness and lassitude gradually lead to coma and death. Rhodesian sleeping sickness resembles the Gambian form clinically, but it has an accelerated time-scale, death occurring in 6–18 months rather than 5–15 years.

AMERICAN TRYPANOSOMIASIS Known as Chagas' disease, this differs completely from the African trypanosomiases. Many people can be infected but remain symptom-free for 30 or 40 years. The parasite that causes it, *Trypanosoma cruzi*, attacks the nervous system.

In some parts of Latin America Chagas' disease accounts for up to 29 per cent of deaths, and there is no effective drug treatment.

Leprosy There are probably about 20 million leprosy sufferers in the world at present. Leprosy today is almost entirely a disease of the Indian subcontinent, tropical Africa, Southeast Asia and South America. It is usually acquired as a result of direct skin-to-skin contact, the bacteria entering through minute abrasions, but there is evidence for respiratory droplet transmission, and for sexual contact transmission. Leprosy varies from a trivial infection to a crippling, disfiguring illness, leading to loss of limbs and eventually death—the skin and peripheral nerves are the important target systems

Cross references
Renal system **132**
Liver **128**
Lymphatic system **108**
Skin diseases **44**

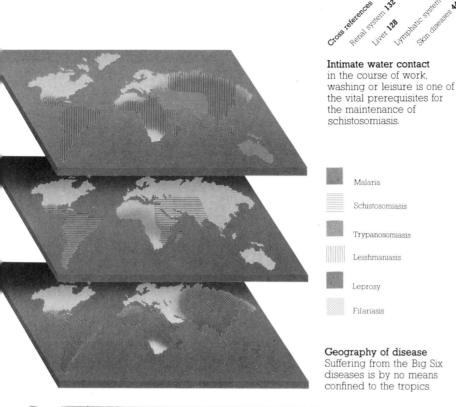

Intimate water contact
in the course of work, washing or leisure is one of the vital prerequisites for the maintenance of schistosomiasis.

Malaria

Schistosomiasis

Trypanosomiasis

Leishmaniasis

Leprosy

Filariasis

Geography of disease
Suffering from the Big Six diseases is by no means confined to the tropics.

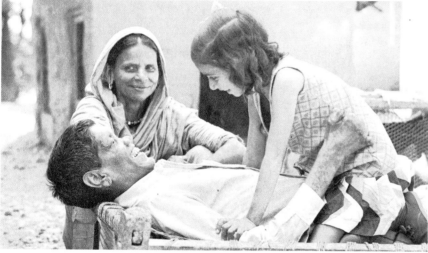

The deformed leper
with fingers, thumbs and often whole limbs missing, was formerly an outcast. Modern drugs and health education have removed traditional fears, and the treated leper now lives a relatively normal life.

for the leprosy bacillus. Leprosy can be controlled by long-term drug administration, but an effective vaccine may soon be developed.

Filariasis This is a collective term for at least eight different infections caused by various species of nematode or roundworm. These are transmitted from person to person by bloodsucking insects. The two most important filarian diseases are Bancroftian filariasis and onchocerciasis: the first is caused by the roundworm *Wuchereria bancrofti*, and is spread by mosquitoes.

Bancroftian filariasis is the most widely distributed of all the major tropical diseases—at least 250 million people are infected at the present time. Numerous control programmes based on mass administration of the drug diethyl-carbamazine citrate, or on insecticidal control of mosquitoes, have been launched since 1947; but

have only succeeded in a few small groups of islands.

The sexually mature adults of *W. bancrofti* colonise the human lymphatic system, progressively damaging and eventually obstructing it. This condition is known as elephantiasis and is most common in the legs and external genitalia.

The second roundworm disease, onchocerciasis, is caused by *Onchocerca volvulus*, and is spread by female blackflies of the genus *Simulium*. The adults of *O. volvulus* live in the skin, where they form large unsightly nodules, cause intense itching and lead to degenerative skin conditions such as 'tissue paper skin' and 'lizard skin'. The most distressing effect of onchocerciasis is blindness, when larval worms migrate from the skin of the face to the eyes. Probably about 40 million people suffer from onchocerciasis, most of them living in the great river systems of West and East Africa. Unfortunately there is no drug suitable for mass campaigns against onchocerciasis. However a 20-year control programme, with WHO as the executing agency, was launched in 1974 covering seven countries of the Volta River Basin in West Africa. All *Simulium* breeding grounds are being sprayed with insecticide.

Leishmaniasis This least common of the WHO 'Big Six' diseases is caused by protozoans of the genus *Leishmania*, transmitted by the bites of tiny midges called sandflies. China, India, Soviet Asia, East Africa, the Mediterranean basin, Venezuela and Brazil are the most important regions for leishmaniasis infections, which can vary from benign, short-lived ulcers, to disfiguring lesions which eat away the nasopharynx and mouth, to a visceral form that causes gross anaemia, and enlargement of the liver and spleen.

Birth control: how and why

Contraceptives are free to all married couples in China. Here technicians at the Nanking College of Pharmacy manufacture contraceptive jelly foil.

The phenomenal growth in the population of this planet and the political, social and economic implications of this growth, have forced the issue of birth control on governments as well as individuals. Mrs Gandhi's policy of encouraging sterilisation by giving away transistor radios, and attempts to develop a satisfactory 'morning after' pill, are just two approaches to a worldwide problem, a problem compounded by those religious leaders who oppose all or most techniques of birth control.

Techniques

Contraceptive measures can be taken by men (condom, withdrawal) or by women (diaphragm, pill, intra-uterine device, douche). Abortion is not generally considered to be a method of contraception, but there is no doubt that it is often used as such, whether the operation takes place in a back street or in a hospital. In many less developed countries prolonged breastfeeding is used, unreliably, as a means of contraception.

The effectiveness of contraceptive methods varies enormously. One way of finding out whether a method is 'safe' or not is to look at its Pearl Index; this is an index based on the number of pregnancies per year in a population of women using a particular method for 100 years and capable of conceiving 12 times a year. So a Pearl Index of 4 for a particular technique means that four women in 100 are likely to become pregnant every year if they use it.

For men Male contraceptive techniques are relatively inefficient. Withdrawal or coitus interruptus is thought to have a Pearl Index in excess of 20. In addition, withdrawing the penis just before orgasm is frustrating for both partners. The condom or sheath, with a Pearl Index of 5, is safer and has the advantage of giving some protection against venereal disease. Most condoms are made of rubber latex and in a variety of styles and colours. They should be unrolled onto the erect penis prior to vaginal entry, and the penis should be withdrawn carefully after ejaculation. Though inexpensive, widely available and easily portable, some couples dislike condoms on the grounds that they reduce sensitivity.

For women A far wider variety of contraceptive methods is available to women. The barrier or diaphragm is usually used with a spermicidal cream or jelly. The coated diaphragm is inserted into the vagina before intercourse and should remain in place for at least six hours after it. This method has a Pearl Index of about 5. The main objection from women is that having to insert a diaphragm before intercourse spoils the spontaneity of the occasion; a few also complain of reduced sensitivity of the vagina. A diaphragm must be fitted individually,

refitted after childbirth, and regularly checked for tears. Only rarely does a diaphragm become dislodged, and then only during female-superior coitus, very active sexual play, or orgasm.

The intra-uterine device or IUD is another effective barrier method (Pearl Index less than 5). Because IUDs are inserted into the uterus and usually left in place for several years, there is no need to remember to take precautions every time intercourse occurs. A wide variety of IUDs have been developed (Lippes loop, shield, spiral, copper T, copper 7), and a woman is fitted with the one that suits her best; her size, age and parity are all taken into account. Though a very popular method of birth control (in the United States, for example, at least five million women use it) the IUD has some disadvantages. Some women find that their periods become heavier. There is also a risk of uterine infection, though this is less frequent with the newer models. Another old problem, that of the IUD being expelled without the woman knowing, has been largely solved by making IUDs with filaments attached to them which protrude through the cervix into the vagina.

The pill Perhaps no recent method of preventing conception has aroused as much controversy as the oral contraceptive pill. This contains varying combinations of oestrogens and progesterones, which prevent pregnancy by inhibiting the development of the egg, inhibiting ovulation, and inhibiting the preparations the uterus makes each month to receive a fertilised ovum. Whilst extremely effective if taken regularly (Pearl Index about 1), there has been much discussion as to its safety.

The pill undoubtedly causes thrombosis, clotting of the blood, in the deep and superficial veins of *some* women. Thrombosis is potentially dangerous of course: if a fragment of a clot breaks away it may pass to the lung, heart or brain. However, it must be stressed that this is extremely uncommon, and to some extent predictable. We know, for example, that women over 35 who smoke are most at risk of thrombosis on the pill. This group of women, and also women with high blood pressure (a condition which the pill may exacerbate), should use alternative contraceptive methods. The less serious side-effects of the pill are nausea, vomiting, depression, fluid retention and headaches.

The other major non-surgical technique of birth control is the rhythm method. This has been approved by the Roman Catholic Church since 1951. Quite simply intercourse must be avoided when ovulation is likely, in the middle of the woman's menstrual cycle. Unfortunately the rhythm method is notoriously unreliable (Pearl Index between 20 and 40). Checking body

Cross references
Fertilisation **20**
Ejaculation **24**
Sperm **25**
Sex hormones **71**

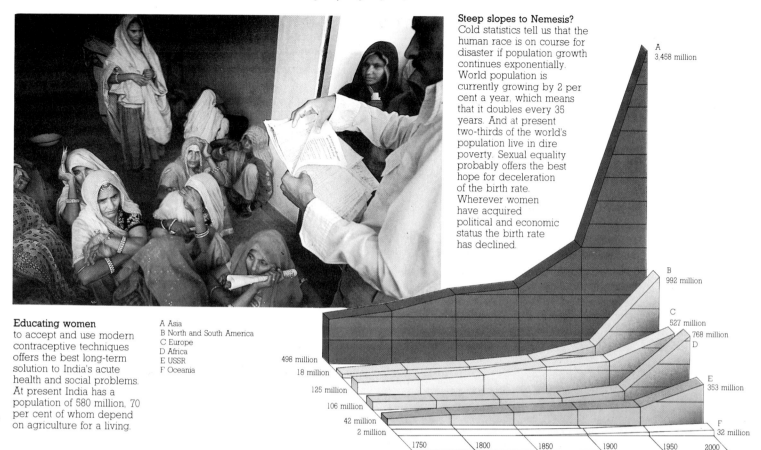

Educating women
to accept and use modern contraceptive techniques offers the best long-term solution to India's acute health and social problems. At present India has a population of 580 million, 70 per cent of whom depend on agriculture for a living.

A Asia
B North and South America
C Europe
D Africa
E USSR
F Oceania

Steep slopes to Nemesis?
Cold statistics tell us that the human race is on course for disaster if population growth continues exponentially. World population is currently growing by 2 per cent a year, which means that it doubles every 35 years. And at present two-thirds of the world's population live in dire poverty. Sexual equality probably offers the best hope for deceleration of the birth rate. Wherever women have acquired political and economic status the birth rate has declined.

A 3,458 million
B 992 million
C 527 million
768 million
D
E 353 million
F 32 million

498 million
18 million
125 million
106 million
42 million
2 million

1750 1800 1850 1900 1950 2000

temperature throughout the month to detect the slight rise in temperature which accompanies ovulation does little to improve reliability.

Surgery The standard surgical technique for rendering men infertile is vasectomy. This is a simple operation which can be done in 30 minutes under local anaesthetic, and involves tying off the sperm tubes, the vasa deferentia, which take sperm into the ejaculate. Similarly, women may have their ovarian tubes tied off to prevent eggs entering the uterus. This is a slightly more complicated procedure requiring a short stay in hospital. Most surgeons perform the operation through a laparoscope, an instrument about as thick as a finger introduced into the pelvic cavity through a small incision in the abdomen. The light source at the end of the laparoscope enables the surgeon to see the ovaries and tubes clearly. The thread used to ligate the tubes is also passed down the scope.

Future developments Potentially, the most convenient form of contraception is the 'day after' pill containing high levels of oestrogens. This is still undergoing trials as nausea is a common side-effect. Long-term contraceptive agents, notably synthetic progesterones, can be injected with an effectiveness of up to six months. So far, attempts at making a pill for men have been unsuccessful.

Whose responsibility?

Many men, married or not, still assume that contraception is the woman's responsibility. With rather odd scrupulousness, many unattached men prefer to have intercourse with women who are 'safe' rather than take precautions themselves. Certainly most women want the right to control their fertility, and so most of them swallow their physical and emotional scruples and take precautions. But in a stable long-term relationship the means of contraception should be agreed between both parties, and be acceptable to both.

Despite the increased availability of contraceptives, it remains axiomatic that the motivation to actually use them is the crucial factor in the success or failure of birth control campaigns. Governments have tried many different ways of encouraging 'responsibility'. Most countries in the developed world, where overpopulation is least acute, have simply relied on the fact that good diet, good housing and good education automatically depress family size. In Russia and China the birth rate is being held in check by more vigorous methods, including indoctrination and positive disincentives. In China, for example, child benefit used to be given for the first two children, but decreased for subsequent children.

Analysing blood samples

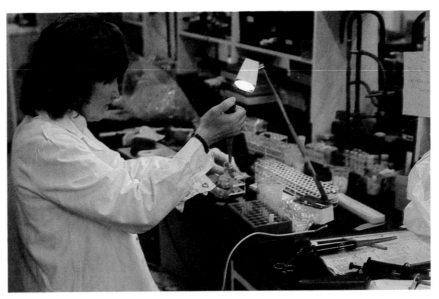

Testing blood samples
is a vital part of clinical and preventive medicine. Not generally appreciated by the public is the fact that testing constitutes a health hazard for the nurses and technicians who take and process blood samples. Hepatitis B is the main hazard, but numerous other infections, including syphilis, can be caught in the laboratory.

No matter how sophisticated diagnostic technology becomes, probably no single test or battery of tests will ever replace a thorough dialogue between doctor and patient, with the patient describing symptoms (the aches and pains he feels) and the doctor checking signs (physical manifestations like lumps, bumps and inflammation). All body substances—blood, urine, faeces, pus, small pieces of tissue—can tell a pathologist something about general or specific body conditions. Here we discuss some of the tests used to confirm (or disprove) diagnoses.

Blood tests

There are many different types of blood test, and new ones are introduced every year, providing further insight into the way the body machine functions. Some of the more routine tests are:

Erythrocyte sedimentation rate (ESR) This procedure is designed to show how long it takes erythrocytes, red blood cells, to separate from plasma, blood fluid, and fall to the bottom of the tube. It is a non-specific test, in that the results will not point to the presence of a specific disease, but they may indicate that something is wrong. In healthy people the sedimentation rate is slow. In diseased people the cells clump together or aggregate, and therefore fall to the bottom of the tube faster. A raised ESR may point to a disease the patient is unaware of, or it may be an indicator of the severity of a diagnosed illness; it can therefore be used to monitor response to therapy—a positive response may be reflected in a change in ESR.

Red and white cell counts The cell content of the blood is important in many ways. A count of blood cells and examination of their size, density and haemoglobin content (haemoglobin is the pigment which gives blood its distinctive red colour) is important in the investigation of anaemia. With this kind of information a doctor can establish if anaemia is due to bleeding, for example, or increased blood destruction, or lack of vitamins or iron. The appearance of the red blood cells can change in response to a wide variety of conditions, including liver and kidney complaints.

Study of white blood cells (the granulocytes, monocytes and lymphocytes) can also be very informative. An increase in certain forms of granulocyte can arise from bacterial infection, an allergy or a cancer. A decrease in their number will alert the doctor to the possibility of disorders of the bone marrow or the spleen. An increase in lymphocytes might indicate a viral infection, whereas a decrease might be the result of certain drug treatments.

Platelet counts Platelets are the cells involved in clotting. Their number may increase in inflammatory or malignant conditions or after surgical removal of the spleen. Conversely, their numbers may drop with some immunity disorders arising from their destruction. A low platelet count can also be attributable to decreased production due to malignancy, infection, drugs or irradiation.

Blood chemistry Measuring various substances in the blood can also provide important clues about the function of vital organs. For example, after a heart attack certain muscle enzymes are released into the blood; their levels indicate the extent of the damage. Further tests will enable the doctor to assess the patient's response to treatment. If the level of muscle enzymes rises rather than falls, further damage may have occurred. Other enzymes are elevated by liver damage, which may also be accompanied by a failure to produce blood proteins in adequate amounts. Blood protein concentrations can be measured. Muscle damage and disorders can also produce changes in enzyme levels. Kidney function can be assessed by the level of urea and other waste products in the blood and urine.

Hormones secreted by the endocrine glands can also be measured in the blood, and sometimes in the urine as well. Occasionally the endocrine glands have to be stimulated so that tests can be performed. In a glucose tolerance test, for example, glucose is ingested to stimulate insulin release into the blood—insulin is one of the hormones which regulates the amount of glucose in the blood and urine. In a normal healthy person a glucose tolerance test produces an increase in the amount of blood glucose which then quickly falls as the pancreas (the insulin-producing gland) produces insulin to promote glucose absorption into the cells. In a diabetic, whose insulin production is impaired, blood glucose levels remain high.

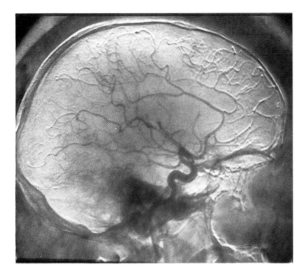

Ultrasound scanning, originally developed as an alternative to X-rays for the purpose of investigating foetal development, is now extensively used for other purposes, for example to confirm suspected tumours, particularly tumours of the upper abdomen, and gallstones.

Cerebral angiography is a highly sophisticated tool used by neurologists to assess the state of the blood vessels in the brain. The procedure is not without risk—the technique is similar to that of coronary angiography.

Specific and sensitive are the two criteria that doctors apply to tests used in preventive screening. The cervical smear (right) comes out well on both counts.

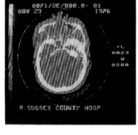

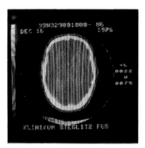

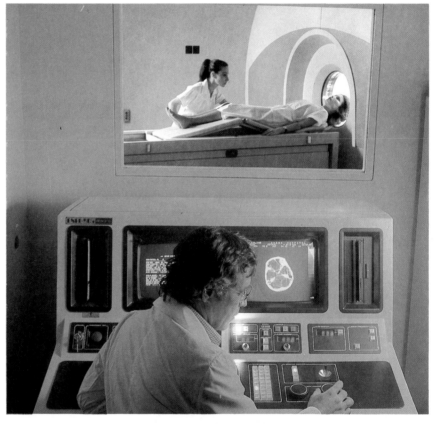

A brain scan can detect intracerebral bleeding (above left) or a tumour in one of the facial sinuses (above right). The procedure involves injection or inhalation of radioisotopes whose distribution in the brain is then visualised on the basis of the radiation they emit.

Infra-red thermography utilises the differential emission of infra-red radiation from body areas of differing temperature and blood flow to detect localised abnormalities. Here the abnormality is a cancerous area in the right breast. Thermography has largely replaced X-rays for the purpose of cancer screening. Ideally, all screening techniques should be non-invasive.

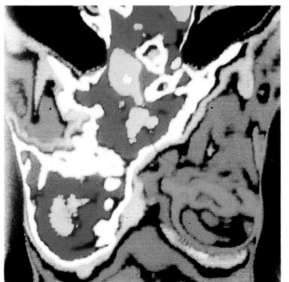

The body scanner represents a marriage between long established technology and new microelectronic engineering. It was developed simultaneously and independently by two scientists, one British and one American, both of whom were awarded the Nobel Prize for Medicine.

Looking inside the body

New technology
A modern haematology lab is capable of handling vast batches of blood samples. Hardware such as this Coulter machine can measure the ratio of red blood cells to the total volume of blood (haematocrit), white cell count, levels of haemoglobin, and many other diagnostic indices. These are interpreted together with clinical data to determine whether a patient is suffering from a blood disorder, anaemia for example. Other samples can be sent to a biochemist for further analysis.

Cannulation and dye techniques

Virtually every artery and vein in the body can be cannulated—a cannula is a very fine tube which can be inserted into blood vessels. Dye is then delivered via the cannula to the vessel in question, and X-ray pictures taken to establish the path the vessel takes and if there is anything wrong with it. Various ducts in the body can be cannulated too (bile duct, pancreatic duct, ureters).

It is now routine in some types of heart disease to assess cardiac function by passing catheters into the heart itself. A catheter passed through a peripheral vein will eventually reach the right side of the heart; a catheter threaded through a peripheral artery will reach the left side. It is then possible to measure pressure in the different chambers of the heart, or take blood samples to measure oxygen levels, or pump dye into the heart chambers and watch the blood flow using X-rays. The coronary arteries can also be cannulated and pumped with dye to see if there are any blockages. This procedure, known as coronary angiogram, is very useful for assessing whether a CHD patient is a suitable candidate for coronary by-pass surgery.

Endoscopy

An endoscope is an instrument for looking inside body cavities. To explore the stomach or small intestine the endoscope is passed through the mouth and throat. To explore the large bowel a simoidoscope (a rigid metal tube) or a colonoscope, both variations on the endoscope, is used, with the anus as the point of entry. A cystoscope is a special scope for exploring the inside of the bladder. A bronchoscope is a special scope for investigating the lung cavities—it is passed through the nose or mouth. The beauty of the modern endoscope is that it is flexible, being made of glass fibre optic bundles which allow transmission of light around curves and corners.

Computer scanning

Computerised axial tomography, CT scanning for short, is a new technique which uses X-rays to build up pictures of body tissues by scanning a series of slices through the head or body at the desired level. This new technology has revolutionised radiology, enabling diagnoses to be made simply and with very little discomfort to the patient. Ultrasound scanning has similar applications to CT scanning, although it is not used for brain scanning because ultrasound will not produce pictures through the skull.

Most organs of the body (lungs, heart, spleen, liver, kidneys) will selectively absorb radioactive isotopes which emit minute and harmless amounts of radiation which can be used to produce pictures.

Cross references
Heart and arteries **104**
Veins **105**
Angina **92**
Ultrasound **138**
Future course of medicine **226**

Biopsy

Tissue biopsy, or the removal of a small piece of tissue for examination under the microscope, has always been a useful diagnostic tool. Bone marrow, liver and kidney biopsies can be done simply and safely under local anaesthetic. At one time other tissue biopsies required minor surgery but biopsy needles are now so fine that surgery is often not necessary. X-ray or ultrasound may be used to visualise the tissues from which samples are required; in this way the biopsy needle can be inserted with great accuracy, and a few cells aspirated for cytological examination.

A cervical smear, for the purpose of diagnosing cervical cancer in women, also comes into the cytological (cell) test category. A small stick rather like an ice lolly stick is used to dislodge a few cells from the lining of the cervix; the cells are then put on a microscope slide, stained, and looked at under a microscope.

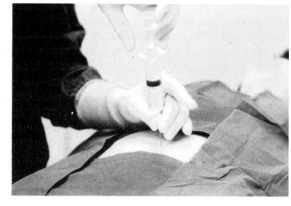

Amniocentesis
involves drawing off some of the amniotic fluid from the womb for analysis. This technique together with ultrasound can detect pre-natal defects such as spina bifida and mongolism.

Diagnostic radiology
Nearly 70 per cent of the radiation we are exposed to comes from natural sources, but the rest comes from medical diagnostic and therapeutic sources. Nevertheless X-rays are invaluable to doctors and dentists; their uses range from plotting the growth of teeth in children to treating malignant tumours. Uncontrolled large doses of radiation can cause cancer.

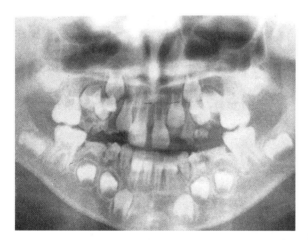

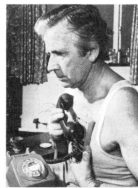

ECG phone check
In some centres where patients live a long way from hospital ECGs can be monitored by telephone. Here a nurse checks the electrocardiogram strip for abnormality. She can even tell when some patients have not been taking their tablets! Heart patients especially

at risk can be given a special transmitter which keeps them in touch with the hospital. The handset, with its amplifier, is held over the heart and the signal transmitted to the hospital. Because the patient is up and about and behaving normally, the information given by such readings is

often more helpful to doctors than readings taken in hospital. ECGs can also be recorded over 24-hour periods on ordinary tape cassettes.

A barium meal
is a routine method of investigating diseases of the digestive system. The patient swallows an unpleasant-tasting mixture containing barium sulphate

which is opaque to X-rays. This picture shows a healthy stomach and duodenum. No surface irregularities due to ulceration can be seen.

Public health: present and future threats

The public health problems discussed here are those which in some measure affect every country in the world. Pollution problems tend to be limited to industrialised countries, and poor public hygiene to tropical and Third World countries, but overpopulation and deforestation are worldwide in their implications. All these hazards to health are preventable in the technical sense. But in the final analysis the solutions to them are political.

Overpopulation

At an international conference on population in Stockholm in 1974 Dr J. F. Patino said: 'Overpopulation has become the most important factor affecting the health of mankind . . . Non-renewable resources are being depleted; disease and stress are bred in crowded living conditions; the environment is being polluted; and material resources are being consumed at appalling rates. The results are manifold: undernourishment, lack of educational opportunities, insufficient housing, poverty, crime, and social and political unrest.'

The statistics back him up in frightening fashion. The population of the world today is a little over 4,000 million. In 1830 it was only 1,000 million, the result of some 250,000 years of thriving and multiplying. By 1930 it was 2,000 million, by 1960 it was 3,000 million, and by 1975 it was 4,000 million. If current growth rates continue unchecked, total world population could be in excess of 7,000 million by the year 2000.

The three essential components of effective action to limit population growth are: political will with solid 'grass roots' backing; wide availability of a range of techniques for limiting family size, with individual choice as to the technique used; and the creation of socio-economic and health conditions which render a high birth rate unnecessary.

This may seem a hopeless dream, but several countries have achieved it in the last 20 years, notably Singapore. In 1957 Singapore had a compound rate of population growth of 3.5 per cent per annum (1.5 per cent above the world average). With the wholehearted support of the government and massive publicity and health education efforts, a family planning programme was launched utilising the whole range of available techniques, made available through government clinics. By 1975 the obtainable annual population growth rate had been reduced to 1.3 per cent with a net reproduction rate of 0.978.

Deforestation

Green plants, and especially large trees, have two effects on the climate of this planet. First, they manufacture their own carbohydrates from water and carbon dioxide and in the process give off oxygen. Thus the balance between oxygen and

carbon dioxide in the atmosphere is determined in large part by the total active biomass of green-leaved vegetation on the earth. And a very important proportion of that vegetation is to be found in the remaining virgin rain forests of South America, Africa and Southeast Asia. Destruction of the largest of these areas, the Amazon forest, could lead to an excessive accumulation of carbon dioxide in the earth's upper atmosphere, an increase in the surface temperature of the earth, and a melting of the polar ice caps. The ecological destruction that would follow would render much of the earth unsuitable for human habitation. On this count alone, the great forests of the world should be of huge concern to us all.

Second, forests are very important in determining rainfall and drainage patterns. Destruction of the Amazon rain forest, which is being felled at a phenomenal rate, could lead to the formation of new deserts in the Americas at a time when the world's growing population will be in desperate need of larger and larger food supplies.

Public hygiene

The two most important components of good public hygiene are safe water supplies and safe sanitation. At the present time 86 per cent of the rural population of the developing countries of the world lack adequate water supplies and 92 per cent

A mature forest tree
takes 200 years to grow but less than 20 minutes to cut down. The pressure of man on his limited natural resources increases with the inexorable increase of population. Deforestation for fuel and farming land, as here in New Guinea, and on an even vaster scale in Amazonia, could change the whole ecology of our globe.

Mass sterilisation,
vasectomy for men and tubal ligation for women, has been used in India to limit population growth. The People's Republic of China has taken a different route: persuasion and readily available contraceptives.

Acute malnutrition
Aid and famine relief flood in to save lives in emergencies, but the long term task is rehabilitation and restoration of the means of self-reliance.

Cross references

Complaints of
the respiratory system **118**
Birth control **210**
Tropical diseases
and WHO **208**

lack adequate facilities for disposing of excreta. In urban areas of the tropics things are only marginally better: 29 per cent of town dwellers have no sanitation facilities whatsoever, and only 28 per cent have sewage disposal systems that could be described as satisfactory.

The practical consequences of these depressing statistics are these: a vast burden of chronic ill health for almost everyone, and for young children, pregnant women, the malnourished, and the frail and aged an ever-present risk of sudden acute disease and death. If one's source of water for drinking and washing is also one's sewer, dysentery, typhoid fever, gastroenteritis, poliomyelitis, infective hepatitis and leptospirosis are a permanent menace. From time to time great epidemics of cholera will strike down even young and seemingly healthy adults. Open sewers are also a perfect habitat for the mosquitoes which carry malarial and filarian infections, and for the snails which transmit schistosomiasis.

The United Nations and the World Health Organization have declared the 1980s an International Drinking Water Supply and Sanitation Decade. The aim is to provide plentiful clean water and safe if simple sanitation for everyone by the year 1990. And the estimated cost? US $300,000 million. To many cynics this is a hopelessly optimistic pipe dream, but for at least two-thirds of the world's population it holds some hope of a livable, if not perfect, life, and may mean the difference between dying and surviving.

Pollution

There are many forms of pollution, but the most obviously hazardous to human health is atmospheric pollution. Anything which pollutes the air we breathe is liable to produce damage, acute or chronic. Over the past century levels of pollutants in the air, especially in the vicinity of large industrial conurbations, have steadily increased. The disastrous London Smog of December 1952 was caused primarily by particulate smoke and sulphur dioxide pollution, and it led to the passing of a very effective Clean Air Act four years later. But in cities such as Tokyo and Los Angeles, where pollution from vehicle exhaust is relatively more important, unburnt hydrocarbons from petrol and diesel fumes, together with carbon monoxide and various nitrogen oxides, react in the presence of strong sunlight to produce ozone. This leads to the formation of a particularly dense and acrid 'photochemical' smog. This is intensely irritating to the mucous membranes of the respiratory tract and greatly aggravates bronchitis and other lung diseases. Legislation compelling car manufacturers to fit 'clean' engines and exhaust filters has now been passed in all major countries.

Ritual bathing
in the River Ganges at Benares. Unfortunately the waters of the Ganges carry a rich cargo of diseases, among them cholera, dysentery, typhoid and poliomyelitis.

Atmospheric pollution
by factory chimneys and automobile exhaust is a real health hazard. The cost of clean air, and clean rivers and clean oceans, is high, but the environmental lobby in most industrialised countries is becoming increasingly vocal and powerful. There are votes in anti-pollution.

Cystitis and prostate troubles

Cystitis (the medical name for inflammation of the bladder) is the name given to a number of unexplained bladder conditions which cause great pain and discomfort to vast numbers of people, usually women. Symptoms include pain, loss of blood from the urethra, the need to pass water frequently and sometimes incontinence.

You should consult your doctor about such symptoms but if he is unable to detect the cause there are various things that you can do. The self-help techniques outlined below have brought comfort to thousands of women.

Preventive measures Whatever you do will bring little relief unless you pay constant attention to hygiene. Wash the perineum, the skin around the anus, vagina and urethra, with lukewarm water three times daily—first thing in the morning, last thing at night and after passing a stool. The perineum also needs washing before and after intercourse, during a cystitis attack and after swimming. Also it must never be allowed to get sticky during hot weather—bacteria thrive in moist conditions.

Never use powder, cream, antiseptic, antibiotic creams or vaginal deodorants. Instead always use warm or cool water with a little pure soap.

Wear clean cotton pants every day. Avoid biological or other strong washing powders. After washing pants, rinse them until the water is absolutely clear, and wash them at home, not in the launderette. Never wear elastic panty-girdles and avoid wearing tights in hot weather.

Check yourself for excess vaginal secretions and if you have any trouble, go to your doctor and ask to be referred to a local clinic which can make an on-the-spot analysis of a vaginal swab.

Cut your pubic hair fairly short, with scissors, not a razor.

If you are prone to cystitis it is absolutely essential that both you and your partner should wash, but not douche, before intercourse. Before washing again afterwards, pass water to flush out any stray germs.

Easing attacks It is possible to minimise the pain of an attack, providing you act quickly. Attacks often begin at inconvenient times like 3 or 4 o'clock in the morning, but there is no point turning over and hoping that the pain will go away. The following drill has helped thousands of sufferers.

Start by passing a urine specimen into a clean container and seal it, so that your doctor can culture any germs.
Drink one pint (0.5 l) of cold water and let your stomach settle.
Make yourself two hot water bottles.
Drink a quarter of a glass of orange juice mixed

Foaming bicarbonate drinks should be part of increased fluid intake during a cystitis attack.

with a teaspoonful of bicarbonate of soda; repeat this process hourly for three hours (heart patients should take advice from their doctors before taking bicarbonate).
Take two mild painkilling tablets (soluble aspirin will do).
Drink a strong black coffee every hour; coffee will make you pass water by irritating the bladder and making the nerve fibres work overtime. But don't drink coffee at any other time.
Before you return to bed drink another half a pint (0.25 l) of liquid—barley water is recommended. Once in bed, place one of the hot water bottles on your back and the other high up between your legs, resting if possible between the labia.
Continue to drink half a pint (0.25 l) of liquid every 20 minutes and pass as much water as possible. Wash the perineum every time you go to the lavatory, taking care to dab rather than rub yourself dry.

These measures should give you a good fighting chance of eliminating the pain. If the attack does not ease within four hours or recurs within 24 hours, tell your doctor.

This advice is based on the technique described by Angela Kilmartin, who set up a self-help group for sufferers in Britain.

Prostate troubles

Resembling a chestnut in size and shape, the male prostate gland lies immediately below the bladder. Its function is almost entirely sexual. Through it pass the ejaculating ducts, from the testes, and the urethra, which empties the bladder. The activities of the prostate, which adds fluid to the semen to

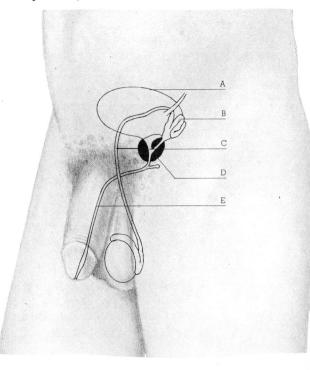

A

B

C

D

E

Cystitis is commonest
in women who are sexually active. This is because the urethra dilates during sexual excitement and may stay dilated for some time afterwards, allowing infectious organisms to pass into the bladder. Cystitis is rare in men because the longer male urethra offers greater resistance to invasion.

The prostate gland
is responsible for most of the volume of seminal fluid. It also produces prostaglandins, hormones which stimulate smooth muscle activity. Urethral obstruction due to enlargement of the prostate occurs in about 40 per cent of men over the age of 60. Only 20 per cent of cases require surgery.

A Bladder
B Seminal vesicle
C Vas deferens
D Prostate gland
E Urethra

assist the force and efficiency of ejaculation, are controlled by testicular hormones.

Some degree of prostate enlargement is almost inevitable in Caucasians over the age of 50. Interestingly this problem is far less frequent in Indian men and almost unknown in West Indian men. The reason for this is not known. It is the peripheral, fibromuscular part of the gland which enlarges rather than the secretory tissue. Enlargement is usually benign, but because the gland bulges up into the bladder wall, urinary symptoms are common, and very annoying. The urine stream is weak and the sphincter controlling the exit from the bladder may not shut properly, resulting in dribbling after urination.

Enlargement brings with it the danger of complete blockage of the urethra, with retention of urine and painful dilation of the bladder. In an acute situation like this a tube may have to be passed through the opening of the penis and up through the urethra into the bladder to re-open the natural channel. In the early stages prostate enlargement may cause increased desire for intercourse, but as time passes impotence is more common.

Treatment for prostate enlargement is surgical. If the operation is performed through an incision in the abdominal wall, bilateral vasectomy is often performed at the same time. Though this means

infertility, libido remains unaltered. The prostate can also be removed using a special operating cystoscope; this is introduced through the penis and cuts the prostate tissue away from the inside.

Like all tissues the prostate may also become infected or malignant. Of the infections venereal disease and tuberculosis (the tuberculosis bacillus attacks many different parts of the body) are the most frequent. The symptoms of infection are a rise in temperature, pain, a frequent urge to urinate, and tenderness over the bladder and prostate (the gland can be felt when examined rectally). Treatment with an appropriate antibiotic is usually successful.

Cancer of the prostate is one of the commonest malignant conditions in men over the age of 65. The symptoms may be the same as those of benign enlargement, but in addition the patient may complain of symptoms due to the spread of cancerous tissue to the bones of the hips and lower vertebral column. Treatment may require a combination of surgery, radiotherapy and oestrogen drugs. The sensitivity of this particular type of cancer to oestrogen is often quite dramatic. Provided the disease is not too far advanced when treatment starts, it can be successfully controlled for several years with doses of oestrogen low enough not to cause the embarassing side effect of breast enlargement.

Dealing with a heart attack

Chest pain is the most common symptom of a heart attack. Often described as 'vice-like' and sometimes resembling indigestion, heart attack pain is persistent. The pain may spread to the arms, back, jaw and occasionally into the upper abdomen. A cold sweat may break out.

Prompt action is vital—some 20 per cent of heart attack patients die within 15 minutes. Alert your doctor immediately; if he or she is not available call an ambulance. If neither is immediately available and the patient does not seem to be too unwell, drive him or her to hospital. If it does not seem possible to move the patient, keep him as quiet as possible until help arrives, give reassurance, and encourage him to rest.

The best position is on the back with both legs raised so that the blood goes to the heart. Loosen clothing, remove false teeth and check the mouth to ensure a clear airway.

Thump the patient's chest if breathing stops. If breathing does not re-start, elevate the chin and apply mouth-to-mouth respiration. To do this, hold the patient's nose between two fingers, breathe into his mouth, wait for the chest to rise and then repeat the process.

If the heart has stopped, trained people will be able to administer cardiac massage; this involves compressing the chest rhythmically to squeeze the heart to keep it going until expert help arrives. Learning the correct cardiac massage technique may help you to save a life. Classes for laymen are now run by organisations such as the Red Cross and national heart associations in an increasing number of countries.

The initial problems attendant on a heart attack tend to fall to relatives, wives in particular, because men are more prone to heart attacks than women. In a recent study about the immediate lay response to a heart attack, two researchers at Edinburgh University, Una Maclean and Aysha Cockshutt, concluded that health education about the management of heart attacks should be directed at women because it is usually they who have to seek help in an emergency.

The Edinburgh study was based on 77 patients who were admitted to the intensive care unit of a large hospital. The patients included 56 men, none of whom had had a previous heart attack. As a result their friends and families had to interpret the signs and symptoms as best they could.

One of the purposes of the study was to establish what influenced the length of time before a doctor, or occasionally an ambulance, was called. The researchers found that the presence of a relative, usually a woman, tended to delay this process. The women were, however, faced with an acute problem: first they had to estimate the seriousness of the man's condition, aided by their knowledge of his customary response to ill health; second, in

The rhythm of life
In severe rate disturbances—bradycardia, for example, where heart rate is so slow that fainting occurs—a pacemaker is implanted under the skin of the chest. This sends impulses to the heart along a catheter electrode, causing the heart muscle to contract at a faster rate.

Cardiac resuscitation
The ABC of resuscitating a patient whose heart has failed is this: Airways—keep them clear; Breathing—tilt the patient's head back, pinch the nose and blow four times into his mouth; Circulation—restore it by thumping on the middle of the chest and then giving five compressions to each breath. This is not as easy as it sounds, but it must be started before the ambulance arrives.

Cross references
Coronary heart disease 96
Myocardial infarction 94
Heart failure 94
Electrical disturbances 95

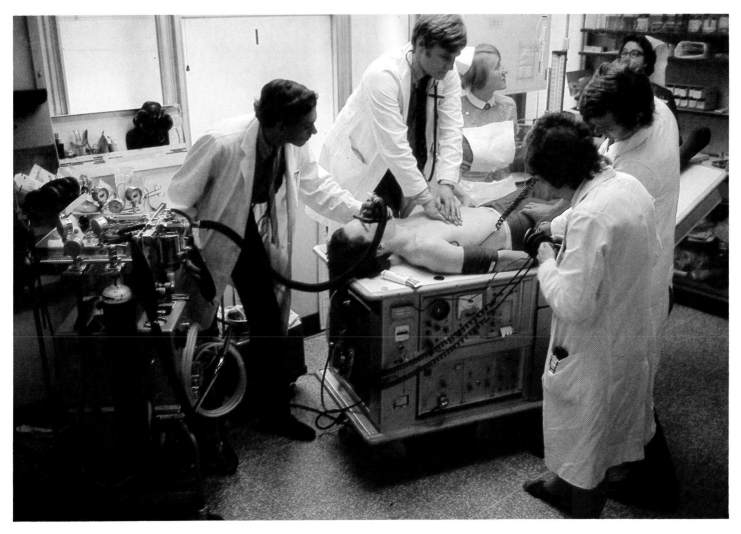

Cardiac arrest
is managed here by cardiac massage. The heart may need to be shocked back to normal by a defibrillator —ambulances carry a portable one as well as oxygen. A tube may be inserted down the trachea to provide artificial ventilation. Various intravenous drugs may also be given. If the patient is conscious, painkillers may be given. Above all the ECG is watched for recurring danger signals.

what was often a rapidly deteriorating situation, they had to decide whether they were justified in taking the 'serious' step of calling in the doctor, thereby defining the man as 'a patient' and the event as 'an emergency'.

The researchers commented: "As the man's physical strength waned, even if the woman thought she should obtain a professional opinion, she had to assume or wrench from its 'natural owner' the 'authority' necessary to make a move which would totally disrupt the family set-up. Not surprisingly, wives and other women in the drama often decided that their first duty was to provide appropriate personal care. As matters got out of hand, however, the struggle over proper management of a developing crisis became more acute, until the man and woman eventually switched roles."

For their part many of the men were exceedingly resistant to the idea of becoming patients. They clung desperately to their image of themselves as being strong, able supporters of their wives and families, men who 'never needed doctors'.

The study also highlighted public confusion

about what constitutes a heart attack. This was summed up in the comment of one young girl: "I never thought my father was having a heart attack because I thought people had to be unconscious."

In many cases relatives and friends supplied all sorts of simple remedies and nursing care. These included changing clothes drenched in perspiration; wiping the patient's brow; giving pain killers, various beverages, foods and cigarettes; and encouraging the patient to breathe fresh air and to keep moving briskly. Some of the heroic measures taken by friends and relatives seemed designed to reassure the anxious woman that the victim was not unwell or desperately ill. And in many cases there was understandable concern among adults about distressing the children.

The researchers concluded: "The woman's response to one kind of serious family illness has shown how extraordinarily difficult it may be to alter behaviour in this area, with so many differing individual considerations at stake. But any health education exercises to do with management of heart attacks must be directed, in the first instance, at women. For it is they who have to cope."

The con brigade: faking sick

Baron Munchausen, the frontispiece to a 1792 edition of his *Travels* published in London.

It is usually fairly easy to diagnose faults in a man-made machine such as an automobile when it breaks down. Diagnosing breakdowns in the body machine is far more difficult, however, not only because the machine itself is more complex but also because patients mislead doctors, sometimes deliberately inventing symptoms.

Most hoodwinking reflects genuine fear and anxiety. For example, a patient may talk about his back when he is really worried about his stomach. Doctors recognise this and structure their consultations accordingly. But there is another sort of hoodwinking which is both mysterious and frightening. It occurs when patients seek treatment they do not need, either for themselves or for their children. Recent cases involving children have included a mother who mixed blood with her child's urine sample; another who fed her child with salt and killed him; and a third who poisoned her child with a drug used for allergies. While it is not known for certain what symptoms the mother who gave her child salt was trying to induce, as she has since committed suicide, excess salt can cause vomiting and some quite extraordinary biochemical reactions. More obviously, blood in the urine can indicate kidney disease or infection of the urinary tract.

British doctors have compared this new trend to the discovery of the battered baby syndrome 15 years ago. They have pointed out that before the mid-1960s doctors were not alert to signs of deliberate baby battering, a syndrome that is now estimated to claim hundreds if not thousands of lives throughout the world each year. It is extremely doubtful whether the consequences of patients misleading doctors match the consequences of baby battering in scale but clearly many parents who expose their children to needless doctoring are likely to demand similar treatment and attention themselves. Deceiving a doctor consumes much time and money. In one case a child was admitted to hospital 12 times, subjected to seven major X-rays, six examinations under anaesthetic and many unpleasant drug treatments. Her urine was analysed 150 times and no less than 16 senior doctors were involved in her treatment.

In another documented case, a mother made bogus patients out of her daughter aged two and her son aged five. The boy had more than 100 investigations for what were described as 'bizarre neurological symptoms'; in fact he had been poisoned with a drug. For six months the girl was treated for diabetes after sugar had been added to her urine. The insulin that she was prescribed could have caused brain damage had not the mother consistently swapped it for distilled water.

According to one theory, parents make patients out of their children in order to express their own anxiety. It might well be that a mother who feels

The illustrious baron carries himself and two coach horses over a 9 ft (3 m) hedge in a single bound, a feat rendered necessary by meeting another coach in a narrow lane. The engraving is by Gustave Doré.

Genuine or not? A busy doctor quickly learns to spot sympathy seekers. But Munchausen patients take care to give substance to their symptoms, making it difficult for the doctor to ignore them.

her child has been neglected medically will fake symptoms to ensure further medical attention. However, this theory does not explain why the same mother exposes herself to needless treatment as well. Case histories in medical journals describe many patients who have faked heart-attack symptoms and altered urine specimens. These are classic hallmarks of the 'hospital addiction syndrome' or Munchausen syndrome. The syndrome takes its name from Baron Heidonymous Karl Friedrick Munchausen (1720–97) whose wildly exaggerated accounts of his military doings inspired an impoverished, exiled German writer, Rudolph Raspe, to write an excessively scathing best-seller entitled *Baron Munchausen's Narrative of his Marvellous Travels and Campaigns in Russia.*

Cross references
Mental abnormality 168
Stress 162
Anxiety neurosis 170

Make-believe symptoms
Children seldom appear at the doctor's on their own initiative. A small but disturbing number of parents, vicariously seeking attention or trying to assuage their own inadequacy, bring their children to the doctor with totally fictitious symptoms.

The Munchausen syndrome

A career in the army
Many Munchausens like to bask in the glamour and bravado associated with 'war wounds'. Recently, from extensive correspondence in a UK medical journal, the exploits of one such 'war veteran', admitted to various hospitals under various aliases, gradually came to light.

Munchausen patients, or Munchausens for short, travel far and frequently in search of treatment, particularly for stomach surgery. They are apt to present themselves as heroes or celebrities, some even dressing the part. One man hired a naval uniform to authenticate his story about being an ex-officer extensively wounded in the battle for the Atlantic. 'Wartime injuries' are extremely popular among older Munchausens as a means of explaining away extensive scarring caused by needless operations.

Another well-documented case is that of a man who 'injured his back falling off a lorry'. He added drama to his plight by making two telephone calls to the emergency services. In the first one he pretended to be a policeman reporting a serious accident and in the second he pretended to be a bystander summoning an ambulance. He was put into splints by the ambulanceman and was admitted to casualty, only to be recognised as a veteran Munchausen. In the classic tradition of this syndrome, he jumped off the stretcher and ran away before he could be persuaded to see the hospital psychiatrist.

Even more bizarre cases are those which involve self-wounding or self-injection. One young woman was referred to hospital by her doctor with a baffling high temperature. The hospital found she had been drawing blood from her arm, mixing it with salad cream and then re-injecting it. She was a Munchausen novice and received psychiatric help.

Most hospitals in fact keep 'black books' listing hoaxers but many people still manage to bluff consultants and undergo the complex operations they so mysteriously seek. Casualty specialists freely admit that the black book system is only partially effective because so many Munchausens assume false names.

Doctors and psychiatrists are particularly mystified by patients who actually yearn for the surgeon's knife. But other motives are easier to understand, such as those of the drug addict who fakes symptoms in order to get a fix; the fugitive who seeks refuge from the police and induces illness by swallowing foreign bodies; the scrounger who seeks free board and lodgings; or the attention-seeker who wants to be the centre of interest. But all these motives explain only part of a bewildering phenomenon, the full extent of which nobody knows.

In the workshop

A glimpse into the future

Car assembly by robots seemed far-fetched ten years ago, but computerised robot systems are now used to manufacture many consumer durables. Computer technology has made equally rapid progress in medicine, notably in prosthetic engineering, brain and body scanning, aids for the deaf and blind, and even the diagnosis and treatment of mental illness.

Let us imagine that you are a 40-year-old married woman with two children living in a city in the year 2050. You have a busy day ahead—a medical and dental check-up—and things are not going well. Your son James, due to sit an important examination, falls over and grazes his leg badly. But at least this is a problem that is quickly dealt with. A quick spray and the wound is bandaged. Yes, that's right, a spray, developed in the last quarter of the 20th century—it comprises a transparent chemical solution which creates a sterile environment that breathes and stretches with the skin.

Next, the family breakfast. A different meal for every member of the family to correspond with their individual nutritional profiles. James's meal is specially chosen to enhance his powers of concentration for his examination. Why the different meals? Analyses of blood samples have shown that the diet which keeps you neat and trim makes your husband put on weight, and is not conducive to adolescent growth. James knows exactly what he should and should not eat. Health education and domestic science are a major part of his school curriculum—it is not only the girls who learn how and, most important, what to eat.

You do not have time to eat breakfast yourself, so you limit yourself to a few pills which meet all your nutritional requirements while also stimulating your taste buds in the same way as a conventional meal.

Next, the medical check-up. Armed with your nutritional and genetic profiles you attend for computer consultation and a blood test to confirm whether your diet is still tailored to your needs.

Then to the cryobiology laboratory (cryobiology is the science of freezing living tissue) where you open a safe deposit box containing your own frozen white blood cells, donated 30 years previously. A technician unfreezes the cells and injects them into you to give your ageing immune system a youthful boost. This is a standard procedure designed to increase resistance to diseases of middle and old age—cancer, arthritis and kidney failure.

Then back to the computer for a print-out liver analysis. Your liver is not the one you were born with. Ten years ago when the computer diagnosed a liver complication, scientists took from your body a group of healthy liver cells and programmed them to form a new liver which was then substituted for the old one without any risk of rejection—recognising the new liver as 'self' your immune system did not attempt to destroy it.

Then to the dental department, no longer the symbol of fear it used to be in the 20th century. The dental drill is a relic of the past and dental decay is removed by a spray. In fact, even the spray is close to becoming redundant for decay itself is becoming increasingly rare in the developed countries. James has never had any decay—vaccines against tooth decay have been in use for 30 years or more.

How fanciful is all this? Surprising as it may seem, some of the changes we have predicted might well become routine within the next few years.

Spray bandages are already used to treat severe burns; computers are already analysing blood samples to see what use we make of food; cryo-preservation of bone marrow already enables replacement of bone marrow in people who develop leukaemia or where bone marrow is damaged by drugs or irradiation, meaning that if your own bone marrow is stored in childhood, and you later develop leukaemia, your leukaemic bone marrow can be destroyed with drugs and irradiation and your stored normal marrow transplanted back into you; scientists have already shown that it is possible to regenerate the limbs if not the internal organs of higher animals such as hamsters using relatively simple bioelectrical techniques.

These are but a few examples which point to an exciting future arising from current research. In the following pages we examine some of the new techniques already in use and some expected to emerge in the foreseeable future.

Artificial hearts

It is predicted that these will be implanted routinely in humans within the next ten years. The first artificial hearts will be implanted in the chest in a natural way, but powered pneumatically by an external source. The long-term aim of researchers is to develop an artificial heart that would be powered by batteries worn around the waist to give the patient complete mobility.

Blindness

Electronic stimulation of the visual centres of the brain may one day enable many blind people to see again. Researchers believe it will eventually be possible to implant tiny television cameras into the eye and house the associated electronics in spectacle stems.

Deafness

In the future electrodes implanted in the inner ear may restore partial or even full hearing to the totally deaf. Diseased or damaged nerves will be by-passed, it is hoped, by wires connecting the ear with the auditory centres of the brain.

Electronic speech

Computers can already be programmed to speak. By the end of the century bioengineers believe that it will be possible for a mute person to speak with the aid of a computer. Such a computer would convert electrical impulses generated by the speaker into a form of speech that sounds human.

Artificial limbs

Scientists are now refining an artificial arm and hand that respond to electric signals from muscles in the amputee's chest, back, stump and shoulders. The arm bends at the elbow and rotates at the wrist. An artificial leg operated by electrical impulses is also being developed.

Even more remarkable are predictions that one day a sense of touch will be incorporated into prosthetic devices. This will mean, for example, that an amputee with an artificial hand will be able to distinguish between the feel of, say, a wine glass stem and a pen. The arm will be coated with electronically sensitised, plastic 'skin' containing nerve-like sensors to enable control of grip—very important if you are handling something fragile like a thermometer. Eventually bioengineers hope to produce a similar type of skin for artifical feet.

Going to the dentist's may not be such a trial in 2000. Doctors are currently perfecting a vaccine against the bacteria responsible for certain forms of tooth decay. For those who will be too old for vaccination to do any good, there is a hope of reprieve from the dentist's drill: a chemical is being developed which simply sprays decay away, leaving the healthy parts of teeth untouched.

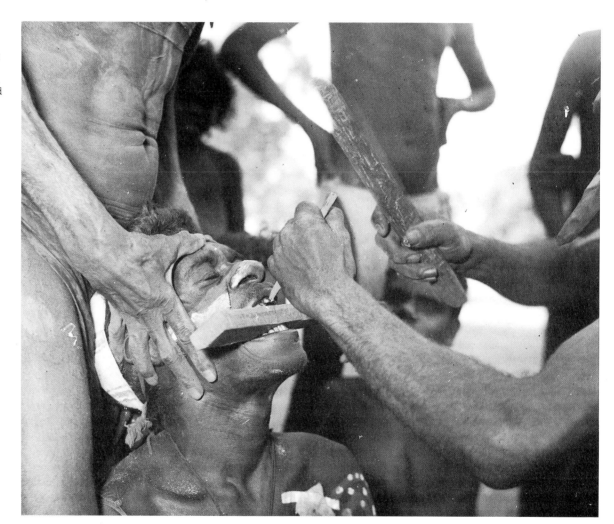

A bionic arm nearly as sensitive as the real thing is in the final stages of development in the United States. The arm responds to electrical signals from muscles in the upper part of the amputee's arm which are relayed via a powerpack to the mechanical arm and hand. A myolectric leg is also being developed.

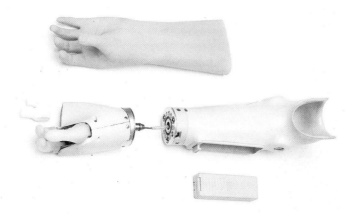

Cancer: new perspectives

Lillian Board
Cancer is no respecter of age or physical fitness. Lillian Board was an Olympic 400m medallist, but she died in her early twenties, a victim of rectal cancer. The likelihood of developing cancer increases with age but if it does develop in young people it often spreads through the body (metastasises) very rapidly.

Cancer accounts for some five million of the 60 million or so human deaths in the world each year. We are still a long way from understanding the causes of cancer. We know it is not a single disease—some cancers are so malignant that death follows within weeks, whereas others may cause death several years later. We know that cancers are characterised by abnormal cell growth and that most cancers are more common with increasing age.

Laboratory-grown cancer cells to test new drugs A new technique developed by American researchers involves taking from cancer patients malignant cells, cultivating them in the laboratory, and then exposing them to various anti-cancer agents to see which is best.

The technique has yet to be fully evaluated, but the idea is to spare the patient many of the unpleasant side effects and psychological distress of successive trial drug treatments. Unfortunately many drugs which destroy animal cancers prove ineffective against human tumours. The great advantage of this *in vitro* technique is that drugs can be tested on human cells from the outset.

Bone marrow transplants These have been routine in some hospitals in the past three or four years, and as a method of first rather than last resort in the treatment of leukaemia, a condition arising from over-production of white blood cells.

Some drugs cause remission of disease, but some patients develop resistance to them and relapse. A bone marrow transplant involves first giving high dose chemotherapy and total body irradiation to destroy the bone marrow cells responsible for over-producing white cells, and then injecting a small quantity of bone marrow from a donor, usually a brother or sister, whose bone marrow is compatible. Once in the bloodstream the transplanted cells automatically seek the bone marrow of the recipient and start producing healthy white cells in appropriate numbers, conferring on the recipient the donor's immunity.

Unusual symptoms: what do they mean? Cancer patients occasionally report changes in their preferences for tastes and odours. This phenomenon, known as specific taste change (STC), is under investigation. In one study at the Western Infirmary in Glasgow, Scotland, some 29 edible substances—including tea, ice-cream, eggs and gooseberries—tasted differently to a number of middle-aged and older women patients. Most of them were receiving treatments for tumours or were subsequently found to have tumours. Some of the women even reported taste changes similar to the cravings and aversions of pregnancy. The cause of this is not understood, but STC may be another early diagnostic pointer.

Vitamin A versus cancer Renewed interest is now being shown in Vitamin A (retinol) both for treating and preventing cancer. Vitamin A occurs naturally in foods such as milk, butter, cheese, liver and fish, and plays an important role in the maintenance of normal growth, bone formation, shedding and repair of skin, eyesight, and reproductive capacity. Animal experiments at the Albert Einstein College of Medicine, New York, suggest that Vitamin A may reduce the severe side effects associated with some cancer drugs.

In one study researchers used the vitamin in conjunction with cyclophosphamide, a potent anti-cancer drug. Like many cytotoxic (cell-destroying) agents cyclophosphamide knocks out cancer cells, but also affects normal tissue, delaying the healing process. Vitamin A is a healer. Rats given cyclophosphamide without Vitamin A lost weight at the rate of 2.6 g per day, but another group of rats given the drug *plus* the vitamin lost only 0.6 g a day because the side effects were less severe. Further experiments on mice with various tumours confirmed the beneficial effects of Vitamin A during drug therapy.

One of the researchers at the Albert Einstein College optimistically commented: "It may be possible to use supplemental Vitamin A at dosages that improve wound healing of cyclophosphamide-treated patients without inhibiting the anti-tumour action of cyclophosphamide".

Could such a simple preventive as Vitamin A foil the development of cancer? The results of a large investigation in Oxford, England, certainly suggest that men who have lower levels of Vitamin A in their blood are more at risk of cancer. Unfortunately excessive Vitamin A damages the liver. However, B-carotene, one of the building blocks of Vitamin A, doesn't. B-carotene is a pigment found in many fruits and vegetables, especially carrots and tomatoes. The famous British physician Sir Richard Doll considers that B-carotene may effectively cut cancer risk. Practising what he preaches, he admits to eating more carrots nowadays.

Interferon The discovery of interferon, and its imminent commercial manufacture by genetic engineering methods, has raised a lot of unrealistic hopes among cancer patients and their families. Interferon is a substance which occurs naturally in the human body, and it is released from various cells and tissues in response to infection. It is one of the body's many natural defence mechanisms.

Trials so far suggest that its effectiveness may be limited to certain types of cancer only (some forms of bone cancer, skin and breast tumours, and lymphomas or cancers affecting the lymph system, for example). Really wide-scale clinical trials will have to wait until it is manufactured in commercial

Cross references
Lung cancer **121**
Immune system **110**
Putting bacteria to work **238**
Immortal cells **242**

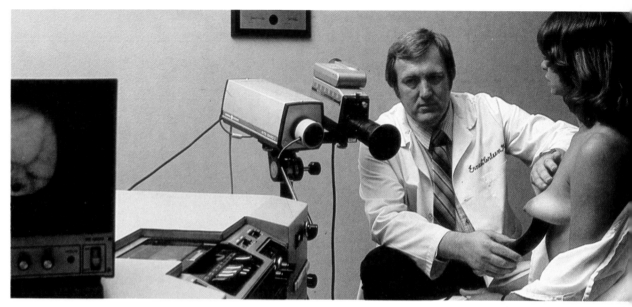

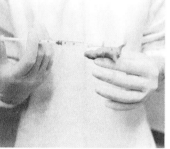

Animal experiments
Although much criticised recently, experiments on animals, such as the one shown here in which human lymphoblast cells are being injected into a newly born hamster, have provided the basis of our understanding and treatment of many cancers.

A Japanese shrine
to the memory of the animals sacrificed in the cause of scientific research—a curious sentiment in the objective world of genetic engineering and cancer research.

Breast cancer alert
It is vital to diagnose cancers as early as possible. Here a diaphanoscope is used to measure the transparency of breast tissue. It works on the same principle as shining a flashlight through your hand in the dark. Any cancerous tissue shows up on the screen as a black area.

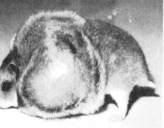

Interferon production
occurs naturally in response to certain tumours. Experimentally, it can be obtained from animals, like this hamster, by transplanting tumours into them. Much work remains to be done to assess the true efficacy of interferon in the treatment of cancer.

quantities, which should happen in the near future.

The anti-tumour potential of interferon was noticed soon after its discovery in the early 1960s. But its career as a 'miracle drug' really began in 1978 when the American Cancer Society backed it with a $2 million research grant. Interferon certainly has impressive properties for reducing some cancers as well as some viral infections, but its acclaim by the media is premature. There is a great deal of research to be done.

Heat and cold Therapy for cancer is sometimes bizarre, especially when the malignancy is unresponsive to standard treatments, and none more so than the 'whole body heating' therapy devised by a team from the University of Mississippi Medical Centre, USA. The preliminary results of this treatment, based on a study of 119 patients with advanced solid tumours and receiving simultaneous drug and/or radiotherapy, were encouraging. Twenty per cent of the patients survived for six months or longer; some are still alive two and a half years later. 'Whole body heating' means what it says: the whole body is heated by external means to temperatures ranging from 106.7° to 107.3° F (41.5°–42.0°C).

What makes these results impressive is that the cancers involved (35 per cent lung, 26 per cent gastrointestinal, 10 per cent breast, and so on) had particularly poor prognoses. Objective evidence of tumour regression was seen in 61 per cent of the 75 patients for whom other therapies had failed. Though no improvement occurred in 16 per cent, the results suggest that hyperthermia (body overheating) is a useful addition to other therapies.

Nor is heat the only potential slayer of cancer cells. Extreme cold appears to destroy them just as efficiently. Cryotherapy, or the rapid freezing of local lesions, is now fairly widely used to treat skin cancers and pre-malignant tissue changes in the mouth. Results from one London dental unit where freezing is extensively used look very encouraging for the treatment of these frightening oral conditions.

Laser therapy Perhaps the ultimate weapon in the temperature war against tumour cells is the laser, now quite commonly used to destroy ominous pre-cancerous tissue changes in the cervix or neck of the womb. Pinhole laser burning of the affected tissue, a simple and painless out-patient treatment, is a far cry from hysterectomy (major surgery involving removal of the womb).

Test tube babies, electromagnetic therapy

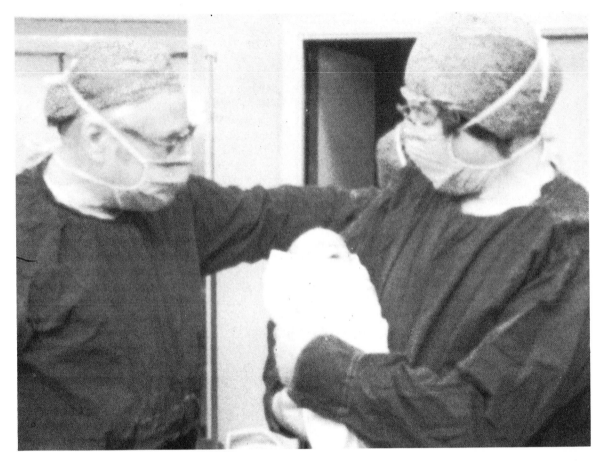

Test-tube baby Louise Brown just after her birth (left) and appearing on American television a year later (below). In June 1981 the first test-tube twins, a boy and a girl, were born in Melbourne, Australia.

The world's first test-tube baby, Louise Brown, was born on July 25, 1978, demonstrating that blocked fallopian tubes—the condition that prevented her mother from conceiving in the normal way—were no longer a bar to motherhood.

An egg removed from Mrs Brown was placed with sperm from her husband in a circular Petri dish—the so-called test-tube—and nurtured for two and a half days. Then the embryo was implanted in Mrs Brown's womb and left to develop normally.

In India doctors have used a different approach which has even wider implications for infertile couples. They removed ripened eggs from the mother, fertilised them with the father's sperm, and then stored them in a deep freeze for 53 days. Then one embryo was thawed and implanted in the mother's womb.

The cellular structure of young embryos is very simple, simple enough for them to be kept on ice for many years. In other words, it may be possible for several children to be conceived at once, or alternatively for their development to proceed as and when the parents want children.

Possibilities like this raise ethical problems which will be debated fiercely by scientists, lawyers and theologians. Would a doctor who carried out *in vitro* fertilisation be legally liable for any malformations? Does the destruction of an embryo

formed in a Petri dish constitute abortion?

The ethics of experimenting with artificial wombs could be equally controversial. Researchers in the USA and Britain are conducting preliminary investigations with animals to assess the potential of artificial wombs. There are many technical problems to overcome, not least the question of how to supply oxygen and nutrients to the foetus and remove metabolic wastes. A naturally growing foetus depends on the mother's heart, kidneys, liver and blood. Thus, an artificial womb would need support from other artificial organs.

Electrical repairs

Body cells speak a language all of their own—a lingua franca of electric signals governing growth, development and repair. If scientists could crack this code, they might be able to communicate directly with cells, instructing them to develop faster or slower, to differentiate, to regroup, and so on. Some scientists believe that this 'soft therapy' could be used to regrow amputees' lost limbs.

Chief among them is Dr Robert O. Becker of the Veterans Administration Hospital in Syracuse, New York. Why is it, he asked, that humans cannot do what the humble salamander does, namely regenerate up to one third of their body mass? His controversial hypothesis is that humans are limited in this respect because they do not produce enough natural electricity. Neither do other animals such as rats.

Suspecting that higher animals could also regenerate lost tissue given the right electrical stimuli, Becker implanted an electrode into an amputee rat. The amputated foreleg regrew as far as the elbow joint, not an ideal result, but it showed that a kind of rebirth is possible, and that the salamander is not in a class of its own.

Dr Stephen Smith of the University of Kentucky Medical School, USA, used a modified version of the same technique to regrow frogs' legs. It worked. The new limbs had the precise anatomical pattern of the amputated limbs, right down to the characteristic webbed feet.

A colleague of Becker's, Dr Andrew Bassett of the Columbia Presbyterian Medical Center, New York, has used 'bioelectricity' to treat troublesome bone fractures on which traditional forms of therapy made no impression. Small electrical coils placed around the injury induce tiny currents in the bone; worn 12 hours a day the coils usually mend fractures within a few months. Therapy is totally painless—the power of the field strength is similar to that beamed from a fluorescent light when you are standing under it. The difference is that the therapeutic field is organised in a different way. Electrical repair of fractures is a process which occurs perfectly naturally in healthy tissue; the mechanical stress of the fracture is converted into electrical energy which guides the repair process.

Becker, Bassett and other advocates of bioelectricity have been criticised by many fellow scientists, but the tide is turning. The US Food and Drug Administration has given the seal of approval to bone healing.

Bones are not the only part of the body to respond favourably to electrical fields. Tissue swelling following bruising or laceration can be reduced by pulsed electromagnetic therapy; new skin growth over burns can be accelerated in a similar manner, and with a considerable reduction in pain; and the calcium that often accumulates in swollen joints as a result of bursitis or a bad sprain can be dissipated electromagnetically. There is even evidence that certain kinds of nerve cell can be regenerated by this method, in which case paralysis may one day be reversible.

The most popular electromagnetic device in use generates high frequency radio waves similar to those that carry television pictures. This energy is pulsed to the injured area in rapid bursts of between 80 and 600 pulses a second. All the patient feels, if anything, is a slight tingling.

Why does electromagnetic therapy work? The hypothesis of Dr Clarence Cone of NASA's Langley Research Center in Virginia is that it lowers the membrane potentials of damaged cells, facilitating the traffic of electrons and ions through their walls and so promoting healing. If this idea is correct it might explain why nerve cells, which have high membrane potentials, are so reluctant to regenerate, and why cancer cells, which have very low membrane potentials, proliferate so rapidly.

The brain itself is an electrical centre which can be affected by external electrical fields to increase or decrease its activity. Advances in this type of therapy may lead to methods of improving memory, concentration and learning ability.

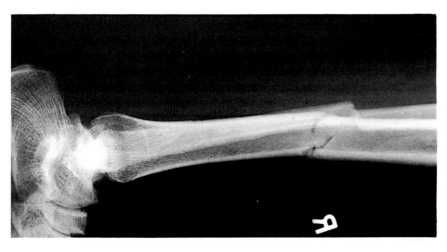

Severe multiple fractures of the leg as shown here could be healed quickly by electromagnetic therapy, avoiding weeks of tedious immobility for the patient. This would be a great advantage to elderly patients whose bones do not heal readily and who quickly lose what mobility they have. Electric currents may eventually be used to regenerate other body tissue, such as heart muscle and damaged nerves and vertebrae in the spinal cord.

Heart transplants

Fifteen years ago the big question where heart transplants were concerned was; can they be done? The question today is rather, should they be done? From a moral and scientific viewpoint there is no reason why heart transplants should not be done as frequently as kidney transplants or corneal grafts. What worries health administrators is the cost. Heart transplants are not cheap—present estimates range from $35,000 to $100,000—but neither, all things considered, is a chronic heart condition. With this in mind the United States has allocated $2 million to study the cost effectiveness of a transplant programme, with a potential annual price tag of $3,000 million.

Survival rates Technically cardiac surgery has come a long way since the first heart transplant on Louis Washkansky in Cape Town in December 1967. The donor was a young woman who died from brain injuries sustained in a car accident. Washkansky's life was prolonged by 18 days. Today survival rates in some centres are 66 per cent after one year, and 50 per cent after five years, much the same as for renal transplants. The record holder for post-operative survival is a Frenchman; he is still alive after 12 years.

It is now recognised that many of the early recipients of 'new' hearts were extremely poor risks. Louis Washkansky, for example, was 54 at the time of his operation and a diabetic. One of the reasons for the recent rise in success rates is that patients are now very carefully selected. Age, psychological stability and general resilience to infection are assessed before the search for a compatible donor heart begins.

Rejection of the donor heart is still a major problem. The drugs currently used to damp down rejection include azathioprine, prednisone and anti-lymphocyte serum (ALS), a combination much favoured by Dr Norman Shumway's team at Stanford University in California. Cyclosporin A is another drug which has solved many rejection problems. The function of these drugs is to suppress the body's immune system, but as a result the patient becomes vulnerable to infections like pneumonia, the main cause of death after transplantation. After a transplant operation patients are monitored non-stop so that signs of infection or rejection can be spotted at the earliest possible moment. Regular biopsy of the tissue of the new heart is the surest way of detecting the increase in lymphocyte numbers that signals rejection. If the first three post-operative months are successfully negotiated, rejection ceases to be a significant risk.

What are the clinical indications for a heart transplant? Some patients are too ill to benefit from transplant surgery, but possible candidates are

Chest open
A metal surgical spreader holds the chest wall and rib cage open, exposing the diseased heart. The surgeon sizes up the donor heart which must be trimmed before the careful work of suturing it to the back wall of the recipient's own heart.

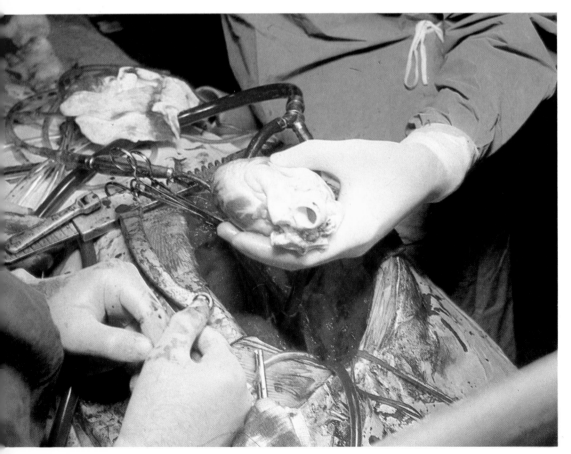

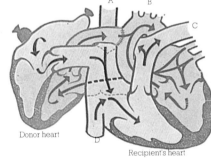

Donor heart

Recipient's heart

A Superior vena cava
B Aorta
C Pulmonary artery
D Inferior vena cava

Piggyback transplant
The donor heart is shown on the left, and the recipient's on the right, with the venous circulation of both shown in blue and the arterial circulation in pink. The superior and inferior venae cavae of the donor heart are cut through and tied off, as are the pulmonary veins going into the left atrium. The aorta is then joined to the aorta of the recipient, and the pulmonary artery grafted to that of the recipient.

How a transplant is done

The drawing on the left shows the right atrium of the recipient's heart cut away as the first stage in its removal. The drawing in the middle shows the insertion points of the tubes taking blood away from the venae cavae and returning it to the aorta. Once the front of the recipient's heart has been cut away, leaving only the back walls of both atria, the donor heart is trimmed to fit and sutured in place. Three of the four sutures can be seen: one around the right atrium, one around the aorta and one around the pulmonary artery; the fourth, around the left atria, is hidden. The incisions where the cannulae were inserted are also stitched up.

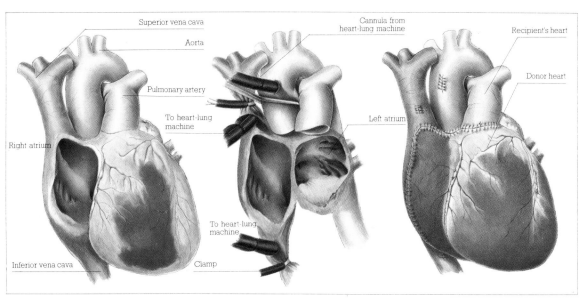

Superior vena cava — Aorta — Pulmonary artery — To heart-lung machine — Right atrium — Inferior vena cava — Clamp — To heart-lung machine — Cannula from heart-lung machine — Left atrium — Recipient's heart — Donor heart

A full transplant

operation takes about five hours. The heart–lung machine (bottom left) takes over the circulation until the transplanted heart can maintain pressure itself.

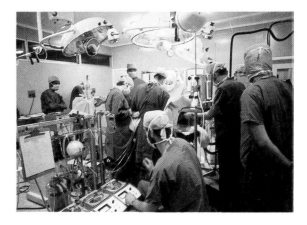

young patients suffering from a cardiomyopathy (heart muscle degeneration of unknown cause) or patients with severe heart disease resulting from recurrent heart attacks ('wall-to-wall infarction') of such severity that life is no longer worth living.

Technicalities and variations The usual procedure is to remove most of the patient's own heart, leaving behind only the back wall of the two upper chambers, the atria, and the pulmonary artery and aorta. The donor or 'new' heart is sewn on first at the septum, the wall between the two atria, and then the junctions between the atria and the pulmonary artery of the donor heart and the patient's own heart are sutured.

To keep the patient alive during the operation he is connected to a heart-lung machine. The veins bringing blood to the heart are temporarily clamped off and the circulating blood is diverted through the machine, oxygenated, and sent back to the patient's aorta. An operation like this is the culmination of many days of work on the part of doctors, nurses, surgeons, administrators and hospital emergency services both at the donor's and recipient's end. And the actual team carrying out the operation may include up to 20 people on permanent standby. The donor heart is paralysed, cooled and kept in a plastic bag surrounded by crushed ice until it is needed. However, there is some debate as to how long a heart can be preserved in this way.

A variation on the transplant technique just described is the so-called piggyback operation. Pioneered by Professor Barnard in 1974, the recipient's heart and lungs are left intact, but supplemented with a donor heart connected in parallel to it. The advantage of this technique is that the patient's own heart, ailing as it is, is left virtually undisturbed. However, room has to be found in the right chest for the extra heart, which entails the risk of lung collapse and infection. Also the two heartbeats have to be synchronised with suitably programmed pacemakers.

Still in the experimental stage at present are heart and lung transplants. The donor lung has to be carefully ventilated to maintain oxygen uptake, carbon dioxide release, and expansion. The advantage of transplanting heart and lungs together is that only three junctions (right atrium, aorta, trachea) have to be made rather than the four shown in the drawings above.

Researchers in Utah, USA, hope soon to be able to implant an electrically powered plastic and aluminium heart (actually little more than both ventricles) into patients whose chances of living without the support of a heart-lung machine following conventional transplant surgery are minimal. Prototype artificial hearts have in fact been tested since 1957, but so far the Federal Drugs Administration has not granted permission to use them. Another alternative is a device which allows a damaged or overworked heart to rest and repair itself.

Microsurgery

Chang, aged 25, lost both his hands in an explosion six years ago. Now, thanks to a toe transplant, he can write letters, use a spoon, hold cups, play cards, pick up needles and unbutton his clothes. He is one of an increasing number of people to have benefited from microsurgery. The microscopes surgeons use to carry out this kind of surgery have a magnification power from ×6 to ×40, and various techniques have been developed for rejoining severed blood vessels and nerves or, in the case of toe transplants, creating completely new links.

Both Chang's second toes were transplanted onto the stump of his right arm to create a new thumb and index finger. The result resembles a lobster claw, but for Chang it means independence. Double or triple toe transplantation is a technique which has been developed to a very high standard in China by Dr Chen Zhong-Wei of the Shanghai Sixth People's Hospital.

Describing the technique recently to surgeons in the West Dr Chen said that three toes is the maximum that can be transplanted safely. There is, he stresses, no point in treating one disability only to create another. Chang can still run and jump as he did before his operation.

The bone from one of his toes (the new thumb) was re-shaped to fit into the contour at the distal end of the radial bone, which, with the ulnar bone, runs from the elbow to the wrist. The bone from the other toe (the new index finger) was also re-shaped to fit the radial bone. The new digits were screwed into place in opposition to each other and at an angle of 30 degrees to allow maximum flexibility and movement—this is an important facet of the operation, for the positioning of our thumbs in relation to our fingers accounts for the amazing ability of the hand. Without a thumb our hands would be little more than crude hooks.

Before this, however, comes the most critical part: knitting together the blood vessels and the nerve fibres. One recent microsurgical operation in Britain—involving the replantation of a severed hand—took 19 hours, such are the complexities of joining arteries and veins only a half a millimetre in diameter. The problems have been eased immeasurably by the development of a new microscope with two or three heads which allows additional surgeons to work on the severed part.

Arteries and veins have to be joined to ensure a good blood supply but it can take between 15 minutes and half an hour to stitch one vein to another. Most surgeons make three stitches 120 degrees apart on the end of the blood vessels, then sew one third of the vessel at a time. Known as triangulation, this method was developed about 80 years ago by a French physician who studied with Lyons' finest lacemaker.

What makes the process so difficult, and extensive training so necessary, is that throughout

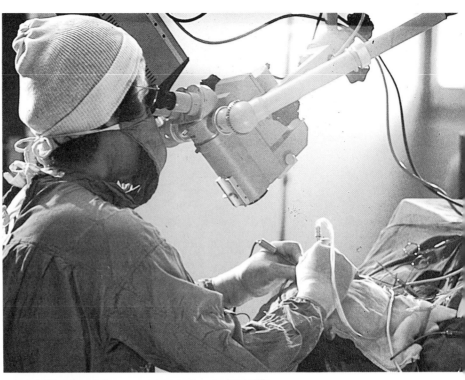

Microsurgery in action
The microscope is useful not only for examining tissue samples, but also for operations which require great precision. Here a double microscope is used to magnify the severed ends of blood vessels and nerves prior to rejoining them.

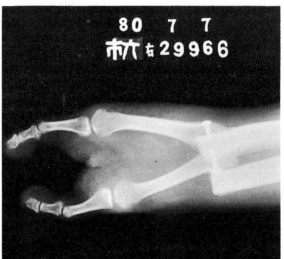

Toes for fingers
Before microsurgery, little could be done to help people who had lost limbs or parts of limbs in wartime or in industrial accidents. Successful attempts at partial reconstruction are now possible. This X-ray picture shows how the radial bone of the forearm has been united with two toes to form a 'pseudo' joint. The toes have been positioned opposite each other so that the important functions of picking up and grasping objects can be maintained.

The restored function
of the reconstructed toe-hand is well illustrated here. The opposition of the new 'thumb' and 'index finger' allows very complex hand movements like writing to be performed with relative ease. Unfortunately the reconstructed wrist joint, and the joints in the transplanted toes, may be more prone to osteoarthritis than normal joints.

the whole operation the surgeon has to hold the needle along with other instruments. A tiny microsurgery needle only 50 microns thick cannot be wielded like an ordinary sewing needle. An 18 micron nylon thread is so fine that it can be blown away by the operating room air conditioning.

The skill in joining up bundles of nerves lies in correct matching. A motor nerve, which triggers movement, needs to be connected to a motor nerve, and a sensory nerve, which registers feeling, to a sensory nerve. A wrong match will deprive both of normal functioning. Under high magnification it is possible to see the bundles of motor and sensory nerves. Yet even a successful operation, according to some surgeons, will not restore total function. For example, the patient is unlikely to be able to distinguish by touch alone a coin from a button, and furthermore, there have been abject failures (resulting in amputation) as well as successes. A numb, uncontrollable limb is worse than nothing.

But patients like Chang in China, Terence Lower in Britain and William Ganote in the USA—three success stories—highlight just what can be achieved. The four fingers of Lower's right hand were left hanging by a thread when it was caught in machinery. He woke up from the anaesthetic expecting to see a stump and was 'over the moon' to see his hand intact again.

Ganote had a double toe transplant after losing four fingers in a printing press. He is reported as saying: 'They move like fingers, they feel like fingers—they're great'.

Physiotherapy plays a big part in restoring function and preventing transplanted or replanted limbs from stiffening while nerves regenerate. The regenerative process works its way gradually towards the fingertips at the rate of about one millimetre a day. From wrist to finger takes about 200 days, though it may take considerably longer for the limb to be fully functional, assuming that function does return.

Patient selection is important. The surgeon has to consider the age of the victim, the type of accident and even personality.

□ Younger patients tend to do better than older ones; the older the patient the easier it is to damage blood vessels. Disastrous tears can result from even the smallest surgical mistakes.

□ With a clean cut, say one from an industrial guillotine, the chances of success can be as high as 90 per cent. In the case of a car accident, resulting in wrenched blood vessels and tendons, the odds may fall to about 10 per cent.

□ The surgeon's decision to operate and the patient's attitude are often linked. Determination and confidence are crucial, as is exercise. The success of the operation cannot be assessed immediately and the patient must always be prepared for the possibility that the final outcome

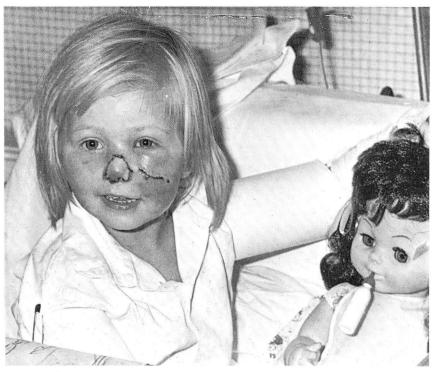

Facial reconstruction
This little girl had her nose bitten off and eaten by a dog. The doctor who was called to the emergency showed great presence of mind in giving the dog an emetic and retrieving the nose. It was then carefully sewn back on with the aid of microsurgery.

may not be as he or she envisaged.

In Shanghai Dr Chen and colleagues followed up 256 patients for three years, analysing the working ability, range of joint motion, muscular power and sensation of replanted limbs. The patients were divided into four grades: 69.5 per cent (Grades I and II) resumed their original work or took up some other work; only 3.5 per cent (Grade IV) had little or no functional recovery.

Microsurgery has many other applications. In the USA, for example, it has almost doubled the success rate of operations to reverse sterilisation. And through what is known as 'free tissue transfer', 'spare muscles' can be moved from a leg to an arm crippled by muscle injury. A patient with a broken shin may lose the thin covering of flesh and skin, but now this can be replaced with fresh skin from elsewhere, and the graft blood vessels joined up with those around the injury. If a long segment of bone is lost, it is now possible to bridge the gap with a vascularised bone graft, and with excellent results.

Surgeons are also envisaging a new era of transplant operations in which the hands of people killed in accidents will be transplanted onto living arm stumps. Surgically, this is possible—the problem lies in how to deal with the body's rejection of the hand as alien. Immunologists have already accepted this challenge but we may have to wait many years for them to find an answer.

Organ transplants and spare part surgery

Corneal grafting
Here a continuous zig-zag suture can be seen around the healing edge of the graft. Donor eyes must be removed and refrigerated in an eye bank within 12 hours of death and used within seven days. The success of this type of transplant is partly due to the fact that there is no blood supply to the cornea, which means that there is no antibody response to it.

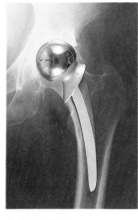

Arthritic hip joints
are now routinely replaced by steel and plastic. More than 100,000 total hip replacement operations are done in the USA and Europe each year. The diseased hip joint is excised and the ball of the joint (the head of the femur) replaced with a stainless steel head which is glued into the femur. The cup of the joint (the acetabulum of the pelvis) is replaced with a cup made of polyethylene.

Not surprisingly the publicity surrounding heart transplantation has distracted attention from major advances in the replacement of other vital organs. The problems of all forms of transplanting and grafting are similar: the body always tries to reject foreign materials, natural or synthetic. But the goal is the same: to improve the quality of life for those whose natural organs have failed.

Kidney transplants One area which has been particularly successful is kidney transplantation. In 1979 over 1,000 kidney transplants were performed in the United Kingdom alone. Survival rates are encouraging, with some of the better centres achieving a 90 per cent survival rate after three months. The best results have been achieved with kidney swapping between identical twins; obviously there is no problem here in matching the tissue type of donor and recipient. Where there is less compatability, as with cadaver donors, survival rates are not as impressive; only 45 per cent of patients survive beyond three years. However, with new methods of tissue typing and more effective anti-rejection drugs such as Cyclosporin A, life expectancy will increase.

Liver transplants A patient with diseased kidneys has a second chance if a transplant fails: the dialysis machine. But a patient with a diseased liver is less fortunate. Liver transplantation is a formidable procedure. The patient is invariably very ill and there is a severe shortage of donor livers. Also the liver is more difficult to preserve before surgery and the operation itself is technically more complex. Despite such problems hepatic replacement has been attempted for almost every kind of severe liver failure, including primary malignancy and cirrhosis. Prognosis after surgery has steadily improved in recent years. In the United States there is a 25 per cent survival rate after one year for adults and approximately 40 per cent for children. Several recipients are still alive after more than five years.

Pancreatic transplants Diabetes is the third leading cause of death in the United States. Though insulin injections maintain many diabetics for many years, there has been much interest recently in the possibility of restoring normal glucose metabolism by transplanting the tissue areas in the pancreas which produce insulin. Unfortunately these areas, the islets of Langerhans, seem very vulnerable to rejection. While transplant research continues bioengineers have developed a continuous insulin-diffusion pump which is worn on the patient's arm. Their next ambition is to incorporate into this device a sensor mechanism which will detect blood glucose levels and stimulate insulin release as and when necessary.

Corneal grafts Sight is our most precious sense and the one most liable to fail with age. Eye banks have been established in most major cities, and there is no shortage of donors. The outer transparent covering of the eye, the cornea, can be replaced by corneal grafting, keratoplasty. This is one of the most successful forms of transplantation practised today. Steroids have helped to overcome problems of rejection and with new microsurgery techniques and new gossamer-fine suturing materials, the patient is out of hospital in less than two weeks.

Cataract, clouding of the lens of the eye, is usually the result of ageing, or sometimes of injury or faulty development. It is now possible to remove the diseased lens and replace it with an artificial one made of inert plastic; however, the replaced lens is not adjustable, so reading spectacles have to be worn to focus near objects. Sight can also be restored by removing the lens and not replacing it; in this case special cataract spectacles are worn which, with the remaining cornea, provide adequate focusing power.

Skin grafting This is one of the oldest forms of tissue replacement, pioneered during the First and Second World Wars for severe burn injuries. As a First Aid measure skin from another species (usually pig) is grafted on to the burn site. Emergency heterografting, as this procedure is known, is necessary to reduce infection and prevent shrinkage and deformity, but such grafts are quickly rejected. Allografts, using human skin, are much more effective and remain in place until an autograft, using the patient's own skin, can be carried out.

Now various types of synthetic skin have been developed as an alternative to heterografts or allografts. A chemical solution is sprayed over the burnt area and sprinkled with a fine powdered polymer. The result is a covering the consistency of a soft contact lens which breathes and stretches with the skin.

Other organs Lung transplants still present overwhelming problems; rejection, and infection and mechanical problems, are common. Bone marrow transplants, involving the injection of small quantities of compatible bone marrow into the blood of leukaemic patients, are also bedevilled by the problem of rejection. High-dose chemotherapy and X-rays are used first to destroy the patient's defective bone marrow.

Because the problems of rejection are less with artificial spare parts huge research effort is being channelled into prosthetic engineering.

Artificial implants Arthroplasty, the replacement of damaged joints, is one of the commonest and

Still able to work
Rehabilitation is vital in maintaining the quality of life for an amputee. Here a disabled worker assembles electronic equipment, a job requiring complex, deliberate movements. Even spine-injured patients can achieve some degree of independence by using their mouth and head to control equipment sensitive to pressure or light.

Homo prostheticus
Plastic arteries, metal heart valves, alloy and polyethylene joints, rubber testes . . . are all part of the arsenal of the spare part surgeon.

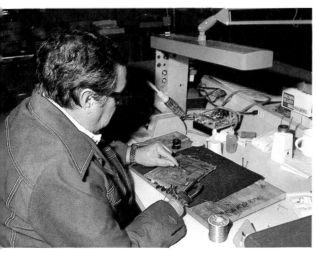

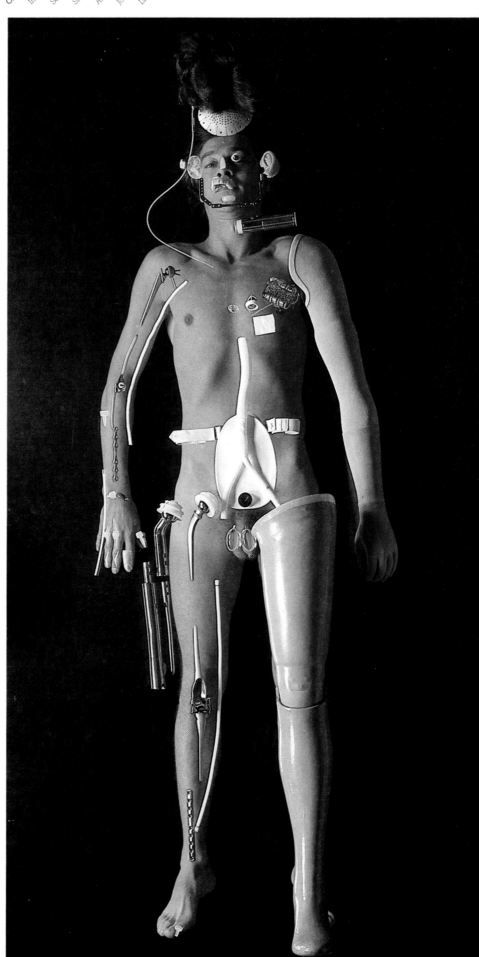

most successful operations performed today. Patients with degenerative joint disease, osteoarthritis for example, are the most frequent candidates. Many thousands of patients have been spared years of chronic pain and increasing disability with total hip joint replacement, a technique pioneered by the British surgeons Charnly and McKee. Bioengineers and orthopaedic surgeons co-operated to develop low-friction artificial joints of stainless steel and plastic, with special cement to weld them to bones. Other joints, knees and fingers for example, can be replaced with artificial implants. But for some patients total limb replacement may be necessary. Peripheral vascular disease of the lower limbs, for example, a condition invariably associated with heavy smoking, can result in gangrene, necessitating amputation above or below the knee. In such cases a 'pylon' is attached to the stump to restore some degree of mobility. In the process of development is a leg prosthesis designed on the same principle as the myolectric arm now being tested in the United States. Electrode implants in the limb stump relay impulses from the adjacent muscles to a tiny powerpack strapped to the body. This transmits signals to mini-motors in the mechanical arm or leg. Taking sophistication even further, scientists are now developing pressure-sensitive skin for artificial limbs.

Harnessing the manufacturing capacity of DNA

Genetic engineering, or recombinant DNA technology as it should properly be called, very nearly failed to get off the ground. When scientists realized the potential of the new techniques at their disposal for changing the very substance of life, the genes, they called a halt to their experiments. The doom-mongers latched on to this unprecedented moratorium, speculating about the bug-eyed monsters, half-human and half-plant, which might have been created if the work had been allowed to continue.

Fortunately the scientists, having got over their initial shock, decided to continue their research but with tight controls over work on deadly infections or cancerous diseases. And, on the whole, the doom-mongers lost interest as widespread excitement greeted first the production of insulin and growth hormone and, more recently, the production of interferon from bacterial cells.

A number of 'breakthroughs' led to the development of techniques whose scientific, industrial, agricultural and medical applications are multiplying almost daily. Scientists had been playing with the sequences of the genetic material DNA ever since James Watson and Francis Crick determined its basic structure in the mid-1950s. But they had to use rather haphazard methods of cutting up the DNA, and found it extremely difficult to decide which specific pieces of DNA controlled the chemical, physical and emotional functions of the body.

Putting bacteria to work Then in 1972 the first 'restriction' enzyme was discovered. These enzymes, more than 80 of which have now been identified, are capable of cutting lengths of DNA at the same specific points each time they come into contact with it. The body needs these natural cutters to dispose of damaged or foreign sections of DNA. Some of the broken ends which are left remain as stumps, while others are cut in such a way that they join easily to another complementary sequence of DNA further down the chain. By carefully working out which restriction enzyme cuts which DNA sequence, scientists have been able to cut only those sections they are interested in, extract the piece of DNA which codes for the substance they are interested in, and then link all the pieces together with the appropriate enzyme.

However, having cut out the piece of DNA they wish to insert, scientists do not reach immediately for their test tubes of bacteria. They need a 'carrier' which will take the new piece of genetic material into the bacterial cell. And that carrier has to be an obliging piece of DNA. While the bulk of their DNA exists within their nuclei, bacteria also have small pieces of DNA outside their nuclei. These peripheral pieces of DNA are called plasmids and replicate independently of the DNA in the nucleus.

A 'stack plate' vessel specially developed in the USA for the culture of interferon from human connective tissue (fibroblast interferon). Although interferon can only be produced from normal human cells at the moment, by this method 200 million units can be produced in eight days.

Scientists realised that plasmids would be ideal carriers for foreign DNA. It is easy to get bacteria to contain several hundred copies of a plasmid, so multiplying gene copies. It is also easy to introduce a small piece of DNA like a plasmid and to isolate it from the bacterium.

This procedure, which forms the essence of genetic manipulation, ran smoothly in the first experiments. The bacterium *Escherichia coli* was singled out as the most likely host. Over the years scientists have put together a complete genetic map of this particular species of bacterium and there is very little they do not know about its habits. So it was an obvious choice. Insulin, the hormone in which diabetics are deficient, was used in many of these early experiments. But having introduced the plasmid containing the insulin gene into the *E. coli* cell, there was a hitch. The DNA replicated but the bacterium was unable to decode the information to produce the insulin itself. *E. coli* had never heard of insulin, so to speak.

Insulin production It took American scientists another 12 months to persuade their *E. coli* bacteria

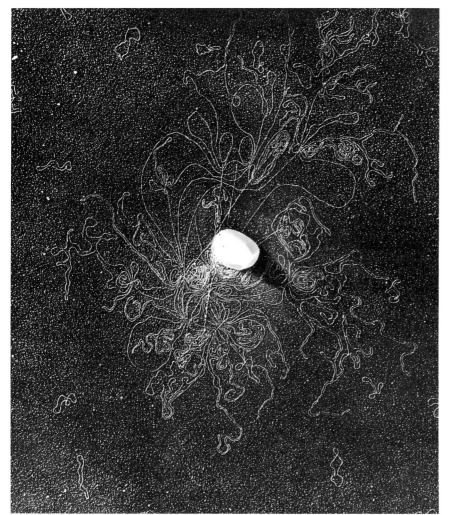

Biologists and bacteria
have both become targets for commercial hijackings. Genetic engineering as an industry is just beginning to show its potential both medically and financially. Left is a Petri dish containing a culture of *E. coli* bacteria.

Escherichia coli,
shown here amidst its own DNA loop magnified 20,000 times. The introduction of human DNA, broken into identifiable fragments, into bacterial cells means that drugs like insulin should be available in commercial quantities by 1990.

to go into production. In the meantime, other researchers were experimenting with genes for two other hormones involved in growth processes, somatostatin and growth hormone (GH).

Even when a bacteria has been induced to manufacture insulin the process is not finished. The cell has to be broken down and the hormone extracted and purified. On top of this, insulin consists of two protein chains, A and B, each made by its own gene, so some bacteria are instructed to produce A and others B. The two chains are later combined.

Trials of human insulin produced in this way got underway in 1980. Initial results suggest that bacteria-produced insulin is just as effective in controlling diabetes as insulin from animal pancreases. And there are added advantages, especially for those diabetics who are allergic and react badly to animal insulins. Scientists are naturally on the lookout for reactions to *E. coli* material which might have become associated with the insulin. Nevertheless, our bodies are very used to *E. coli* bacteria—they are permanent residents in the human intestine and the body is accustomed to

keeping bacteria away from those areas where they would do harm. Nevertheless it was the fact of *E. coli* living in the human gut which originally alerted scientists to the dangers of genetically manipulating bacteria. The fear was that if bacteria containing genes for a deadly infection found their way out of the laboratory, the first place they would seek refuge would be the human gut. In fact laboratory-bred bacteria are a rarified breed, too accustomed to optimum conditions to live for long in the rigorous conditions of the outside world.

Commercial production of insulin and interferon is now in progress and projects for smaller-scale production of growth hormone and other drugs are also proceeding. It is important that these substances are produced in quantity, because the use for them is increasing yearly. Diabetics live much longer than they used to, requiring insulin supplies for many decades; in fact doctors have forecast an insulin shortage by 1990. Growth hormone is at present available only in limited amounts since it has to be extracted from the pituitary glands of dead people; genetic manipulation could ensure an unlimited supply.

Gene manipulation: ethics and limitations

The superhuman being?
One of the aims of genetic
engineering is to implant
healthy genes into
genetically defective cells.
But the prospect of
producing a race of
supermen by this method is
unutterably remote.
Purification of the human
gene pool would in any case
weaken our capacity to adapt
and survive.

Interferon This drug produced from bacteria for the first time at the start of 1980, is one of the most interesting anti-cancer prospects yet found. But much wider testing is needed before we know which cancers can be effectively treated. Indeed, much of the early optimism may prove unfounded. Using traditional methods, only 100 mg of interferon can be made from 65,000 pints (38,000 l) of blood. The cost is enormous and purification process often unsatisfactory. So the announcement that bacteria had been pressed into service to produce the drug aroused predictable excitement.

The genetic engineering industry

Bioengineering is a multi-million dollar business, headed by a number of American and European commercial companies. These companies develop and market the products of genetic engineering, either working in conjunction with universities, or

trying to entice academics away from their laboratories. There have been fears that companies with huge financial backing might cream off the best research scientists into a system where money is no object and grant applications would become a thing of the past.

Legality In 1980 some remarkable legal wranglings in the United States culminated in a broad patent for two techniques essential to all genetic engineering being granted to the scientists at Stanford University and the University of California who developed them. It took the authorities seven years to reach this important decision. It will mean, in effect, that American scientists wishing to use the techniques will have to get the permission of the Stanford and California groups and hand over a proportion of any profits made from their commercial application.

Another historic decision made in America during the summer of 1980 concerned the patenting of living organisms. The organism concerned was a bacterium developed by the General Electric Company to digest oil from water surfaces. It had enormous money-making potential as an 'oil slick eater'. After a lengthy legal battle the courts decided in favour of General Electric and set a precedent in the US for patenting new life forms.

The legal situation is clearer in the United Kingdom where it is quite feasible to apply for a patent not only for an organism carrying the human genetic material but also for any carrier of the new genetic material, the messenger genetic material involved in the production process, and the finished product isolated from the bacterial cells.

A major fear of scientists is that researchers who make key discoveries in the field of genetic engineering will be loath to tell their colleagues for fear of being beaten in the race to patent commercially viable products. Companies which have been set up to market such products work in unusual secrecy.

In 1981 American scientists were still fighting over the ownership of the original cells used to develop the process for bacterial interferon production by the Swiss company Hoffmann La Roche and an American genetic engineering firm called Genentech. The strange saga began with University of California researchers sending cells cultured from the bone marrow of a dying leukaemia patient to a researcher at the National Cancer Institute, allegedly on the understanding that the cells would go no further. However, they were passed on to scientists at the Roche Institute of Molecular Biology, funded by Hoffmann La Roche. Further work led to the development of cells which would produce interferon, and Genentech was brought in to develop the process. Interferon was duly extracted and the researchers who owned the original cells claimed that their cells had been misappropriated by Roche and Genentech.

Ten years ago the idea of scientists going to litigation over ownership of test tubes full of bacteria worth fortunes would have seemed extremely far-fetched, not to say fantastic.

Human guinea pigs

The only reason why genetic engineering methods were initially developed with bacteria was because bacteria have less DNA than other micro-organisms and because most of it had been thoroughly 'mapped'. Man, with his 23 pairs of chromosomes and thousands of genes, is a much more complex proposition. Nevertheless, the first attempts at inserting genetic material into humans were made towards the end of 1980.

The human guinea pigs were women, one Italian and one Israeli, with the rare inherited blood disease thalassaemia. This is often lethal since the blood cells responsible for carrying oxygen do not function properly. The disease, in its most lethal form, is most common in Mediterranean countries. The two women were injected with the genetic material, which, when decoded, gives rise to the protein enzyme missing in thalassaemia. The experiment failed and led to enormous criticism of the man who performed it, Dr Martin Cline, because of the lack of previous experimental work in animals.

It was difficult enough persuading bacteria to decode the DNA for insulin, but in man—or woman in this case—the problem is far more difficult because of the amount and complexity of genetic material in every human cell. Large areas of the human genetic map remain unplotted, and to further complicate matters it seems that the DNA for any particular protein is not found in one continuous piece in the DNA but in parts separated by 'nonsense' DNA, which is not decoded. Some scientists believe that this 'nonsense' material regulates just when and where the surrounding DNA is decoded. This is the intricate puzzle which has stood in the way of human genetic engineering so far.

What is the point of inserting a missing piece of DNA into a human chromosome if one doesn't know how to 'turn it on' to produce the vital proteins? Dr Cline managed to insert the necessary gene but he could not get it to work in his thalassaemic patients.

Far into the future

Once scientists have learned the secrets of these regulatory genes—and there is little doubt that they will eventually—the possibilities for correcting genetic abnormalities in human chromosomes will be endless. Genetic engineering in bacteria is only

the beginning. It takes little imagination to see the ethical and biological problems this new technology will pose, however.

However, this is looking many decades, and possibly centuries, into the future. The more immediate potential for gene therapy in humans lies in a few rare diseases such as thalassaemia, sickle cell anaemia, Lesch-Nyhan syndrome (where patients have strong and inevitably lethal self-destructive impulses) and phenylketonuria (which causes severe physical and mental defects if untreated). It is only in these diseases that scientists have even a small grasp of the genetic defects and regulatory processes involved. Genetic manipulation of diseases arising from a complex interaction of faults in a variety of body systems is a very long way off. And manipulation of complex emotional and physical interactions is beyond the horizon of even the most imaginative genetic engineers working today.

Many of the fears of the genetic engineers of the early 1970s have proved unfounded. None of the terrible accidents predicted by the Jeremiahs of the time have materialised. Nevertheless, as awareness of the possible dangers of all new forms of technology grows, the combination of self-imposed and legal restrictions on genetic manipulation is also growing.

Massive meteor craters such as this, the world's largest in Arizona, USA, are a reminder that alien organisms could reach us from outer space. For all our tinkering with terrestrial life forms, outer space is still the most likely source of monsters. The ability to manipulate genetic material might conceivably be our only defence against potentially devastating microbes.

Sickle cell anaemia is a serious genetic disorder of the blood in which the red blood cells are distorted and unable to carry oxygen efficiently. As this map shows, the disease is most prevalent in Africa and in certain foci around the Mediterranean. One 'advantage' of sickle cell anaemia is that it confers protection from malaria. Is this why it is prevalent in areas where malaria has been endemic? Eight per cent of American blacks carry the sickle cell trait; few in whom the condition is particularly serious reach maturity.

Lifespan and the mortal cell

The tremendous triumphs of modern medicine have done very little to alter human life expectancy. The reason for this is that the human lifespan is biologically ordained, just as the duration of human pregnancy is ordained. For the half-century from 1900 to 1950, life expectancy in North America rose by a mere 20 years, mainly because of a better understanding of hygiene, a rise in living standards, and the successful use of medicine to treat conditions that formerly caused death before the age of 65. From 1900 to 1969 the gain in life expectancy at 65 and 75 years of age was only 2.9 and 2.2 years respectively.

Some modern experts in ageing, however, believe that in the not too distant future there will be few deaths in youth and middle age and that most of the elderly will maintain vigorous good health almost to the end of their lives, at the age of 85 on average. Dr James Fries, a physician at the University of Stanford, California, believes that in a society where disease is virtually eliminated and deaths are due to natural causes, two-thirds of all deaths would occur between the ages of 81 and 89, and 95 per cent between the ages of 77 and 93.

The mortal cell In an attempt to find out why ageing occurs and how it can be prevented, or at least postponed, scientists have evolved a new field of study, the cell biology of human ageing. Such studies have now moved out of the area of eccentricity and have become an area of enquiry for the world's top biologists; immortality is no longer a concept belonging to science fiction. In 1981 Dr Leonard Hayflick, a leading authority on the cell biology of human ageing at the Bruce Lyon Memorial Research Laboratory in Oakland, California, made a significant discovery. He and his colleagues found that when five fibroblast cells from a human embryo were placed in a culture medium they underwent a finite number of doublings and then died. Even when cultured under optimum conditions, death followed after 50 doublings. The conclusion was that the death of these cells was not due to an environmental inadequacy but to some inherent property of the cells themselves; in other words, we carry our own death warrants written in our cell structure.

This conclusion was further substantiated by taking cells that had undergone a number of divisions, or doublings, and freezing them. The lowered temperature arrested biological activity. Various stages of cell division were selected as the freezing points and samples were stored at reduced temperatures for varying lengths of time. The cells were then reconstituted and allowed to divide further in a culture medium. The cells doubled up as before but only to the allotted 50 times. Cells arrested at 10 doublings, for example, continued through another 40 doublings before dying, while cells arrested at 45 doublings added only another 5 doublings before death. This was the case no matter how the length of the freezing time varied.

Logically, therefore, cells taken from an adult rather than an embryo would not be able to divide 50 times because a certain amount of ageing had already taken place. So Hayflick and his colleagues tried culturing normal adult fibroblasts to see what would happen. Result? Their total number of doublings was significantly less than those of the embryo cells, a finding which indicates an inverse relation between the age of the human donor and the *in vitro* (outside the body) proliferation capacity of these cells.

Old before one's time Another avenue of research was the phenomenon of progeria, or precocious ageing, a condition in which a patient at the age of 10 shows physical signs of ageing that are normally found in a person of 70. Fibroblasts were cultured from patients suffering from progeria to discover to what extent the cells would multiply and survive. It was predicted that their lifespan would be measurably shortened. The assumption proved to be correct. Cells from progeriatric patients divided between two and ten times, where the normal values were between 20 and 40.

The next step was to demonstrate that what happened outside the body also happened *in vivo* (in the body). In order to do this, cells were labelled so that they could be identified. The labelled cells were transplanted from one genetically identical host to another as soon as the donor approached old age. Such cells did not survive beyond their programmed limit. The injury of transplantation seemed to have little effect. Survival appeared to be related only to the age of the grafted cells.

There is a wide variation in the lifespan of different species. To take an extreme pairing, the mayfly lives for only a few hours while an elephant lives for many decades. Experiments were carried out to see if there was any correlation between the population doublings of cultured normal fibroblasts and the mean maximum lifespan of the species. The findings were not conclusive, but a trend became apparent. For example, normal embryo fibroblasts from a tortoise, with a lifespan of about 150 years, were grown in culture media and achieved doublings of up to 125. In contrast, normal embryo fibroblasts from a mouse with a lifespan of 2½ years managed to double between 14 and 28 times.

Immortal cells The experimental evidence outlined so far suggests the strong possibility of a direct relationship between the ability of cells to divide and the process of ageing. The conclusion is almost inescapable: that all cells die in the

Cross references
Division of cells 17
The gene machine 13
Ageing 156
New perspectives on
cancer 226

end—with one startling exception. This exception is a disturbing one. In cell culture laboratories throughout the world, cancer cells taken in 1952 from a human carcinoma at the mouth of the womb have continued, even to this day, to flourish through innumerable doublings.

The discovery of 'immortal cells' presented a major headache to biologists interested in senescence, until it became clear that such cells were abnormal; only cells which show a fixed number of doublings are normal. Abnormality in the immortal cells could be due either to a morphological deviation in the nucleus and chromosomes (genetic material) when compared to the genetic material of the cells from which they were originally derived, or there could be a distinct difference in the way the genetic material of the immortal cells expressed itself when compared to the genetic expression of the cells from which they arose. This can be shown by taking a mortal cell and infecting it with a cancer virus. The infection brings about a fusion of the genetic material of the virus and that of the cell, making the genetic material abnormal. The immediate result is that the cell becomes immortal.

Human senescence is not only caused by one or more important cell populations losing the ability to divide and replenish. Further experimental work has shown that this is only part of the ageing process. Major functional changes take place in normal human cells grown outside the body and are expressed well before the cells lose their capacity to replicate. The ending of the cell's ability to divide is only one functional deterioration whose genetic basis may be similar to that known to occur in non-dividing cells such as those of the brain and muscle. Dr Hayflick summed this up by saying that it was not his contention that age changes result necessarily from loss of function in any class of cells. Function loss may be measured as reduced capacity to divide, or any of a myriad of other deteriorations which characterise ageing cells.

Defiance of death
has been the main motive of medical research throughout history. But recent research seems to indicate that each one of us, and every cell in our body, has a finite lease of life. If all deaths were due to natural causes, 95 per cent of us would die between the age of 77 and 93.

Omm Seti
née Dorothy Eady in London, England, in 1904, fell downstairs at the age of three and was so severely concussed that she was presumed dead. She recovered, but from then on had continual, vivid dreams about a temple in Egypt which she felt was her home.

Eventually she went to live in Abydos, the site of the temple of Seti I (1318–1304 B.C.), the temple in her dreams. Although she never claimed she was a reincarnation of an Egyptian priestess, she felt she had returned to a 'long-lost and well-loved home', where she died in 1981.

Cryobiology and experiments in cell division

Genetic control of cell division If the loss of proliferation capacity in a cell population is an expression of ageing, which on evidence appears to be the case, then it is important to locate and understand the mechanism that controls this finite repetitive capacity in order to manipulate it in an attempt to increase the human lifespan.

Through a very ingenious experiment, Hayflick and his colleagues proved that the proliferation mechanism is genetically controlled. This was shown by taking cultured cells and treating them with a chemical called cytochalasin B. This caused the cell to extrude its nucleus and, by means of centrifugation, millions of cells without nuclei (i.e. without genetic information) were obtained. These anucleated cells were called cytoplasts and they remained alive for several days. Using a special technique, the genetic information of old cells was introduced into young cytoplasts, while the nuclei of young cells were introduced into old cytoplasts. As a result young cells were produced with old genetic information and old cells with young genetic information. Studies of the remaining population doublings showed that young cells with old genetic information had less replication power than old cells with young nuclei. The conclusion was that the lifespan of man is fixed and that it is genetically programmed into his cell structure.

Cell differentiation All the different cells in the human body arise from just one fertilised cell, the ovum or egg. This is made possible because of two processes: cell division, which allows cells to multiply; and a series of 'one-way' differentiation processes which cause cells to take up different functions. Cell differentiation is the result of the activation of certain genes while others are repressed, thus preventing the formation of unwanted proteins. The mechanism of repression is not yet understood but it is almost certainly chemically controlled.

In 1977 a South African Medical Research Council Unit in the Department of Medical Biochemistry at the University of Stellenbosch Medical School reported an interesting research achievement which tends to support the chemical determination of differentiation. The investigators took a culture of cells removed from a mouse embryo that closely resembled fibroblasts, the cells that form scar tissue. The culture was treated with a chemical called 5-azacytidine and the cells reacted by differentiating into muscle cells. They not only stood up to examination under the microscope but also contracted under chemical stimulation in the same way as muscle cells. Similar results have been achieved using other chemical compounds.

It is very likely that ageing is the end result of differentiation and represents a failure to divide or

Buddha and the immortals
A Tibetan *tanka* painting showing Buddha surrounded by those who, through repeated incarnations and adherence to the 'noble eightfold path', have attained Nirvana. In this perfect state man becomes immortal, having merged with the life of universe 'as the dewdrop slips into the shining sea'.

The state funeral
of Winston Churchill in 1965. Churchill was 91 when he died, and became Prime Minister for the second time at the age of 75. His mind, exercised by the problems of statesmanship, remained active almost to the end. But the accumulated experience and wisdom of many old people is destroyed and fragmented by the physical process of ageing.

a failure to continue accurately to make the functional cell proteins. If this is so, then the most likely control agent is chemical, superimposed on the differentiation programme of each cell. Ageing may represent a further chemically-controlled repression of genes. As this form of control is more clearly understood and the genetic messages unravelled, the possibility of the control of ageing will become a reality.

Cryogenics—the freezing of life It has often been suggested that deep-freezing could be of great help in keeping diseased human beings preserved alive until such time as the disease from which they are dying can be cured. In the United States a number of organisations have been formed to push ahead with experimental work in cryogenics. Examples are the Life Extension Society of Washington, the Immortality Research and Complication Association, and the Anabiosis and Longevity Institute of New York. Various people have paid large sums of money to ensure that when they die their bodies will be preserved by freezing, in the belief that the techniques of successful revival will eventually be developed. In 1967 a retired professor of psychology in California, Dr James H. Bedford, set aside more than $4,000 for this purpose before he died of cancer at the age of 73.

The technology of cryogenesis is reasonably simple. Immediately after his death, Dr Bedford was injected with heparin, a substance that prevents clotting of the blood. His chest was then opened and his heart massaged in order to supply his brain with oxygenated blood until such time as his body could be connected to a heart-lung machine. Once on the machine, his temperature was progressively lowered to 48° F (8° C) by packing ice around his body. Most of the blood was then withdrawn and replaced with a solution of salt plus a solvent known as DMSO (dimethyl sulphoxide). The temperature of the body was then lowered to −110° F (−79° C) and the body was flown to Phoenix, Arizona, for storage in liquid oxygen at −310° F (−190° C).

The process appears fairly straightforward but unfortunately the freezing of organs and entire bodies is not that easy. Damage occurs in tissues kept at low temperatures for long periods and further damage takes place when the temperature is raised again. This is caused in part by the physical changes that take place in liquids at low temperatures, inducing stresses in surrounding tissue. To take just one aspect, as water in the cell freezes not only does the concentration of salts build up to a damaging level, but the change in state creates a change in volume and the crystals puncture the cell wall.

Were it not for the fact that any researcher learns early on to use the word 'impossible' with caution,

Cross references
Division of cells **17**
Fertilisation **20**
Ageing **156**
Future course of medicine **226**

Ancient Egyptian pharoahs believed themselves to be gods and immortal. To fit them for the journey from death to immortality they had themselves embalmed and entombed, together with all the artefacts necessary for eternal life.

Slow but sure Tortoises have a very sluggish metabolism, and apart from the sea anemone, and the sponge, which are in a sense immortal because they reproduce vegetatively, have the longest lifespan of any terrestrial animal. The black Seychelles tortoise holds the record: 170 years.

The fleeting existence of most butterflies coincides with the flowering season of the plants they feed on. Butterflies live only for a few days or weeks, just long enough to mate and lay eggs. Two generations may develop in the course of a single summer.

most scientists would be tempted to place such work in the realm of the ridiculous. Only a few years ago it would have been thought impossible that mammalian cells such as blood cells, spermatozoa, fibroblasts, or any tissue capable of conversion into single cell form, could be stored at low temperatures for years. Yet it has been shown that a suspension of cells in nutrient solution mixed with DMSO can be cooled to −310° F (−190° C) and then stored. When required, the cells can be thawed and washed, and full physiological function is restored.

The evidence that man's long search for immortality is gaining ground is disturbing; although long-term survival may benefit the individual, there is cause to think that it would be of great harm to the species as a whole. Senescence and death are an evolutionary necessity. If all organisms were immortal, there would be no need to reproduce. If there were no reproduction there would be no rewriting of cell programmes, and no change. Each species would lose the potential to adapt. Though it may, in theory, be possible to control our own biology, would we ever adapt psychologically to life everlasting?

In conclusion

We have shown that in various ways the machines we build are modelled in our own image to extend our natural capacity. However, even the most sophisticated man-made machines are primitive compared with the human body. The body is not a machine, but a machine plus, the first wonder of the universe.

The body machine analogy, nevertheless, provides an invaluable insight into the way we function and underlines the need for proper maintenance and servicing. But there are potential risks as well as gains in looking at ourselves as mechanical beings.

Writing recently in the American journal *Psychiatric Opinion* Dr Leah Davidson commented: "To be cool, to have no feelings, to be mechanical in the performance of sex, these are the ideals of much of our society. Our TV hero stereotypes are Bionic Man and Bionic Woman—part robot, part human. Sex is used by these creatures to acquire power and control . . . We are becoming changelings. The bad fairy has stolen our feelings and we no longer believe that we have to exchange them with one another."

It is often said that machines are de-humanising, but we cannot blame machines for the faults we build into them. Certainly the way we use and think of them shapes our lives and, in an ever-increasing number of cases, our deaths.

Shortly before his death a bulletin about President Tito of Yugoslavia said that he was suffering from "heavy stomach bleeding, heart weakness, cardiac rhythm disturbances, kidney failure, pneumonia and diabetes." Any one of these complications could have killed him, yet his death was delayed by life supports.

In an editorial, appropriately titled 'A doctor's dilemma', *The Houston Post* commented that after his surgery President Tito "seemed sufficiently on the road to recovery to warrant first one then another life saving emergency measure. To have denied them would have been unethical and not in keeping with modern medical practice. At the time he and his doctors were averse to the idea of prolonging his life artificially should he become terminally ill. But gradually, as one machine after another replaced a function of his body, Tito began to sink. He is now in a coma. It is fairly sure that he is being kept alive only by the massive system of life support equipment. Nothing now can reverse the progress of his illness or restore him to consciousness, much less to precarious health.

"It is probable now that his protracted illness has allowed time in Belgrade for political forces to resolve their differences and plan an orderly transition. But the physicians in charge face a question: do they continue to keep alive a man who can no longer live in the real sense of the word? If not, who will make the decision to withdraw the supports?"

Medical or surgical use of machines is beneficial only for as long as it can prolong the quality of life. Quality should take precedence over quantity in the cause of dignity. This means that we have to review constantly with the utmost vigilance what is done in the name of progress. It should not be beyond us to safeguard the future against the bad fairy, in the guise of rampant technology, but at the same time derive benefit from new knowledge.

We are all born to die, yet until recently medical students were taught to regard the death of a patient as a therapeutic failure. Now both inside and outside medicine the taboo of death is itself living on borrowed time. In the last 15 years or so the number of publications about death and dying has increased by almost 1,000 per cent. New methods of treating the terminally ill are showing that the boredom, fear and loneliness of dying can be transformed through pain-controlling drugs and pastoral support. Unfortunately for many terminal patients dying is still rather like war: 90 per cent boredom and 10 per cent fear. But the climate is changing slowly. The special needs of the dying patient are being recognised in an increasing number of countries. There is in the English city of Sheffield a small cottage hospital called St Luke's. What makes St Luke's special is that it was the world's first purpose-built hospital for the chronically sick. It has been described as a place where there isn't a 'parking meter on the end of every bed'. Progress like this is not reflected in newspaper headlines but it is as important, if not more so, than that which is.

In all phases of life we should recognise the special properties of the body machine. It demands many different kinds of fuel, not least self-respect, dignity, pride, love, excitement and challenge, all the things which cannot be measured quantitively on a fuel gauge and which will never be incorporated into the machines we make.

Health quiz

Health quiz

Cover up the right hand column on each of the following pages and don't peep until you have ticked your answers in the left hand column!

Scoring

Between 75 and 90 You have read this book very carefully and have assimilated a lot of interesting information about the body machine.

Between 50 and 75 Your understanding of the body machine is about average. You will probably feel stimulated to re-read sections of this book and others to increase your knowledge.

Less than 45 Your knowledge of the body machine is average. You probably only read those sections that interested you before you tackled the quiz.

True or False?

Answers

1 The average man contains 4½ gals (20 l) of water. [TRUE] [FALSE]

False. About 60 per cent of the body weight of an average man weighing about 145 lb (66 kg) is water, equivalent to 9 gls (40 l).

2 Proteins are formed by linking amino acids; all but 10 of the 23 different amino acids in the human body can be synthesised by the body cells.

True. The 10 we cannot synthesise must be consumed in the diet in the form of protein.

3 DNA (deoxyribose nucleic acid) molecules form proteins by linking together amino acids.

False. This function is done by RNA (ribose nucleic acid) after it has copied the chemical coding from DNA.

4 Two brown-eyed parents will only produce brown-eyed children.

False. If both parents have a recessive 'blue-eyed' gene they have a one in four chance of having a blue-eyed child.

5 People with an XXY chromosome pattern are individuals who have female genitalia externally, but lack female sex organs internally.

False. The condition described is Turner's syndrome (XO). XXY is Klinefelter's syndrome, associated with men who are sterile, with under-developed male genitalia and often some female development.

6 Women are carriers of haemophilia; they do not actually suffer from it.

True. One of the most famous carriers of haemophilia was Queen Victoria, whose eighth child, Prince Leopold, died of severe bleeding after a trivial fall.

7 Each sex cell contains 23 pairs of chromosomes.

False. Sex cells divide by meiosis which results in 23 single chromosomes, not 23 pairs.

8 Follicle stimulating hormone (FSH) causes ovarian follicles to ripen and rupture, releasing eggs or ova.

False. FSH does stimulate ovarian follicle growth, but it is luteinising hormone, secreted in response to oestrogen, which triggers ovulation.

9 Sperm survive inside a woman's body for 12–24 hours.

False. Sperm usually survive for 24–48 hours, increasing the chances of conception occurring.

10 The chances of conceiving a boy or a girl are equal.

False. More males are conceived, but are more prone to death in the womb; this results in an almost equal ratio of male to female births.

11 There are 206 bones in the normal adult.

True. At birth we have 300 bones, some of which fuse together in early life.

12 The femur or thigh bone can withstand 1,200 lb of pressure per square inch (85 kg/cm²) when we walk.

True. This is due to the complex structure of bone, which is composed of collagen fibres hardened and strengthened with calcium and other mineral salts.

13 Muscles consist of actin and myosin fibrils.

True. These two sorts of fibrils partly interlock with each other; it is the moving closer together of their interlocking teeth during contraction which shortens muscle length.

14 The parasympathetic nervous system stimulates the heart, increasing the force and rate at which heart muscle contracts.

False. The sympathetic nervous system does this; the parasympathetic nervous system has an inhibiting effect on the heart.

15 Keratin waterproofs skin.

True. Nevertheless, prolonged immersion in water will lead to penetration of the keratin barrier, causing skin to wrinkle.

16 Black and white people have equal numbers of melanocytes, the cells which produce the skin pigment melanin.

True. The difference in the skin colour of different races lies in the productive capacity of their melanocytes.

17 Albinos, people who lack melanin, have white hair, pink skin and blue eyes.

False. Melanin is also required to give eyes colour; therefore albinos have pink, colourless eyes.

18 Psoriasis of the skin can be associated with a form of arthritis of the joints.

True. Fortunately this complication of psoriasis is a fairly rare condition.

19 There are 100,000 hairs on the average head, each one of which grows for about three years.

True. The growth rate is about 1½₅ in (1 mm) every three days, equivalent to about 5 in (12.5 cm) a year.

20 In the course of a day 200 gals (900 l) of blood are pumped through the heart.

False. At a rate of 10–15 pints (5.5–8.5 l) per minute, some 2,000 gals (9,000 l) of blood are pumped by the heart in a day.

21 The second heart sound is due to closure of the tricuspid and mitral valves.

False. The first heart sound is caused by closure of these valves; the second is caused by closure of the aortic and pulmonary valves.

True or False?

#	Question			Answers
		TRUE	FALSE	
22	All heart murmurs are associated with an abnormality within the heart.	☐	☐	False. Murmurs are often heard in perfectly normal hearts—these are sometimes called innocent murmurs.
23	Many athletes have a resting pulse rate of 45 beats a minute or less.	☐	☐	True. Fitness reduces the resting heart rate.
24	The normal heartbeat is stimulated by electrical impulses from the heart's natural pacemaker, the atrio-ventricular (AV) node.	☐	☐	False. The AV node is only a 'relay station'; the impulses are generated by the sinus node—this is the true cardiac pacemaker.
25	There are three main coronary blood vessels supplying blood to the heart.	☐	☐	True. The right coronary artery and the left, which divides the two main branches.
26	The Scots, who are believed to have the world's highest mortality rates from coronary heart disease (CHD), have very high levels of blood cholesterol.	☐	☐	False. The Scots do not have particularly high levels of cholesterol, but they do have high triglyceride levels.
27	Stress has been shown to be associated with an increase in cholesterol levels.	☐	☐	True. In one North American study the cholesterol levels of accountants were found to increase during the peak period of their working year, two months before everyone's tax returns were due.
28	Between 1963 and 1973 coronary heart disease among Americans aged between 37 and 75 fell by a quarter.	☐	☐	True. This has been attributed to a decrease in consumption of tobacco and saturated animal fats, and to increased intake of polyunsaturated vegetable fats.
29	Ventricular fibrillation (VF) of the heart is invariably fatal unless normal rhythm is restored within a few minutes.	☐	☐	True. VF is usually treated with electrical shock (defibrillation).
30	The transmitting part of the nerve cell is a thin projection known as a dendrite.	☐	☐	False. A dendrite's job is to receive, not transmit, nerve impulses. It is nerve axons, which differ in length from a fraction of an inch (several millimetres) to about 3 ft (1 m) and in diameter from about 0.5–20 microns, which ensure that impulses are transmitted.
31	A fatty substance called myelin, which is wrapped around nerve fibres, slows up the speed at which nerve impulses travel.	☐	☐	False. The thicker the sheath of myelin the quicker impulses travel.
32	The average weight of the human brain is just over 3 lb (1.4 kg).	☐	☐	True. In contrast a gorilla's brain weighs about 1 lb (0.45 kg).
33	Alpha brain waves usually occur when one is thinking hard and has one's eyes open.	☐	☐	False. Alpha waves usually occur when the eyes are closed, although experienced meditators can maintain alpha activity with their eyes open.
34	Thyroid stimulating hormone (TSH) is secreted by the pituitary gland.	☐	☐	True. It is one of ten hormones secreted by the anterior lobe of the pituitary, and triggers the thyroid gland to produce hormones.
35	Excess prolactin can cause infertility because it prevents sex hormones from stimulating the ovaries.	☐	☐	True. An excess of prolactin can sometimes be treated with the drug bromocryptin which suppresses prolactin production.
36	A baby is much better at hearing very high pitched sounds than an old person.	☐	☐	True. A baby can hear sounds with frequencies up to 20,000 cycles per second, but an elderly person is lucky if he or she can hear sounds of 12,000 cycles per second.
37	We do not dream during rapid eye movement (REM) sleep.	☐	☐	False. Experiments have shown that sleepers woken during REM sleep are in the middle of a dream.
38	Sleepers deprived of REM sleep suffer from various emotional disturbances and even hallucinations.	☐	☐	True. Sleep deprivation has been used as an effective brainwashing technique.
39	A newborn infant sleeps 16 hours a day on average.	☐	☐	True. The need to sleep diminishes with age, decreasing to an average of about 7½ hours in adulthood.
40	Every day about 200,000,000,000 red blood cells are produced by the bone marrow.	☐	☐	True. These last about 110–120 days in the circulation.
41	Failure to absorb vitamin B_{12} results in pernicious anaemia.	☐	☐	True. Before this vitamin could be synthesised, sufferers were treated with a diet of vitamin-rich raw liver.
42	Leukaemia is a blood disease characterised by overproduction of red blood cells.	☐	☐	False. Leukaemia literally means 'white blood', and is due to excess manufacture of white blood cells.
43	Platelets are cells which help blood to clot at the site of a cut or wound.	☐	☐	True. They do, but platelets are only part of the complex process which results in blood clotting.
44	Group A blood contains anti-A antibodies.	☐	☐	False. Group B blood contains anti-A antibodies; group A blood has anti-B antibodies.

True or False?

Answers

45	Rhesus or 'blue' babies are born to mothers who have Rhesus positive blood.	☐ ☐ TRUE FALSE	False. The mothers of blue babies have rhesus (Rh) negative blood and Rh positive antibodies which attack the blood cells of the baby who is Rh positive.
46	Blood tests can prove that a man is the father of a child.	☐ ☐	False. Blood tests can only conclusively prove that he is *not*.
47	Varicose veins are associated with sedentary occupations.	☐ ☐	False. Occupations which demand prolonged standing—being a policeman or a housewife—are more commonly associated with varicose veins.
48	Prolonged immobility can cause you to faint.	☐ ☐	True. This causes a temporary decrease in blood flow to the brain; soldiers standing on parade for long periods sometimes faint.
49	The systolic blood pressure of a young man at rest is 80 mg Hg.	☐ ☐	False. His diastolic pressure would certainly be about 80 mm Hg, but his systolic pressure would be much higher, probably around 120 mm Hg.
50	In the average 80-year-old systolic blood pressure would be quite a lot higher.	☐ ☐	True. This is due to the fact that ageing arteries lose their elasticity.
51	Casual blood pressure readings may give an entirely erroneous idea of a person's blood pressure.	☐ ☐	True. A person may have a falsely high recording if anxious or under stress.
52	High blood pressure can cause kidney failure and strokes as well as coronary heart disease.	☐ ☐	True. Diagnosis and treatment of hypertension can reduce the incidence of strokes and kidney failure.
53	The amount of oxygen in an average adult's body at any one time is enough to keep him alive for four minutes, provided he is resting.	☐ ☐	True. If he was strenuously exercising, he would only have enough oxygen to keep him alive for one minute.
54	Colour images in the eye are registered by the rod cells of the retina.	☐ ☐	False. The rods are for monochrome vision; colour images are registered by the cone cells of the retina; surprisingly we have more rods, principally used for night vision, than cones.
55	There are only three different types of cone cells, each sensitive to only one of three colours, red, blue and green.	☐ ☐	True. Other colours are perceived as combinations of these colours.
56	Most colourblind people are unable to identify red or green.	☐ ☐	True. Inability to identify blue is rare.
57	Pupil size may reflect the degree of stimulus we obtain from what we see.	☐ ☐	True. A man's pupils have been shown to increase as much as 30 per cent in diameter when he sees a beautiful woman.
58	Pancreatic juice contains three enzymes (lipase, trypsin and amylase) which break down fats, proteins and starch in preparation for their absorption by the intestine.	☐ ☐	True. Lack of pancreatic juice can cause malabsorption.
59	Bile salts are important in aiding the absorption of fats.	☐ ☐	True. They break down or emulsify fats prior to absorption.
60	Digestive processess are regulated by hormones secreted in the blood.	☐ ☐	True. Food in the duodenum stimulates the release of these hormones; these in turn cause the release of pancreatic juices and bile from the pancreas and gall bladder.
61	Blood flow through the kidneys is about 430 gals (1,930 l) per day.	☐ ☐	True. Only about a thousandth of this is converted into urine.
62	Each kidney contains about one million nephrons or filtering structures.	☐ ☐	True. If unwound and placed end to end, these would stretch for more than 50 miles (80 km).
63	Reabsorption of water by the nephrons is controlled by a hormone called aldosterone.	☐ ☐	False. Aldosterone from the adrenal gland controls the reabsorption of salt. Water reabsorption is controlled by anti-diuretic hormone (ADH) produced by the pituitary.
64	The liver stores glycogen, which is a source of energy.	☐ ☐	True. The liver cells manufacture and store glycogen from glucose and turn it back into glucose when energy is needed.
65	The liver produces many of the blood clotting factors.	☐ ☐	True. If the liver is damaged blood clotting may be impaired.
66	Obstruction of the bile ducts can cause jaundice.	☐ ☐	True. This is called an obstructive jaundice and is associated with a light-coloured stool and dark urine, because large amounts of bile enter the blood rather than the intestine.
67	Cirrhosis of the liver is now the fourth most common cause of death in adult white males in the USA.	☐ ☐	True. Cirrhosis is usually caused by excessive alcohol consumption.

True or False?

68	The pancreas usually produces 2½ pints (1.5 l) of alkaline pancreatic juice a day.	☐ ☐ TRUE FALSE	**Answers**

Answers

68 The pancreas usually produces 2½ pints (1.5 l) of alkaline pancreatic juice a day. ☐ ☐ TRUE FALSE

True. Because it is alkaline, pancreatic juice helps to neutralise the acid entering the small intestine from the stomach.

69 The secretion of pancreatic juice is entirely regulated by hormones. ☐ ☐

False. It is also partly controlled by nervous stimuli relayed from the brain via the vagus nerve in response to food coming into contact with the taste buds.

70 Cells can only undergo a finite number of divisions or doublings before dying. ☐ ☐

True. Experiments have shown that cells taken and frozen for varying periods of time, and then thawed and cultured, have the same division capacity regardless of the length of time they were frozen for.

71 Cancer cells only double a finite number of times. ☐ ☐

False. It would appear that in culture some cancer cells can continue to replicate indefinitely.

72 Someone who sleeps 7 or 8 hours a day, maintains proper weight and refrains from smoking is likely to live longer than someone who doesn't. ☐ ☐

True. These are three of the 'seven health habits' which have been found to have a positive correlation with longevity.

73 Married men live longer. ☐ ☐

True. In the Alameda County study, death rates among 30–49-year-old unmarried men were double those among married men. The same was true of 50–59-year-olds.

74 Smokers are ten times more at risk from lung cancer than non-smokers. ☐ ☐

True. In the USA there are 84,000 deaths a year from lung cancer.

75 Smoking does not cause increased levels of carbon monoxide in the blood. ☐ ☐

False. Up to 15 per cent of the haemoglobin in the blood of heavy smokers may have carbon monoxide attached to it, preventing it from absorbing oxygen.

76 Many alcoholics suffer from anaemia. ☐ ☐

True. This is usually due to poor diet deficient in folic acid, which is necessary for blood production.

77 For every female alcoholic there are seven or eight male alcoholics. ☐ ☐

False. Not any more; there is now one female alcoholic for every four or five male alcoholics.

78 Exercising until it hurts is good for you. ☐ ☐

False. Painful exercise can be dangerous if you are unfit, because it places an undue strain on the heart.

79 Leading a sedentary life does not put people at greater risk of coronary heart disease. ☐ ☐

False. Many studies have shown that people who lead sedentary lives are more liable to coronary heart disease than those who take regular exercise.

80 People with coronary heart disease should avoid taking exercise. ☐ ☐

False. Many studies have shown that graduated exercise can help some people with coronary heart disease to improve their cardiac performance.

81 Coronary heart disease is largely restricted to Western countries. ☐ ☐

True. The incidence of coronary heart disease is much lower in the Third World.

82 In Western people atherosclerotic changes in blood vessels are present in early life. ☐ ☐

True. In post-mortem studies of US airmen killed in Korea, nearly half showed a significant degree of atherosclerosis, and their average age was only 22.

83 Angina is often associated with pain in the jaw and down the arms. ☐ ☐

True. Although heart pain is commonly felt in the chest, it frequently moves into the jaw and down the left or both arms.

84 After a heart attack 12 per cent of sufferers die within 15 minutes. ☐ ☐

True. Prompt action can sometimes save lives.

85 Obsessive and compulsive neuroses rarely occur together in an individual. ☐ ☐

False. They occur together so frequently that they are clinically regarded as two sides of the same coin.

86 Hysterical neurosis usually develops as a way of avoiding unpleasant situations. ☐ ☐

True. Although it is only natural to try to avoid unpleasant situations, avoiding measures can be taken to extremes, resulting in actual loss of motor or sensory functions.

87 Hypochrondria may be a means of gaining 'secondary attention'. ☐ ☐

True. Hypochondriacs sometimes use their 'poor health' as a means of obtaining sympathy and favours.

88 Manic depression involves continuous depression and hopelessness. ☐ ☐

False. On the contrary it involves alternating episodes of manic behaviour.

89 Diabetics have to use animal insulins because it is not possible to produce human insulin. ☐ ☐

False. Genetic engineering has led to the production of 'human insulin' (insulin chemically and biologically identical to human insulin) in the laboratory.

90 Transplanted toes can functionally replace lost hands and fingers. ☐ ☐

True. This has been pioneered in China where double or triple toe transplants have been performed.

Index

Acknowledgements

Medical advisers

Professor R. J. Berry, Department of Genetics,
The Royal Free Hospital School of Medicine,
London, United Kingdom
Professor Derek Burke, Department of Biological
Sciences, University of Warwick, United Kingdom
Dr Ian W. Caldwell, Department of Dermatology,
Jersey General Hospital, Channel Islands
Professor Ian Craft, Department of Obstetrics and
Gynaecology, The Royal Free Hospital, London,
United Kingdom
Edward Ihnatowicz, Department of Mechanical
Engineering, University College, London,
United Kingdom
Margot Hartman, Research Fellow, Sleep Laboratory,
St George's Hospital, London, United Kingdom
Dr J. W. Hinton, Department of Psychology,
University of Glasgow, United Kingdom
Dr Abba Kastin, Tulane University School of
Medicine, Louisiana, USA
Dr Geoffrey Knowles, Chest Clinic, Kingston
Hospital, Surrey, United Kingdom
Dr C. Ogg, Renal Unit, Guy's Hospital, London,
United Kingdom
Mr Neil S. Painter, Senior Surgeon, Manor House
Hospital, London, United Kingdom
Dr Kelvin Palmer, Research Fellow, Department of
Medicine, The Royal Free Hospital, London,
United Kingdom
Professor Ivan M. Roitt, Department of Immunology,
Middlesex Hospital Medical School, London,
United Kingdom
Dr J. R. Silver, National Spinal Injuries Centre, Stoke
Mandeville Hospital, Aylesbury, United Kingdom
Dr D. de Wied, Rudolf Magnus Institute for
Pharmacology, State University of Utrecht,
Netherlands
Dr Roger Williams, Liver Unit, King's College
Hospital, London, United Kingdom

Contributors

Jenny Bryan, *General Practitioner*, London,
United Kingdom
Lorraine Fraser, *General Practitioner*, London,
United Kingdom
Liz Grist, *General Practitioner*, London,
United Kingdom
Dr David Isenberg, Department of Rheumatology,
University College Hospital, London,
United Kingdom
Peter Merry, Chairman, Medical Journalists'
Association, United Kingdom
Elizabeth Morse, Senior Scientific Officer, British
Nutritional Foundation
Dr Henry Purcell, The Medical News Group, London,
United Kingdom
Dr Brian Southgate, Ross Institute of Tropical
Hygiene, London School of Hygiene and Tropical
Medicine, United Kingdom
Dr Paul Williams, General Practice Research Unit,
Institute of Psychiatry (University of London),
United Kingdom

Text review

Dr R. E. Pounder, Senior Lecturer in Medicine,
The Royal Free Hospital, London, United Kingdom
Bryan Silcock, Science Correspondent, *The Sunday
Times*, London, United Kingdom

We would also like to thank the following people for
permission to quote or excerpt:

Milton Diamond and Arno Karlen, *Sexual Decisions*
(Little Brown & Company)
Robert Kastenbaum, *Growing Old—years of fulfilment*
(Hamlyn)
Angela Kilmartin, *Cystitis—a complete self-help guide*
(Hamlyn)
David L. Player, Director of Scottish Health
Education Group, Edinburgh, United Kingdom
Lindsay Knight and *Mind Out* magazine
Leonard Kristal, *Understanding Psychology—a personal
perspective* (Harper and Row)
Christiaan Barnard, *Good Life, Good Death*
(Prentice Hall)

Finally, for their meticulous editorial assistance our
thanks go to Bull Publishing Consultants, Susan Kemp
and Anne Hardy; and for their administrative and
secretarial skills to Zahida Hirjee, Sue Morawski and
Lesley Taylor.

Credits

Photographs

Aliza Auerbach   42 top right
American Cancer Society   205 left
All Sport   34 bottom left
Australian Information Service   40 bottom right
Yael Braun   138, W. Braun 159 right
Dr Chen Zhong-Wei (Sixth People's Hospital, Shanghai) 234 middle and bottom
John Cleare/Mountain Camera   119 top right
Colorific   238 top, Potter Dressler/Life © Time Inc. 1980 239 left and bottom right
Colorsport   71 top right
Daily Telegraph **Colour Library**   172 top, 196 top, 197 left, 214, 236 right, 221, S. J. Allen 220 top and 239 top right, M. Goddard 204 bottom and 220 bottom, L. L. T. Rhodes 214, 237 left, Mark Saunders 217 top, Shaun Skelly 213 top right, P. Thurston 244 bottom, P. Ward 237 right, A. Woolfit 243 bottom
Ruth Eisenhardt   97 top, 197 right
Fiat   226 top left
Jozef Gross   156
BBC Hulton Picture Library   10, 67 left, 222 top left
Alan Hutchinson   19 bottom, 73 top, 177 bottom, 209 top right, 216 bottom
Institute of Ophthalmology   236 top
Keystone Press Agency   15 top, 103 bottom, 198
London Scientific Fotos   13 bottom, 20 top, 36 right, 45 left, 46 bottom left, 49 left, 52 top, 57 bottom left, 105 (3) bottom, 117 middle top and bottom, 130 top right, 136 top
Don MacKenzie   81 bottom
The Mansell Collection   17 bottom, 129 right, 130 top left, 222 top right
Medical Illustration Support Service   131 top left
Monitin Mica Kirshner   92 right
P. Morris   216 top left
Multimedia Publications Inc.   15 middle, 24 left, 26, 29 top, 30, 31 top, 42 top left, 60 bottom right, 64 bottom left, 65 bottom left, 68 left, 92 right, 94 right, 99 bottom, 140 bottom right, 144 top, 147 middle right, 148 top right, 171 top, 180, 190 top left, 195 top, 201 left, 206, 211 left, 212, 213 bottom left, Miki Koren 12 top right, 44, 51, 53 top right, middle left and right, 72 top, 75 bottom, 90 top, 99 top, 103 left and right, 104 top left, 112, 115 left, 117 bottom, 120 bottom, 121 bottom, 141 top, 144 bottom left, 147 top left, middle and right, 148, 149 bottom, 150 top, 153 top right, 157 bottom right, 165 right, 172 right, 176 left, 179 left and top right, 184 top, 188 bottom, 189 top, 204 left, 207, Lisa Mackson 67 right, 213 middle right, Shaun Skelly 183 top right, Israel Sun 29 bottom, 43 bottom, 56 bottom left, 59 bottom left, 70 top, 78, 84, 107 right, 119 top left, 133 top right, 165 top left, 167 bottom, 170 left, 171 bottom, 175 top and bottom, 176 top right, 185 top, 188 middle right, 196 top, 200 top and bottom, Sergio Trippodo 53 top left, 97 middle
NUJ/T. A. Wilkie   62 left
Jil Paul   43 top right
Alex Poignant   227 top
Paul Popper Limited   41 bottom left
Popperfoto   40 bottom left, 71 middle, 86 left, 89 top right, 110 top, 132, 215 bottom, 230 bottom, 235
Rex Features   15 bottom, 24 right, 25, 34 bottom right, 38, 39, 41 top, 42 bottom left and right, 46 top left, 56 top right, 57 top left, 61 top, 64 bottom, 75 top, 85 right, 101 top left and right, 105 top left, 114 bottom right, 116 top, 119 bottom, 120 top, 129 middle, 143, 145 right, 149 top, 150 bottom left, 152 top left, 157 top, 158, 167 top, 169, 173, 174 bottom left, 183 bottom, 184 bottom, 186 right, 193, 201 top right, 202, 204 right, 209 bottom left, 216 top right, 217 bottom, 222 bottom, 223, 224, 228 top, 229 bottom left, 230 top, 234 top right, Agence de Presse 106, Stefano Archetti 47 bottom, Baccon/Gibod 63, Giancarlo Bonora/Pierluigi Picture Feature Services 139, Paul Brown 61 bottom, Francois Duhamel 229 top, A. Ganor 73 bottom, Patrick Frillet 98, Thomas Furey 17 middle, Hellbruegge/Friedel 144 bottom right, 146, Matsumoto 229 bottom middle, Ralph Merlino 41

top right, Brian Moody 194 right, H. Nathan 35 top left, J. Player 114 top right, Sigla 120 top, Sipa Press 41 top left, 45 top right, 56 middle, 58, 79, 88, 101 bottom, 105 top left, 113 top, 115 right, 160 top right, bottom left and right, 172 bottom left, 174 bottom, 199, 224, 229 bottom left, 234, Willison/Sipa 120 top, Goksin Sipahioglu 187 top, Kathy Tracy 240, D. Turner 174 top left, Villard 67 bottom, J. M. Vincent 59 middle, 165 bottom left
Royds London Limited 218 left
Searle Research and Development   238
David South   243 top
Spectrum   11, 65 top left and bottom right, 76, 77, 114 top left, 190 bottom right, NASA 134 top
St Bartholomew's Hospital   40 top right, 55 bottom, 125 middle, 127 bottom, 231 bottom, G. Moss 129 bottom, D. Sexton 68 right
Hugh Steeper Ltd   227 bottom
Sunday Times/**Ian Yeomans**   232 left, 233 bottom
Tao Clinic   46 bottom right
UNICEF Nagata   186 left
University of Newcastle upon Tyne   41 bottom right
Colin Urquhart   163 Bottom, 194 top
Vision International   55 top, 80 bottom, 136 bottom, 137 top, 160 top left, 170 top, John Coldblatt 188 top, CNRI 20 bottom, 21 bottom, 32 left, 46 bottom middle, 48 top left, 80 bottom left, 89 top left, 109 bottom right, 111 left, 121 top left and right, 125 bottom left, 213 top and middle left, bottom right, 215 top right, middle left, 245 top right, Explorer (A. Bertrandy) 208 middle left, (Blond) 40 middle right, (Hervy) 197 middle, (M. Moisnard) 145 left, (Nivoliez) 93, (Paillard) 160 top left, (Peino) 69, (R. Sidney) 157 top right, (Tenrel) 245 top right, Robin Fletcher 110 bottom, 245 bottom left, Ed. Holt 245 top left, K. Hundt 183 top left, Paolo Koch 31 bottom, 59 top, 74, 182 right, 185 bottom, 189 bottom, 208 bottom right, 210, 241 left, Scala 22, 219, 244 top, Anthea Sieveking 62 right, 71 bottom, 72 bottom, 111 bottom, 113 bottom, 124 left, 125 top left, 134 bottom left, 140 top and middle, 141 bottom, 142, 147 bottom, 179 bottom right
John Watney Library   93, 94 left, 95, 97 bottom, 134 bottom right
James Webb   108 bottom, 109 bottom left, 126 top, 127 top, 208 bottom left and (2) top right, 215 bottom right
World Health Organization   82 left, 86 top left, 89 middle left, 126 bottom, 157 bottom left, 203, T. Farkhas 34 top, D. Henrioud 17 top, A. Kochar 56 bottom right, E. Mandelmann 86 top left, 159 left, P. Almasy 87
Zefa/Rosmarie Pierer 89 bottom right

Illustrations

Olivia Beazley   233 top
Martin Bronkhorst   104 left
Jane Cope   162
John Davies   32 right, 36 left, 50, 80 top, 151, 232 right
Christopher Forsey   12 right
David Gifford   35 middle
Henry Grant   cover design
Richard Lewis   12 left
Josephine Martin/The Garden Studio   104 right, 124 right
Charlotte Emma Styles (Multimedia Publications Inc.) 14, 16, 18, 19 right, 21, 23, 27, 28, 33, 35 bottom, 37, 49, 51 middle, 52 bottom, 54 top left, 57 top right, 60 top left, right and bottom, 63 bottom, 65 top right, 81 middle left, 82 top right, 83 bottom, 85 top left, 86 bottom right, 90 bottom, 92 left, 102, 117 bottom left, 125 bottom right, 128, 129 top, 130 bottom right, 133 top left and bottom right, 137 bottom, 152 bottom left, 218 right
Terry Oakes   9 bottom, 135, 161, 181 bottom, 225, 247, 248
Kathy Wyatt   154, 155
Tassos Xeni   96, 100, 107 left, 122, 191, 196 bottom, 197 bottom, 209 top left, 211 right, 241 right
Wolfgang Mezger   190 top right

Multimedia Publications Inc. have endeavoured to observe the legal requirements with regard to the rights of the suppliers of graphic and photographic materials